Lifeboat Directory

A comprehensive guide to British lifeboats, covering selected pulling and sailing lifeboats, steam lifeboats, motor lifeboats, inshore lifeboat types, boarding boats, training boats and selected independent lifeboats

Nicholas Leach and Tony Denton
Ships in Focus Publications

Ships in Focus Publications
18 Franklands
Longton
Preston PR4 5PD

ISBN 978-1-901703-30-6
Copyright © NICHOLAS LEACH 2013
Typesetting and design by Nicholas Leach.
Printed by Amadeus Press Ltd, Cleckheaton

The right of NICHOLAS LEACH to be identified
as the Author of this work has been asserted

Cover Lizard's 16m Tamar Rose (ON.1300) at
sea off Kilcobben Cove.

Page 1 Relief lifeboats Atlantic 75 Gordon
England (B-701) and 14m Trent Henry Heys
Duckworth (ON.1213), from Weston and Barry
Dock, on exercise in the Bristol Channel.

This page Salcombe's 16m Tamar Baltic
Exchange III (ON.1289) off Start Point.

Page 4 The first 13m Shannon class lifeboat,
Sir Jock and Lady Slater (ON.1308), off Poole.

Acknowledgements

The idea for this book came about a couple
of years ago and it represents the culmination
of many years of work, research and pursuing
lifeboats old and new. In order to complete the
book, however, I have been have assisted by
many people who have supplied information
and photos, and I am very grateful to them all.
At the RNLI, Barry Cox, Elise Chaney, Nathan
Williams, Adrian Frogley, Glyn Ellis, Kate Cooney
and Captain Hugh Fogarty have all helped, and I
am grateful to them for facilitiating my research,
supplying photographs and providing up-to-date
information. The records of the late Grahame Farr,
held at the RNLI's library in Poole, were consulted
and proved to be of much value. Phil Weeks very
kindly proofed various parts of the book, looked
through several drafts and suggested numerous
changes and improvements, as well as obtaining
recent photos of some of the lifeboats, and I am
extremely grateful for his contribution. Martin
Fish supplied extra photos and suggestions for
improvements. And finally, I am very grateful to
the many people who supplied photographs for
possible inclusion; individual contributors of the
photos are listed on page 158.

Nicholas Leach
Lichfield, March 2013

Lifeboat Directory
Contents

Lifeboat Directory
Introduction

The scope of this book

The intention of this lifeboat directory is to provide a comprehensive guide to the lifeboats that have been built in the 20th and 21st centuries, while also including details of a few older boats that are historically significant or which are still in existence, either on display at museums or under private ownership. It therefore covers all of the steam and motor lifeboats built by the RNLI as well as a selection of pulling and sailing lifeboats. The body of the book is arranged in order of the boats' Official Number (ON), which runs in a broadly chronological order. Also included are brief details of the various inshore lifeboats, boarding boats, training boats and hovercraft that have been designed, developed and operated by the RNLI. The ILB fleet is too numerous to include in its entirety, and so just the main types of ILBs have been included.

The pulling and sailing lifeboats have been selected with consideration to their current situation, so all of those preserved and on display are included, while several in private ownership are listed if they are in good condition or are good representations of privately-owned pulling lifeboats. The pulling lifeboats section is not comprehensive, and for those seeking a full list of such lifeboats the annually-published Lifeboat Enthusiasts' Society Handbook is recommended. The photographs show the lifeboats in their most recent guise, where available, although as obtaining recent photos has not always been possible some photos show the boats when in service.

While this book is intended essentially for reference purposes, readers will see by looking through the entries, which more or less show

The Cullercoats pulling lifeboat Co-operator No.1 (ON-571), which served the station from 1907 to 1937, being launched from her carriage. A 37ft twelve-oared self-righter, she was one of several hundred lifeboats of a similar design built during the 19th and early 20th centuries. Very few of these pulling boats emain in existence, but a few have been completely restored and are used for fund-raising and publicity purposes.

the lifeboats in chronological order, how lifeboat design has evolved over the past two centuries, and the many different types of lifeboat that have been built. The advancement of lifeboat design has been an ongoing process, with naval architects and RNLI designers harnessing the latest technology and building techniques, together with available materials, to create the best possible rescue boat.

Lifeboat variety

The variety of lifeboat types is considerable, with different designs being developed to cater for certain local conditions, such as where a treacherous bar had to be crossed to get to sea as at Salcombe and Appledore, or for undertaking rescues in specific conditions and locations, such as inflatable inshore craft being

used close to rocks or in shallow water. One of the determining factors governing lifeboat design is the method by which the boat will be launched. A boat which lies afloat has fewer restrictions on its size and weight than one which goes down a slipway, or which is launched across a beach. For example, when the 47ft Tyne was developed one of the design criteria was that it had to fit into existing lifeboat houses, so its height and length were limited by the size of the boathouses. Similarly, if a lifeboat is being launched from a carriage across a beach, and recovery involves dragging it out of the water, the boat's weight and size are important considerations as, the larger and heavier the boat, the more powerful the equipment needed to manoeuvre it when ashore.

When shipbuilding was undertaken largely by

Official Numbers

The numbers for lifeboats used in this book follow the RNLI's Official Numbers (ON) order. The origin of Official Numbers can be traced back to the Southport and St Annes lifeboat disasters of December 1886. Following these tragedies, the RNLI's Committee of Management realised that the design of lifeboats had to be improved and that disasters must not befall existing lifeboats. So, the well-known yacht designer George Lennox Watson, of Glasgow, was asked to become Consulting Naval Architect to the Institution and design a new lifeboat.

Meanwhile, to ensure the existing lifeboat fleet was of an adequate standard, the Chief Inspector of Lifeboats, Captain H. W. Chetwynd, RN, and his assistants drew up a list of these boats for testing to a much more exacting standard than any applied hitherto. The numbering system was introduced as the lifeboats were tested. There were 290 station lifeboats and 20-30 more reserve lifeboats, all of which were surveyed. Each boat was allocated a number, recorded in a large volume,

and this served as the Official Number of the lifeboat concerned throughout the rest of its active life. This system has continued, and so since the 1880s every new lifeboat has been given an Official Number, abbreviated to ON, by which it can be identified.

The latest addition to the numbering of lifeboats has been the introduction of Operational Numbers. These numbers indicate, by their first two digits, the class of lifeboat and refer to the type's hull length; for example, 52-?? indicates a 52ft Arun, while 12-?? indicates a 12m Mersey, the first class to use metric numbers. The first boat to have an Operational Number was 44-001 (but had no Official Number), purchased from the United States Coast Guard in 1964. Lifeboats of the 37ft Oakley class were the first RNLI boats to which Operational Numbers were given.

The prototype 17m Severn Maurice and Joyce Hardy (ON-1179) on trials shortly after being completed. Together with the smaller 14m Trents, the 17m Severns were the first RNLI all-weather lifeboat type capable of speeds up to 25 knots. (By courtesy of RNLI)

12m Mersey Lifetime Care (ON-1148) was the first RNLI lifeboat to be built of fibre-reinforced composite. She was built in 1988 and was used for a series of intense proving trials before being placed in the Relief Fleet in October 1989. (By courtesy of RNLI)

The prototype 17m Severn Maurice and Joyce Hardy (ON-1179) on trials shortly after being completed. Together with the smaller 14m Trents, the 17m Severns were the first RNLI all-weather lifeboat type capable of speeds up to 25 knots. (By courtesy of RNLI)

hand and wood was the material used in boat construction, standardisation was not seen as necessary. In the era immediately following 1945 no two lifeboats were identical, and even boats of the same class, such as the 42ft Watsons, were different in many ways although their basic hull form and size was the same. The size and deck layout of the Watsons, Liverpools and Barnetts, motor lifeboats that once made up the bulk of the lifeboat fleet, varied from boat to boat and even sisterships were not identical.

Standardisation

However, with the introduction of glass-fibre and fibre-reinforced composite for lifeboat hulls, which were constructed from the same mould, the lifeboat fleet in the 21st century has become considerably more uniform. The first GRP-hulled boats were the Aruns, followed by the commercially-developed Bredes. The Mersey class was the first to be built from a composite fibre material, fibre-reinforced composite (FRC), which was very light yet extremely strong and durable. The next classes of lifeboat that were developed, the Severns, Trents and Tamars, were also built of FRC and this material has proved ideal for the RNLI's lifeboats. In fact, the FRC hulls of the 17m Severns, for example, are deemed so good that they have a life-saving career projected to be in excess of 50 years.

With standardisation being applied wherever possible by the RNLI, and achievable through the use of composite materials, the lifeboat fleet of the 21st century consists of classes where boats in each class are more or less identical in shape, layout and dimensions. During the early years of the 21st century, the Institution was keen to reduce the number of lifeboat types so that the cost of maintenance, repairs and spare parts was kept to a minimum while still ensuring the boats were of the highest standard. The intention is to operate as few different types as possible, with just three all-weather lifeboat classes to be in service when the Shannon build programme completes by 2020. This is almost the complete opposite of lifeboat design and building during the previous 150 years, where boats were sometimes designed as one-offs to cope with conditions at a particular station.

While a large degree of standardisation has taken place in the offshore fleet, this is less true of the inshore fleet. The introduction of the inflatable inshore lifeboat in 1963, followed by the development of the rigid-inflatable Atlantic class in the 1970s, brought a new dimension to the lifeboat service. While this book only touches upon inshore lifeboats, for many years they have been the workhorse of the lifeboat service, carrying out more rescues and saving more lives than their larger counterparts.

As well as the standard inshore lifeboats, the RNLI has gained a plethora of other boats and craft, ranging from small dinghies to large training boats. Information about these has been included as far as possible, although space permits for only basic details of the smaller boats, such as the X boats, XP boats and Y boats, most of which operate as daughter craft from all-weather lifeboats.

In addition to the all-weather and inshore lifeboats, the RNLI has taken over lifeguard services and introduced specialised lifeguard craft as a result. Many lifeguards use the Arancia inshore rescue boat, developed in New Zealand where the craft are still built, while Rescue Water Craft (RWC) are also deployed at many beaches. As well as life-guarding, the RNLI has created a specialised flood rescue team, which uses inflatable boats in areas of flooding. The team was formed in 2000, and has six divisional teams strategically positioned to respond to a flood anywhere in the UK or Ireland within six hours. Each team has two inflatable boats, which are former ILBS, as well as a rescue van, a Land Rover, and ancillary equipment.

The other kind of craft in widespread use are boarding boats, which take crews out to lifeboats kept at moorings. Although

D class inflatable inshore lifeboats, such as Henley Eight (D-701) at Withernsea, have become the workhorse of the RNLI's fleet and more than 100 of the type are in service around the UK and Ireland. (Nicholas Leach)

The 3.8m Arancia rescue boat, used extensively by RNLI lifeguards, is also used for flood response, with Arancia A-06-FR on a training exercise for the RNLI Flood Rescue Team at the Tees Barrage white water centre. (Martin Fish)

The restored pulling and sailing lifeboat Robert and Ellen Robson (ON-669) at Whitby.

alongside pontoon boarding has become more widespread, meaning the number of boarding boats in service has been reduced, a significant number are still in use. Some stations, such as Humber and St Mary's on the Isle of Scilly, operate purpose-designed and -built boats to board the lifeboat. Some boarding boats are stripped-down D class inflatables with the canopy removed, extra fendering added and powered by standard 40hp engines. Some stations use an old D class inflatable as a boarding boat, often carrying equipment similar to an ILB but with a 'BB' prefix. Larger Sillinger twin-engined inflatables are used at stations where the lifeboat mooring is exposed.

The latest lifeboats in the fleet are included in this book, but inevitably a work such as this will go out of date reasonably quickly as new boats are built and enter service. The information is correct as at 31 January 2013.

Significant lifeboats

Because the entry for each lifeboat in the main body of the book is, due to space constraints, necessarily brief, the following section describes some of the more significant lifeboats and why they are noteworthy. Describing any one lifeboat as more significant than another is inevitably a subjective matter, and almost all of the lifeboats described in this book will have saved many lives throughout their careers, and thus all are worthy in their own way. However, the following are notable for either their design, being the first of their class, or their service record.

ON-231 Duke of Northumberland • The first steam lifeboat, ON-231 was built in 1889 and used for extensive trials to prove steam power could be used for life-saving. She was the RNLI's first powered lifeboat, and went on to have a distinguished service career lasting more than 30 years, saving more than 300 lives.

ON-343 J. McConnel Hussey • ON-343 was a standard self-righting pulling lifeboat, built for service at Folkestone, but was converted with an engine in 1903-4, when a single 10hp Fay & Bowen engine was fitted, and thus became the RNLI's first motor lifeboat.

ON-350 Bradford • ON-350 was the second RNLI motor lifeboat, being converted with a single 30hp Briton motor in 1906 and then serving at various stations in the north-east.

ON-478 Helen Peele • ON-478 was the first and only steam tug built by the RNLI. She served at Padstow throughout her operational career and worked in conjunction with the pulling lifeboat ON-475. She saw service with the Admiralty from 1917 to 1919, and was sold in May 1929 after undertaking much fine rescue work at Padstow.

ON-560 Maria • ON-560, a 40ft Watson, was the RNLI's first purpose-built motor lifeboat. She was completed in 1908 and was basically a standard sailing lifeboat fitted with an engine. She was used for extensive trials before going on station at Broughty Ferry.

ON-561 John A. Hay • ON-561, a 42ft self-righter, was the RNLI's second purpose-built motor lifeboat and served at Stromness, in Orkney, where she was better equipped to deal with the strong currents and heavy seas than the pulling lifeboat she replaced.

ON-578 William Cantrell Ashley • ON-578 was the last sailing lifeboat in service with the RNLI. She was built in 1907 and spent 41 years on station at New Quay before being replaced.

ON-613 Henry Vernon • ON-613 was one of the first motor lifeboats, built in 1910, and served at Tynemouth and Sunderland. While at Tynemouth, she was involved in the epic service to the 7,400-ton hospital ship Rohilla with 229 crew and medical staff aboard in October 1914. Pulling lifeboats from Whitby, where the ship had stranded, were unable to get close enough

Two early motor lifeboats destined for the Orkney stations of Stromness and Stronsay, John A. Hay (ON-561) and John Ryburn (ON-565), with the Thurso pulling lifeboat Sarah Austin (ON-585) alongside the quay at Thurso. The three lifeboats left London Docks on 15 April 1909 and began an epic journey north under their own power. Although the boats reached their stations safely, the passage had not been without incident, with the motors breaking down on several occasions, but overall it proved that the use of motor power was viable in lifeboats. Hitherto, new lifeboats had been delivered to their station by steamship or railway, and so the voyage by sea as far as Orkney was a major undertaking. (By courtesy of RNLI)

to the wreck to effect a rescue. But ON-613 was brought south from the Tyne and succeeded in reaching the casualty and saving 50 lives.

ON-669 Robert and Ellen Robson • The last pulling lifeboat in RNLI service, ON-669 was built in 1918 for Tramore in Ireland, later went to Aberdeen and ended up at Whitby, from where she was withdrawn from service in 1957. She was then placed on display as the centrepiece of the town's lifeboat museum.

ON-656 Hearts of Oak • ON-656 was the last Norfolk & Suffolk sailing lifeboat to be built. The N&S lifeboats were large beach-launched boats, primarily intended for sailing, and were used exclusively at East Anglian stations, where they were well liked by their crews.

ON-671 The Brothers • In 1923 ON-671 was the first lifeboat to be registered with the Registrar General of Shipping, under the Merchant Shipping Acts, and given an Official Number. Since 1928 all lifeboats have been thus registered, with the exception of 44-001. The number is either stamped inside the boat or carried on a plate in the cabin or wheelhouse.

ON-682 William and Kate Johnston • ON-682 was the first Barnett lifeboat to be built. She measured 60ft in length and was the first lifeboat with twin engines and twin propellers, and as such was a significant advance.

ON-700 K. E. C. F. • ON-700 was the first Watson lifeboat with two engines and, in 1927, she became the first lifeboat to be fitted with wireless-telegraphy. She was the only one to be so equipped at that time as a certified operator was needed. In 1929 sets were installed in three more lifeboats, ON-718 William and Harriot at Stornoway, ON-719 Queen Victoria at St Peter Port and ON-725 Sir William Hillary at Dover.

ON-701 N. T. • ON-701 was the only lifeboat to be fitted with two engines driving a single propeller. Subsequent twin-engined lifeboats were fitted with twin propellers.

ON-725 Sir William Hillary • ON-725 was a special 64ft high-speed lifeboat built for Dover with the primary aim of rescuing airmen ditched in the English Channel. She could reach 17.5 knots and was constructed to specifications

The 60ft Barnett William and Kate Johnston (ON-682) leading the line-up of lifeboats moored off the Embankment on the Thames in July 1924 for the International Lifeboat Conference, which was held to mark the RNLI's centenary. Lifeboats from France, Netherlands, Sweden and Denmark were in attendance, along with the RNLI's 45ft Watson motor J. W. Archer (ON-685) destined for Teesmouth. The Dutch lifeboat Brandaris, seen to the right, was a 60ft 2in by 15ft 7in twin-screw motor lifeboat, powered by two 45hp engines, and carried a crew of four. She was vying with the RNLI's new 60ft design as the world's largest and most sophisticated lifeboat. Built in 1923, Brandaris served at Terschelling for almost 40 years.

different from any other contemporary motor lifeboat. She only served for ten years, 1930 to 1940, before being taken over by the Admiralty.

ON-731 Lady Jane and Martha Ryland • ON-731 served at Lerwick for 28 years and in the Reserve Fleet for another 11 years, making her one of the RNLI's longest-serving lifeboats. She was the first lifeboat to serve Shetland, where heavy seas and strong currents, combined with the long distances to be covered to reach casualties, made operating a pulling and sailing lifeboat in the area unfeasible.

ON-733 Mary Stanford • Built for service at Ballycotton, ON-733 served the station for almost 30 years and was used in the famous

The 51ft Barnett Lady Jane and Martha Ryland (ON-731) served at Lerwick from 1930 to 1958, as the first lifeboat in Shetland, during which time she is credited with saving 80 lives.

gold medal-winning service to the Daunt Rock Lightvessel on 7 February 1936. The lightvessel got into difficulty off the Cork coast in a south-eastern gale, with rain and snow. The lifeboat was away from station for 79 hours and the crew had only three hours sleep during the 63-hour rescue, in which the lightvessel's seven crew were saved. She is the only lifeboat to be awarded a Gold medal for gallantry, the boat getting the award as well as the Coxswain.

ON-777 H. F. Bailey • ON-777 was stationed at Cromer and used for some of the most famous rescues in the history of the RNLI. She was at Cromer for just ten years, including the Second World War years. During that time she saved more than 500 lives, including almost 450 during the war, launching over 150 times.

ON-809 Helen Blake • A unique, one-off design, ON-809 was intended to serve in the relatively sheltered waters of Dublin Bay and, at just 28ft in length, can be regarded as the forerunner of the inshore rescue boat. She was

The 51ft Barnett Mary Stanford (ON-733) off Ballycotton, Co Cork. She served the station for almost 29 years and was involved in the famous Daunt Rock rescue. (By courtesy of Ballycotton RNLI)

The 46ft 9in Watson cabin motor Elizabeth Rippon (ON-865) was the first of her class with a cockpit amidships, which was later enclosed to provide a greater degree of protection for the crew than on previous lifeboats. She served the RNLI for almost 30 years, primarily at St Helier. (By courtesy of RNLI)

The 46ft 9in Watson Douglas Hyde (ON-896), pictured during her naming ceremony at Rosslare Harbour on 5 June 1952, was not only the first lifeboat to use radio direction-finding equipment on service but was also involved in the epic medal-winning service to the tanker World Concord. (By courtesy of Rosslare RNLI)

stationed at Poolbeg for more than 20 years and is credited with saving five lives.

ON-840 Henry Blogg • ON-840 was the first 46ft Watson with a midship steering position, and was a complete redesign of the Watson deck layout. The bow had to made lower to improve visibility from the midships cockpit where the wheel was positioned.

ON-856 Susan Ashley • ON-856 was the first lifeboat to be built with an aluminium upperworks; this was an easier-to-work material than the double diagonal wood, which had been used for lifeboats' upperworks previously.

ON-865 Elizabeth Rippon • ON-865 was the first 46ft 9in Watson motor lifeboat to be built with midship steering and a deck cabin. Previous lifeboats of the class had open cockpits aft.

ON-896 Douglas Hyde • In 1955 ON-896 was the first lifeboat to use radio direction finding equipment on service. She served with the RNLI for more than 20 years, first at Rosslare Harbour.

ON-907 William Taylor of Oldham • ON-907 was fitted, in 1954, with 48hp Gardner 4LW diesel engines, the first time a commercial diesel engine had been fitted to a new lifeboat. Previous engines had been built to RNLI plans.

ON-942 J. G. Graves of Sheffield • The first 37ft Oakley lifeboat, ON-942, was the first modern lifeboat to be fully self-righting without sacrificing stability or seaworthiness, as had been the case with previous self-righting designs. All subsequent lifeboat designs have been fully self-righting.

ON-954 Solomon Browne • ON-954 served at Penlee for 21 years before being tragically wrecked on service on 19 December 1981 when going to the aid of the motor vessel Union Star. All eight of her crew, together with the eight crew of Union Star, were lost. This is the last time that an RNLI motor lifeboat and her crew have been lost on active service.

ON-964 The Baltic Exchange • ON-964, while on station at Salcombe, capsized on service on 10 April 1983 and her emergency air-bag inflated, righting the boat and helping to ensure that no crew members were lost. This was only the second time that a self-righting air-bag had been used on service, but it undoubtedly helped to ensure no crew lost their lives.

ON-968 Earl and Countess Howe • In 1963 ON-968 was the first lifeboat to be equipped with radar. She was also the first of just five 48ft Oakley lifeboats to be built, which employed the water ballast transfer method of self-righting first used in the 37ft Oakley design.

ON-987 Charles H. Barrett (Civil Service No.35) • ON-987 was the first of only three 70-71ft Clyde class rescue cruisers built by the RNLI. They were originally manned by full-time crews and patrolled large sea areas, being based in the Bristol Channel and around Orkney and the Pentland Firth. This proved not to be an effective way to operate, and they subsequently served as lifeboats.

ON-1001 John F. Kennedy • ON-1001 was the first of the steel-hulled Waveney class lifeboats to be built. The Waveney, based on a US Coastguard design, was also the first fast lifeboat class with the RNLI. It was not based on a displacement hull shape which had been used hitherto. The design was also fully self-righting and thus marked a major breakthrough.

ON-1018 Arun • ON-1018 was the first 52ft Arun class lifeboat to be built. Capable of between 18 and 20 knots, the Arun represented

a new direction for lifeboat design. It had a fully enclosed wheelhouse, a flared bow, a broad beam for stability and a flying bridge, and the hull was also fully self-righting.

ON-1025 Sir William Arnold • ON-1025, the second Arun class to be built, was involved in a fine Gold medal-winning rescue on 13 December 1981 when she was launched to the motor vessel Bonita, which was listing heavily 40 miles north of Guernsey. Coxswain Michael Scales and his crew saved 29 people in hurricane force winds and heavy seas.

ON-1037 Edward Bridges (Civil Service & Post Office No.37) • ON-1037 was the first 54ft Arun class lifeboat to be built, and served at Torbay for almost 20 years. She was involved in a Gold medal-winning service on 6 December 1976 when she saved the crew of the motor vessel Lyrma, which was in difficulty in gale force winds and heavy seas.

ON-1049 Tony Vandervell • ON-1049 was the first lifeboat to be built with a glass-reinforced plastic hull. All previous lifeboats had been built either of wood or, occasionally, steel, but ON-1049 set a trend and almost all subsequent Arun lifeboats were moulded from GRP, with the

The first 48ft Oakley class lifeboat, Earl and Countess Howe (ON.968), was the first lifeboat to be equipped with radar and the only one of her class with an aft steering position. (By courtesy of RNLI)

The 37ft 6in Rother James Cable (ON-1068, on left) escorts 12m Mersey Freddie Cooper (ON-1193) to Aldeburgh in November 1993. James Cable was the last of the RNLI's displacement lifeboats to leave service.

Mountbatten of Burma (ON-1069) was one of three Medina class lifeboats to be built by the RNLI, none of which saw active service.

use of wood for construction gradually ceasing.

ON-1052 City of Bradford IV • Built for service at the remote Humber lifeboat station at Spurn Point, the 54ft Arun ON-1052 became famous after being involved in several remarkable rescues during the winter of 1978-79 which earned her coxswain, Brian Bevan, the Gold, Silver and Bronze medals, and he became the only lifeboatman to receive the three awards at the same Annual General Meeting.

ON-1066 • The un-named prototype 33ft Brede was the first lifeboat class to be based on a commercially-designed hull. Only 12 Bredes were completed and the design, which was regarded as an intermediate type, had limitations placed on its operational service.

ON-1068 James Cable • ON-1068 was the last displacement lifeboat to be built by the RNLI and she served at Aldeburgh for 11 years. When replaced in November 1993, she was also the last such lifeboat in the fleet.

ON-1069 Mountbatten of Burma • The first of three large rigid-inflatable Medina type lifeboats, ON-1069 was used extensively for trials and was hailed as a breakthrough in design. However, problems with finding a suitable propulsion unit resulted in the Medina project being halted without any of the boats entering service. However, the Netherlands

lifeboat service successfully proved the design and now uses large rigid-inflatables exclusively.

ON-1100 Snolda • ON-1100 was the only steel-hulled Arun class boat, and was built to assess this material for that class, but the high cost involved in using steel precluded its further use.

ON-1148 Lifetime Care • ON-1148, a 12m Mersey, was the first lifeboat to be built with a fibre-reinforced composite hull. While the first Merseys were built from aluminium, ON-1148

was built as a full size prototype and used to test the strength and durability of FRC. Not only could FRC withstand the rigours of beach launching, which often involves being dragged over shingle and sand, but boats built from the material were also lighter than those of aluminium. Using an FRC mould also meant that series production was relatively fast.

ON-1179 Maurice and Joyce Hardy • ON-1179 was the first 17m Severn and as such was the first all-weather lifeboat with a maximum speed of 25 knots.

ON-1280 Peter and Lesley-Jane Nicholson • The first 16m Tamar lifeboat to enter service was ON-1280. The Tamar class, designed to be slipway launched, have state-of-the-art technology on board and are the most sophisticated lifeboats ever built. The specially-designed seats and SIMS computer system were among many significant advances.

ON-1308 Sir Jock and Lady Slater • ON-1308, the prototype Shannon class lifeboat, was significant because she was the first RNLI all-weather lifeboat to be powered by waterjets rather than propellers. The E class lifeboats on the Thames, introduced in 26002, are waterjet-driven, but ON-1308 was for use at sea.

The Shannon class lifeboat Sir Jock and Lady Slater (ON-1308) was the first all-weather lifeboat to be powered by waterjets.

Part 1
Pulling and Sailing Lifeboats

Hundreds of pulling and sailing lifeboats were designed and constructed by the RNLI during the 19th and 20th centuries, and before the RNLI's founding in 1824 many other man-powered lifeboats had been built by the variety of local organisations that took up the mantle of sea rescue before a national organisation had been established.

The first pulling lifeboats were those built by Henry Greathead at South Shields and by Thomas Costain in Liverpool for work on the Tyne and Mersey respectively. Greathead has claims to be the inventor of the lifeboat, a contentious issue beyond the scope of this work. However, he did build 39 lifeboats during the early 1800s and his design was subsequently adapted by other builders, mainly in the north-east. One Greathead-built boat survives, Zetland at Redcar, along with two similar boats, Bedford and Tyne.

When the RNLI was founded in 1824 as the National Institution for the Preservation of Life from Shipwreck, a title used until the 1850s, its first lifeboats were small, usually less than 30ft in length, and rowed by ten or fewer oars. One type was developed by George Palmer, an Essex MP who joined the RNLI's Committee of Management in 1826, and the other by Newbury boatbuilder William Plenty.

In the 1850s the National Shipwreck Institution, as the organisation had become known, was reformed and renamed, and a new type of lifeboat was developed. A prize offered for a new design was won by Great Yarmouth boatbuilder James Beeching, whose plans were considered to be the best. His design was improved by James Peake and became the self-righting type that dominated lifeboat construction for more than half a century. The standard self-righter, with a limited range, was a light pulling lifeboat and became the mainstay of the lifeboat fleet for many years.

Meanwhile, on the East Anglian coast an unusual design was developed, known as the Norfolk & Suffolk type. Based on the beach yawl used by beachmen for salvage work on the outlying sands, the N&S type was a large non-self-righting sailing craft, over 40ft in length, intended primarily for sailing. It was favoured almost exclusively in East Anglia, and was used to perform many heroic rescues. The RNLI developed its own non-self-righter in the 1890s, when George Lennox designed a large sailing lifeboat. Unfortunately, few N&S and Watson lifeboats survive today.

The last pulling lifeboats were built in the immediate post-1945 era, by when motor power had almost completely taken over. But it is fitting that the last pulling lifeboat built by the RNLI, Robert and Ellen Robson, survives, as a tribute to the men who pulled the oars, often through tremendous seas, facing them with only strength, courage and determination.

The 34ft self-righting lifeboat Queen Victoria (ON-112), which served at Bembridge from 1887 to 1902, on her carriage and being taken from her lifeboat house.

Zetland

31' x 10'6" North Country • Henry Greathead, South Shields
Built 1802 • Redcar 1802-80
Sold 9.1932 • Zetland

After service at Redcar, Zetland was given to the local townsfolk, and was used for display, processions and fund-raising, until being placed on permanent display in the 1960s. She is the oldest surviving lifeboat in the world and is on display in the Zetland Lifeboat Museum in Redcar (pictured).

Tyne

32' x 10' North Country • Edward Oliver, South Shields
Built 1833 • South Shields 1833-87
Sold 2.1931 • Tyne

After a long career serving at South Shields, Tyne was placed on display next to the Lifeboat Memorial, South Shields in May 1894. The boat and its shelter were moved to their current location in South Shields (pictured) during the mid-1930s, and were rebuilt following bomb damage in 1941.

Bedford

32'9" x 11' North Country • Lambert, South Shields
Built 1886 • South Shields 1886-1939
Sold 1939 • Bedford

Bedford served at South Shields for more than 40 years, and in October 1968 went to the Exeter Maritime Museum where she was displayed until the demise of the museum. She then went to Eyemouth (pictured) where she is kept in storage by Eyemouth International Sailing Craft Association.

112 • Queen Victoria

34' x 7'6" Self-righter • Forrestt • F 53
Built 1887 • Bembridge 1887-1902
Sold 11.1902 • The Ark/ Queen Victoria

112 was sold in 1902 and converted into a houseboat in Bembridge. By the 1990s she had been acquired for display at Bembridge Maritime Museum and in 1997 was moved to The Classic Boat Museum, Newport. She was used at fund-raising events and was at Arreton Barns Craft Village from 2010.

353 • Alfred Corry

44' x 13' Norfolk & Suffolk • James Beeching • B 6
Built 1893 • Southwold No.1 1893-1918
Sold 3.1919 • Alba/ Albemarle/ Thorfinn/ Alfred Corry

353 was sold in 1919 and was converted into the yacht Alba. Later renamed Albemarle and Thorfinn, she was used as a houseboat in Heybridge Basin. In 1976 John Cragie bought her and had her rebuilt at Rowhedge. In 1994 she was restored at Lowestoft (pictured) for display at Southwold in a museum.

393 • Samuel Fletcher of Manchester

36'2" x 8'10" Watson • Forrestt • F 98
Built 1896 • Blackpool 1896-1930
Sold 10.1930 • Samuel Fletcher of Manchester

393 was sold in 1930 to Blackpool Corporation and used as a pleasure boat from 1930 on Stanley Park Lake and to take people across the lake to Blackpool Zoo. She was in this role until the 1990s. Since 2009 she has been out of the water at Sea Cadets HQ (pictured) but in 2012 went into storage.

397 • Edward Birkbeck

34' x 10' Norfolk & Suffolk • James Beeching • B 9
Built 1896 • Winterton 1896-1925
Sold 4.1925 • Mirosa/ Edward Birkbeck

397 was sold in 1925 and was converted to a yacht fitted with a Watermota petrol engine in 1947. She was based at Cardiff, Dartmouth, Falmouth and Plymouth, and by the 1990s she was at Conwy (pictured), later moving to Port Penrhyn and Deganwy. In 2013 she was taken to Winterton for restoration.

399 • Francis Forbes Barton

40' x 10'4" Self-righter • Rutherford • RF 956
Built 1896 • Broadstairs 1897-1912, Reserve 3A 1912-24, North Deal (War Emergency) 1915-21 • Sold 11.1924 • Path/ Francis Forbes Barton

399 was sold in 1924 and, fitted with an engine, was based on the Thames. By the early 1990s she was on the river Colne near Rickmansworth, later being moved to a car park in Uxbridge. By 1997 she was at Littlehampton (pictured), and in 2012 was taken to Lincolnshire to be restored.

406 • St Paul

38' x 12' Norfolk & Suffolk• James Beeching • B 10
Built 1897 • Kessingland No. 2 1897-1918, Kessingland 1918-31
Sold 1931 • Stormcock/ St Paul

406 was sold in 1931 and converted into a yacht named Stormcock kept on the south coast in the Portsmouth area. In 1994 she went to Chatham Historic Dockyard and in April 1996 was placed on display (pictured). She is being gradually restored there and is part of the Lifeboat Collection.

417 • Jane Anne

37' x 9'3" Self-righter • Thames Ironworks • TI 21
Built 1898 • Irvine 1898-1914, Reserve 1915-22, Falmouth 1922-28
Sold 1928 • Jane Anne

417 was sold in 1928 and was at the RNLI Depot, Poole in the 1980s in a poor condition. In the early 1990s she was moved to the Scottish Maritime Museum at Irvine (pictured), where she was taken out of the water to be restored. By 2004 she had deteriorated and was in a very poor condition.

435 • James Stevens No.10

37' x 9'3" Self-righter • Thames Ironworks • TI 39
Built 1900 • St Ives 1900-33
Sold 1933 • Patricia Mary/ Mary Andrew/ James Stevens No.10

435 was sold in 1933 and became a yacht at Kirby le Soken, Walton-on-Naze by the 1990s. She was kept at Great Oakley until being sold in 1999 to a York owner. In 2002, fitted with an engine, she went to St Ives (pictured) after being restored. Since 2011 she has been at Lelant Saltings up for sale.

461 • Chapman

35' x 10' Liverpool • Thames Ironworks • TI 67
Built 1901 • Groomsport 1901-20, Reserve 1920-24, Hilbre Is 1924-38
Sold 8.1939 • Harbinger/ Peggy LR41/ Chapman

461 was sold in 1939 and was used as a Glasson Dock Pilot Cutter based at Sunderland Point. After further sales, she ended up at Hesketh Bank. By 2001 she had been moved to Cammell Laird, Birkenhead for restoration and in 2011 was taken to the old boathouse at Hoylake (pictured) to be displayed.

473 • Sarah Pilkington

35' x 8'6" Self-righter • Thames Ironworks • TI 78
Built 1901 • Stornoway 1901-18, Reserve 1918-19, Watchet 1919-44
Sold 3.1945 • Sarah Pilkington/ The Flying Column/ Manyana

473 was sold in 1945 and, after being converted into a yacht and fitted with an engine, was based at Brightlingsea, Walton and Oulton Broad. She later moved to moorings on the river Bure, near Great Yarmouth, and to Acle in the late 1990s. By 2003 she was on the river Cam in Cambridge (pictured).

475 • Edmund Harvey

42' x 11'6" Self-righter • Thames Ironworks • TI 82
Built 1901 • Padstow 1901-29
Sold 5.1929 • Trevone

475 was sold in 1929 and was converted into a ketch owned in Padstow. She had several other owners and was based at Yarmouth, Lymington and Neyland before being bought from Faversham by Simon Evans in 1993 and taken to St Denis les Sens, France (pictured), for use as a charter boat.

489 • Ryder

35' x 8'6" Self-righter • Thames Ironworks • TK 2
Built 1902 • Looe 1902-30
Sold 7.1930 • Halmay III/ Ryder

489 was sold in 1930 and converted into the pleasure boat Halmay III based at Bristol, Wyke Regis and Chesil Beach. By 1987 she was derelict but she was restored and placed on display in Weymouth. By 2001 she became a seagoing exhibit at Polperro and has visited Fowey (pictured).

495 • Louisa Heartwell

38' x 10'9" Liverpool • Thames Ironworks • TK 8
Built 1902 • Cromer 1902-23, Cromer No.2 1923-31
Sold 5.1931 • Waiora/ Louisa Heartwell

495 was sold in 1931 and converted in 1932 at Kings Lynn into a single screw ketch. She was kept at Brancaster and later Barry Dock. By the 1990s she was in use as a houseboat at Grand Union Canal, Rickmansworth, moving in 1997 to the Chichester Canal, adjacent to Chichester Marina.

521 • James and Mary Walker

38' x 9'4" Watson • Thames Ironworks • TK 51
Built 1904 • Anstruther 1904-33
Sold 4.1933 • Cameronia/ Ishbara/ James and Mary Walker

521 was sold in 1933 and eventually became the yacht Ishbara, based at Falmouth. She was at Santa Eulalia, Ibiza in 1985, but by the 1990s had moved to Preston Dock and in 2008 was at Gallows Point, Beaumaris. In June 2010 she was donated to Anstruther and returned there to be restored (pictured).

530 • Oldham

38' x 9'4" Watson • Thames Ironworks • TK 61
Built 1904 • Abersoch (Penrhyndhu) 1904-30
Sold 1930 • Grey Dawn

530 was sold in 1930 and converted into a yacht based at Barry Dock for many years, and was out of water there during the 1990s and early 2000s. In 2007 she was offered for sale and moved to Milford Haven (pictured). By 2009 she had been sold and was at Skipool Creek, Poulton-le-Fylde.

533 • Thomas Lingham

34' x 9'4" Rubie self-righter • Thames Ironworks • TK 65
Built 1904 • Rhosneigir 1904-24, Reserve 1926-37
Sold 1937 • David Scott/ Thomas Lingham

533 was sold in 1937 and became a private yacht around the south coast. In June 1984 she was delivered to the National Lifeboat Museum, Bristol, for restoration. In 1994 she was moved from Bristol 1994 to Simon Evans' yard at St Denis les Sens, France (pictured) and was moved to Migennes in 2012.

535 • Charlie Medland

43' x 12'6" Watson • Thames Ironworks • TK 67
Built 1904 • Mumbles 1905-24, Southend 1924-28, Reserve 1928-36, New Brighton No.2 1936-38 • Sold 1.1939 • Charlie Medland

535 was sold in 1939 and used as a yacht until 1965, then a houseboat. In 1970 she was bought by Simon Evans' family who sold her in 1974, but Simon Evans bought her back in 1976 and took her to France. She went to St Denis les Sens (pictured) in the 1980s, and moved to Migennes in 2012.

536 • J. C. Madge

41' x 11' Liverpool • Thames Ironworks • TK 68
Built 1904 • Sheringham 1904-36
Sold 6.1936 • J. C. Madge

536 was sold in 1936 and became a yacht. She was at Brancaster in 1984 and moved to Lincoln in 1985. In 1991 she was restored at Oulton Broad, and was then displayed at Muckleburgh Collection, Weybourne. After being stored at Aylsham, she was displayed at the Mo Museum, Sheringham.

538 • Jones-Gibb

38' x 9'4" Watson motor • Thames Ironworks • TK 72
Built 1905 • Barmouth 1905-39
Sold 6.1939 • Thrift

538 was sold in 1939 and used as a private yacht at Hamble and Chatham. By the 1990s she was at Faversham and later moved to Queenborough and Dover. By 2005 she was at Bowling Canal Basin, Dumbarton (pictured), and by 2009 had been taken to Sand Point Marina, Dumbarton, to be restored.

558 • Prichard Frederick Gainer

35' x 8'6" Self-righter • Thames Ironworks • TK 96
Built 1906 • Lynmouth 1906-44
Sold 8.1944 • Lynmouth/ Pritchard Frederick Gainer

558 was sold in 1944 and, fitted with two Ford engines, was converted into a cabin cruiser with a large forward cabin. She was used on the Great Ouse, and kept at Waterbeach (pictured) in summer and St Ives, Huntingdonshire in winter. In 2001 she had moved down river to Priory Marina, Bedford.

562 • John and Naomie Beattie

35' x 8'6" Self-righter • Thames Ironworks • TK 100
Built 1906 • Aberystwyth 1906-32
Sold 1.1933 • Chiquita/ John and Naomi Beattie

562 was sold in 1933 and, fitted with an engine, became the pleasure boat Chiquita at Stourport. She moved to Porthcawl and cruised the Bristol Channel. By the 1990s she was restored and on display at Swansea Industrial Transport Museum, moving to the museum's store at Landore (pictured).

574 • Brothers Brickwood

35' x 8'6" Self-righter • Thames Ironworks • TL 14
Built 1907 • Brighstone Grange 1907-15, Reserve 1915-18, Scarborough 1918-24 • Sold 11.1925 • Abalone/ Dornovaria

574 was sold in 1925 and, although little is known of her early history, by the 1990s she was at Rainey Island on Strangford Lough in use as a yacht. She was later kept at Donaghadee Marina (pictured) before moving in 2004 to Torrevieja Marina, Alicante, Spain as a yacht and houseboat.

578 • William Cantrell Ashley

35' x 10' Liverpool • Thames Ironworks • TL 18
Built 1907 • New Quay 1907-48
Sold 1949 • William Cantrell Ashley

578 was sold in 1949 and used as a workboat at the Outward Bound Sea School, Aberdovey. By 1986 she was a fishing boat at Milford Haven and in the early 1990s was due to be displayed at New Quay. Since 1991 she has been stored at Nantgarw, Cardiff (pictured) for possible future display.

583 • Charles Henry Ashley

38' x 9'4" Watson • Thames Ironworks • TL 23
Built 1907 • Cemaes 1907-32
Sold 5.1932 • Charles Henry Ashley

583 was sold in 1932 and was used as a pleasure boat on Anglesey. In 2006 funding was found for a complete restoration, and the Cwch Ashley Boat Cemaes charitable trust oversaw a restoration at Classic Sailboats, near Caernarvon. She was rededicated at Cemaes on 10 May 2008 (pictured).

593 • General R. Dudley Blake

35' x 8'3" Self-righter • Thames Ironworks • TL 35
Built 1909 • Black Rock 1909-35
Sold 1935 • St Therese

593 was sold in 1935 and was largely unaltered, being used as a trip boat at Howth (pictured) in the 1980s and 1990s. In 2003 she was removed from Howth following a dispute. The latest reports indicate she is storage somewhere in central Ireland, but her exact whereabouts are unknown.

594 • William Riley of Birmingham & Leamington

34' x 8' Self-righter • Thames Ironworks • TL 37
Built 1910 • Upgang 1909-19, Whitby No.2 1919-31
Sold 11.1931 • Whitby II/ William Riley

594 was sold in 1931 and, under several owners, was kept on the river Severn. She was restored as a yacht and toured the south-west, being kept at Barnstaple. By 2005 she was semi-derelict, but was acquired by a group in Whitby (pictured), returned there and was fully restored for use fund-raising.

597 • Lizzie Porter

34' x 8'6" Self-righter • Thames Ironworks • TL 40
Built 1909• Holy Island 1909-25, North Sunderland 1925-36
Sold 1936 • Lizzie Porter

597 was sold in 1936 and was removed from a mud berth in the river Trent by the Army after she had been left partially submerged for years. She was taken to Bristol where she was restored at the National Lifeboat Museum, moving to Chatham Historic Dockyard (pictured) in April 1996 for display.

605 • Charles and Eliza Laura

40' x 11' Watson • Thames Ironworks • TL 49
Built 1910 • Moelfre 1910-29
Sold 3.1929 • Salvor

605 was sold in 1929 and was a work boat based at Ramsgate (pictured) and was reconditioned 1982-84 by a Richmond builder. After deteriorating at nearby Richborough, she was again restored and was at Ramsgate until 2009, when purchased by a Spirit of Dunkirk group and taken to Darwen.

607 • James Leith

42' x 12'6" Norfolk & Suffolk • Thames Ironworks • TL 52
Built 1910 • Pakefield No.1 1910-19, Caister No.1 1919-29, Aldeburgh No.2 1930-35 • Sold 8.1936 • Robin Hood II/ James Leith

607 was sold in 1935 and became a houseboat at Poole having had a large wheelhouse added, as well as a petrol engine driving a single screw. Her original mast and sails were retained. By 1996 she was at Chatham Historic Dockyard on display as part of the Lifeboats Collection (pictured).

611 • Jane Hannah MacDonald

35' x 8'6" Self-righter • Thames Ironworks • TL 56
Built 1910 • Appledore 1910-22, Res 1922-33, Flamborough 1933-38
Sold 1938 • Jane Hannah/ Jane Hannah MacDonald

611 was sold in 1935 and, fitted with an engine, she was used by the Sea Scouts, and participated in the Dunkirk evacuation. She became a fishing boat but by 1990 was in a coal yard near Stoke, and had been for at least 20 years. In 1992 she was taken to St Denis les Sens, France (pictured).

618 • Henry Finlay

35' x 8'6" Self-righter • Thames Ironworks • TL 66
Built 1911 • Macrihanish 1911-30, Teignmouth 1930-40, Res 1940-45
Sold 7.1945 • Teignmouth Belle/ Henrietta/ Henry Finlay

618 was sold in 1945 and operated as a pleasure and trip boat out of Teignmouth and Torquay, moving to Exmouth in the mid-1990s. In 2003 she was purchased by Peter Lucas and taken to Old Mill Quay Boatyard, Old Mill Creek, Dartmouth (pictured), for restoration.

623 • Docea Chapman

34' x 8' Rubie self-righter • Thames Ironworks • TL 71
Built 1911 • Withernsea 1911-13, Easington 1913-33, Reserve 1933-38, Padstow 1938-39 • Sold 3.1939 • Girl Maureen/ Louisa II

623 was sold in 1939 and became a fishing boat operating out of Padstow owned by Tommy Morrissey, who renamed her Girl Maureen. In 1982 she was sent to Lynmouth for display at the local Tourist Information Centre but was later moved to The Power of Water Exhibition, Glen Lyn Gorge (pictured).

627 • Kate Walker

35' x 8'8" Self-righter • Thames Ironworks • TL 76
Built 1911 • Lytham 1912-31, Porthoustock 1931-42
Sold 1.1946 • Jarusia/ Kate Walker

627 was sold in 1946 and became the motor yacht Jarusia registered in London. She was kept at Woodbridge, Aldeburgh and Slaughden Quay, considerably altered. Since the 1980s she has been at Felixstowe Ferry (pictured) in a mud berth, heavily converted with a wheelhouse and cabin.

636 • James and John Young

35' x 11' Liverpool • Thames IW, completed RNLI • TL 87
Built 1913 • Ardrossan 1913-30, Reserve 1930-39
Sold 4.1939 • Alma of Southampton/ James and John Young

636 was sold in 1939 and converted into the motor yacht Alma based at Southampton. By the 1990s she was being restored for display at Exeter Maritime Museum. In about 2002 she was taken to Eyemouth (pictured) and was kept in storage by Eyemouth International Sailing Craft Association.

637 • Staughton

40' x 11' Watson • Thames Ironworks/Saunders • TL 88/ S2
Built 1915 • Reserve 1915-19, New Brighton No.1 1919-30
Sold 1.1931 • Viator

637 was sold in 1931 and become the yacht Viator and was based around Anglesey. In 1965 she was at Bangor and in 1971 she broke from her moorings and sank in Cemaes Bay. In the 1990s she was used for fishing out of Port Penrhyn (pictured), until about 2000 when she was broken up.

652 • Joseph Ridgeway

35' x 8'10" Rubie self-righter • Summers & Payne • SP 67
Built 1915 • Stonehaven 1916-34
Sold 3.1934 • Sarah Louise/ Logos/ El Pamadero/ Joseph Ridgway

652 was sold in 1934 and was heavily converted while operating under three different names. She was bought by Simon Evans in 2009 and taken to Saint Denis les Sens, France (pictured) via the river Yonne. During the passage the top of the hull deteriorated. She moved to Migennes in 2012.

662 • Ernest Dresden

35' x 8'10" Rubie self-righter • Saunders • S 20
Built 1917 • Courtown 1917-25, Reserve 1925-27, Port Isaac 1927-33
Sold 12.1933 • Courtown/ Ernest Dresden

662 was sold in 1933 and became a motor boat at Ramsgate and Wisbech. She was ashore at King's Lynn by the 1980s and in 1993 the owners of the house where she had been abandoned gave her to Simon Evans, who took her to St Denis les Sens, France (pictured), and then to Migennes in 2012.

669 • Robert and Ellen Robson

34' x 8' Self-righter • Saunders • S 29
Built 1918 • Tramore 1918-23; Aberdeen No.2 1924-39 & 1943-47; Whitby No.2 1947-57 • Display from 1958 • Robert and Ellen Robson

669 was the last pulling lifeboat to be built for the RNLI and she had a varied service career, ending her days at Whitby. After being withdrawn from service, she was used for display purposes at Whitby, ending up as the centrepiece of the Lifeboat Museum housed in the old boathouse (pictured).

478 • Helen Peele

95'6" x 19'6" Steam tug • Ramage & Ferguson
Built 1901 • Padstow 1901-29
Sold 5.1929 • Helen Peele

After service at Padstow (pictured) towing the pulling lifeboats, the unique steam tug 478 was sold out of service in May 1929 for £500. What became of her or where she was based is not known, but she was last reported being used as a yacht tender on the Clyde in March 1964.

Part 2
Steam Lifeboats and Motor Lifeboats 1904-1930

The first powered lifeboats operated by the RNLI were driven by steam. Although only six steam lifeboats were built by the RNLI, as well as a steam tug which was used in conjunction with a sailing lifeboat, they proved to be fairly successful. The first steam lifeboat, Duke of Northumberland (ON.231), was launched on the Thames and made her first trial trip on 31 May 1889. Her engine, with its 'patent tubulous pattern' boiler, produced 170hp and drove hydraulic pumps. The last steam lifeboat was withdrawn in 1928 with the boats having given very good service.

Steam had its advantages over pulling and sailing lifeboats, but it also had several drawbacks and the advent of the internal combustion engine pointed the way ahead for lifeboat design. The first RNLI motor lifeboats were converted pulling lifeboats, and five lifeboats were thus modernised between 1904

and 1912, by when the first purpose-built motor lifeboat had entered service. The early experiments with engines in lifeboats were rather hit and miss, as many problems had to be overcome before powered lifeboats were ready for sea rescue. Although the problems were gradually solved, the early motor lifeboats, being all single-engined, still carried auxiliary sails in case of engine failure.

Following the end of the First World War the RNLI developed several new motor lifeboat types and undertook a major building programme with the aim of phasing out the pulling and sailing lifeboat. A significant advance came in 1923 when the 60ft Barnett type was designed and built. Fitted with twin engines driving twin screws, she represented a major breakthrough and was the most powerful craft of her generation. The engines were housed in separate watertight engine

rooms, and she also had a rudimentary shelter which offered a degree of protection for the crew, another significant advance.

Following the introduction of the twin-engined 60ft Barnett, smaller motor lifeboat designs with twin screws were developed. In 1927 the first twin-engined 45ft 6in Watson motor was completed, and in 1928 the first 51ft Barnett entered service. Meanwhile, smaller motor lifeboats were introduced, including 40ft Self-righters, 40ft 6in Watsons and a single-engined 35ft Self-righter, which was light enough to be launched by carriage. This was adapted and, starting in 1929, a series of 35ft 6in motor self-righters was built for stations where carriage launching was employed. By 1930 the RNLI's fleet of 194 lifeboats consisted of 90 motor lifeboats, of which 50 were Watsons; of the 102 pulling and sailing lifeboats, 72 were self-righters.

The 40ft self-righting motor lifeboat Henry Vernon (ON-613) sailed from her station at Tynemouth down to Whitby in November 1914 to undertake an epic rescue, saving the survivors from the hospital ship Rohilla, and proving the worth of the motor lifeboat. (By courtesy of RNLI)

231 • Duke of Northumberland

50' x 14'3" Steam • R. and H. Green • G 227
Built 1889 • Harwich 1890-92, Holyhead 1892-93, New Brighton 1893-97, Holyhead 1897-1922 • Sold 1923 • Duke of Northumberland

After service at Holyhead, 231 was sold out of service in 1923, but nothing is known of her location or use until the 1990s. Then, in 1994, she was found in a completely derelict condition at Ready-Mix Concrete, Terrace Road, Widnes (pictured), where she was slowly being covered in waste concrete.

362 • City of Glasgow

53' x 16' Steam • R. and H. Green • G 289
Built 1894 • Harwich 1894-97 and 1898-1901, Gorleston 1897-98
Sold 10.1901

After service at Harwich (pictured) and Gorleston, 362 was sold out of service in 1901 to a Harwich-based owner. She was replaced after a short RNLI career because she suffered from mechanical faults and poor reliability, but nothing is known about her time under private ownership.

404 • Queen

55' x 16'6" Steam • J. I. Thornycroft • TH 325
Built 1897 • New Brighton 1897-1923
Sold 1924 • Queen/ Robert Hughes

After trials (pictured) and a long career on station at New Brighton at the mouth of the river Mersey, 404 was sold out of service in 1924. She had become a pilot tender in Lagos, Nigeria by the 1970s, a role for which she was unaltered, but it is not known whether she is still in existence.

420 • James Stevens No.3

56'6" x 15'9" Steam • J. S. White • W 1054
Built 1898 • Grimsby 1898-1903, Gorleston 1903-08, Angle 1908-15, Totland Bay 1915-19, Dover 1919-22, Holyhead 1922-28
Sold 1.1929 • Helga

420 was the most widely travelled of the steam lifeboats, and after service at several stations including Gorleston (pictured), she was sold in 1929. She became the yacht Helga but was reportedly lost off Porthdinllaen in 1935.

421 • James Stevens No.4

56'6" x 15'9" Steam • J. S. White • W 1055
Built 1899 • Padstow 1899-1900
Wrecked on service 11.4.1900

421 served at Padstow (pictured) for just over a year before she was wrecked on service to the ketch Peace and Plenty, of Lowestoft, with the loss of eight of her crew on 11 April 1900, and was subsequently broken up. The station's pulling lifeboat, Arab, was also wrecked going to the same vessel.

446 • City of Glasgow

56'6" x 15'9" Steam • J. S. White • W 1101
Built 1901 • Harwich 1901-17
Sold 12.1917 • Patrick

After service at Harwich (pictured), 446 was sold to the Admiralty and converted into a patrol boat, renamed Patrick. While in Admiralty service she saved the lone survivor from the German submarine UC-1, a minelayer, which hit one of its own mines off the Sunk Lightvessel.

343 • J. McConnel Hussey

38' x 8' Self-righter • Converted to motor 1904 • Wm Ellis • E 6
Built 1893 • Folkestone 1893-1903, Newhaven 1904, Tynemouth
1905-11, Sunderland 1911-14 • Sold 1914

Built as a pulling lifeboat for Folkestone, 343 was the first RNLI lifeboat to be
converted to motor when she was fitted with a single 10hp Fay and Bowen
two-cylinder petrol engine. She was sold out of service in 1914 but her
subsequent use and whereabouts are unknown.

350 • Bradford/ Reserve No.2B

42' x 11' Self-righter • Converted to motor 1906 • Woolfe • W 253
Built 1893 • Ramsgate 1893-1905, Reserve 1905-07, Seaton Snook
1907-09, Seaham No.2 1909-11, Teesmouth 1911-17 • Sold 1918

Built as a pulling and sailing lifeboat for Ramsgate (pictured), 350 was
converted to motor in 1906 when she was fitted with a single 30hp Briton
petrol engine. She was re-engined a year later with a 30hp Tylor engine. She
was sold in 1918 but her subsequent use and whereabouts are unknown.

407 • Michael Henry

37' x 9'3" Self-righting • Converted to motor 1906 • Thames IW • TI 15
Built 1897 • Newhaven 1897-1905 & 1908-12, Dunmore East 1914-19
Sold 1919

407 was converted to motor in 1906 while in service at Newhaven. She
was fitted with a 24hp Thornycroft petrol engine, but was re-engined in
1913 with a 20hp Gardner engine for service in Ireland. She was sold out of
service in 1919 but her subsequent use and whereabouts are unknown.

432 • James Stevens No.14

43' x 12'6" Norfolk & Suffolk • Conv to motor 1906 • Thames IW • TI 32
Built 1900 • Walton and Frinton 1900-28
Sold 6.1928 • Mardee/ James Stevens No.14

432 was converted to motor in 1906 and sold in 1928 to a Maldon-based
owner, and she became a fireboat during World War II, then a houseboat on
the river Blackwater. In the late 1990s she was taken to Titchmarsh Marina
and restored to seagoing condition (pictured), a project completed in 2009.

463 • Albert Edward

45' x 12'6" Watson • Converted to motor 1912 • Thames IW • TI 70
Built 1901 • Clacton-on-Sea 1901-29, Arranmore 1929-32
Sold 10.1932 • Marion/ Albert Edward

463 was sold in 1932 and became the trawl fishing yacht Marion. By the
late 1960s she had been converted to a motor yacht on the river Deben at
Ramsholt. By 1993 she was at Fox's Marina, Ipswich. From the mid-2000s she
was at Woodbridge (pictured) and in 2011 moved to Haven Marina, Ipswich.

560 • Maria

40' x 11' Watson motor • Thames Ironworks • TK 98
Built 1909 • Broughty Ferry 1910-21, Portpatrick 1922-29, Pwllheli
1930-31, Shoreham Harbour 1931 • Sold 7.1932 • Passerelle

560 was sold in 1932 to a Leigh-on-Sea owner and was converted into a
yacht. She was re-engined in 1951, again in 1962 and with a Thornycroft
diesel in 1973. She was at Ramsgate in 1977 and by 1983 was owned at
Canvey Island (pictured). It is believed she was burnt at Allington in 1991.

561 • John A. Hay

42' x 11'6" Self-righting motor • Thames Ironworks • TK 99
Built 1908 • Stromness 1909-28, Fenit 1928-32
Sold 9.1932 • unknown

After service at Stromness (pictured) and Fenit, 561 was sold out of service in September 1932 for £60 to an owner based at Westcliffe-on-Sea. However, details of her subsequent use and whereabouts are unknown, or whether she is still in existence.

563 • Charterhouse

40' x 10'6" Self-righting motor • Thames Ironworks • TL 1
Built 1908 • Fishguard 1909-30
Sold 2.1931 • Marian/ Charterhouse

563 was sold in 1931 and was converted into the yacht Marian, based for many years in North Wales (pictured), at Conway and then at Port Penrhyn, Bangor. In 2009 she was donated by her owner to Fishguard station for display, and was taken to Goodwick, where her restoration is being undertaken.

565 • John Ryburn

43' x 12'6" Watson motor • Thames Ironworks • TL 3
Built 1908 • Stronsay 1909-15, Peterhead No.2 1915-21, Broughty Ferry 1921-35 • Sold 2.1935 • Vigilant/ Bembo

565 was sold in 1935, had a number of owners and was converted into a yacht. Registered at Caernarfon and re-engined with Bergius and later Ailsa Craig diesels, she was at Caernarfon (pictured) in the 1990s with a sheet covering her. She remains opposite Caernarfon castle, slowly deteriorating.

595 • William and Laura

43' x 12'6" Watson motor • Thames Ironworks • TL 38
Built 1909 • Donaghadee 1910-32, Arranmore 1932-35
Sold 4.1935 • Libo

After service at Donaghadee (pictured), 595 was sold in 1935 to a London-based owner, who sold her on to a Twickenham-based owner. She was converted into a yacht with an all over cabin, and was reported to be at Barnstaple, but details of her subsequent whereabouts are unknown.

602 • Elliot Galer

38' x 10' Watson motor • Thames Ironworks • TL 46
Built 1910 • Seaham Harbour 1911-36
Sold 11.1936 • Quest

602 was sold in 1936 and had several owners who based her on the south coast. In 1976 she was for sale at Falmouth and was subsequently refitted as a yacht with four berths and a 70hp Ford diesel. She was later reported at Anstruther, Dingle in 1980, and as being lost off Milford Haven in the 1980s.

603 • Helen Smitton

38' x 10' Watson motor • Thames Ironworks • TL 47
Built 1910 • St Abbs 1911-36
Sold 11.1936 • Paloma

603 was sold in 1936 and was used as a work boat and yacht on Strangford Lough. She was kept at Whiterock, Strangford Lough, and by the 1990s she was at a farm on the west side of Strangford Lough (pictured). In 2006 she was sold and was moved to Dale, outside Milford Haven, for restoration.

609 • Robert Theophilus Garden

40' x 10'6" Self-righting motor • Thames Ironworks • TL 54
Built 1910 • Wicklow 1911-37
Sold 5.1937 • Sirius

609 was sold in 1937 and was used by a youth training agency operating out of Stourport Yacht Club named Sirius (pictured). By the mid-1990s she was being used as a houseboat in the Marina at Milford Haven. She was reported to have been sold in 2003 to Sheerness and transported to Iceland.

613 • Henry Vernon

40' x 10'6" Self-righting motor • Thames Ironworks • TL 58
Built 1910 • Tynemouth 1911-18, Sunderland 1918-35
Sold 10.1935 • Rohilla

613 was sold in 1935 for £200 to a London-based owner who had her converted into a motor yacht at Bosham. During the 1939-45 war she was requisitioned and was taken to Dunkirk. Details of her post-war activity are lacking, but as a yacht she was broken up in the Bay of Biscay in the 1990s.

614 • General Farrell

40' x 10'6" Self-righting motor • Thames Ironworks • TL 59
Built 1911 • St Davids 1912-36
Sold 3.1936 • Isle of Iona

After service at St Davids (pictured), 614 was sold in 1936 to an IOM owner. She was converted into the yacht Isle of Iona before being sold on and taken to London. In 1979 she was in West India Docks, privately owned but used by Sea Scouts. She was last reported at Great Yarmouth in 1983.

620 • William MacPherson

43' x 12'6" Watson motor • Thames Ironworks • TL 68
Built 1912 • Campbeltown 1912-29, Aldeburgh No.2 1930, Pwllheli 1931-40 • Sold 9.1940 • Carn Ingli

620 was sold in 1940 to the Corporation of Edinburgh. She subsequently had a series of owners and was converted into the screw ketch Carn Ingli based in Southampton. By the late 1960s she was a yacht at Gzira, Malta, but was broken up in 1999/2000 (pictured), with her remains at Marsaxlokk.

621 • Frederick Kitchin

43' x 12'6" Watson motor • Thames Ironworks • TL 69
Built 1912 • Beaumaris 1914-45, Reserve 1945-48
Sold 5.1948 • Lady Pat/ Jackie Maxwell/ Ballyheo Dream

621 was sold in 1948 and, with a cabin added, was at Sunderland in the 1970s. By the 1990s she was at Davey Bank, Newcastle, and in 1998 was sold, being taken to Blyth (pictured) to be refurbished. She went to Grimsby, and sank but was raised. She then moved to a marina at Ely, Cambridgeshire.

622 • Alexander Tulloch

43' x 12'6" Watson motor • Thames Ironworks • TL 70
Built 1912 • Peterhead No.2 1912-14
Wrecked on service 26.12.1914

622 served at Peterhead for two years before being wrecked on service on 26 December 1914 (pictured) to the trawler Tom Tit. She hit rocks at the entrance to the harbour, with three of her crew of ten being drowned. The motor, air cases and other equipment were salvaged after the disaster.

628 • Sir Fitzroy Clayton

38' x 9'9" Self-righting motor • Thames Ironworks • TL 77
Built 1912 • Newhaven 1912-18 & 1919-30, Lizard 1918-19, Reserve
1930-33, Fleetwood 1933-35 • Sold 8.1935 • La Moye

628 was sold in 1935 to an owner who converted her into a cabin cruiser.
She was registered at Barrow in 1941 and used as a motor yacht until 1945,
after which she became a houseboat. She was reported at Bowness, Lake
Windermere in 1985, but was broken up the following year.

641 • Lady Rothes

42' x 11'6" Self-righting motor • Thames IW/Saunders • TL 92/S 6
Built 1914 • Fraserburgh 1915-37
Sold 3.1937 • Liberty Belle/ Wandering Albatross/ Albatross/ Lady Rothes

641 was sold in 1937 and was converted into a yacht, for use on the Clyde
and west coast of Scotland, home ported in Tobermory. By the 1990s she was
semi-derelict at Kerrera Island, Oban, moving later to Loch Feochan. In 1998
she went to Fraserburgh to be restored but was destroyed in 2001 (pictured).

642 • John Taylor Cardwell

40' x 10'6" Self-righting motor • Thames IW/Saunders • TL 93/S 7
Built 1914 • Arklow 1915-38
Sold 5.1938 • Arklow/ Bridget

642 was sold in 1938 and used by the Royal Navy around Kintyre in World
War II. She was later on the Humber until bought by a North Wales owner
in the 1970s, and converted into a yacht and based at Port Penrhyn, Bangor.
In 2008 she was extensively refitted as a gaff schooner (pictured).

646 • Henry Frederick Swann

40' x 10'6" Self-righting motor • Saunders • S 11
Built 1917 • Tynemouth 1918-39 and 1941-47, Reserve 1939-41
Sold 12.1947 • Wearsider/ Survival

646 was presented by the RNLI to the 3rd Tyne Sea Scouts in 1947. She was
used in Sunderland, but by the 1990s was on the Tyne in private ownership.
She was a fishing boat on the Tyne until 2006, when she was acquired by
the North East Maritime Trust and moved to South Shields to be restored.

647 • Ethel Day Cardwell

40' x 10'6" Self-righting motor • Saunders • S 12
Built 1917 • Teesmouth 1917-24, Port Erin 1925-39, Reserve 1939-42
Sold 6.1942 • Bay Monarch

After service at Teesmouth and Port Erin, 647 was sold out of service for
£100 in June 1942. She was renamed Bay Monarch, but details of her use,
whereabouts and any conversion to her are unknown. Whether she is still in
existence is not known either.

648 • Elsie

45'x 12'6" Watson motor • Saunders • S 13
Built 1919 • St Mary's 1919-30, Helvick Head 1930-46, Reserve 1946-50
Sold 1.1951 • Happy Return

648 was sold out of service in January 1951 to Horace Kimber who sold
her on again in about 1955. She was then converted into the yacht Happy
Return at Ilfracombe (pictured), and taken to Tahiti at about the same time.
Information about her use and whereabouts since then is not known.

649 • Duke of Connaught/ Shamrock

45' x 12'6" Watson motor • Saunders • S 14
Built 1919 • Baltimore 1919-49, Reserve 1949-51
Sold 1.1952 • Shamrock

649 was sold in 1952 to a Crosshaven-based owner but nothing is known of her until she was reported under conversion at Bowling Basin, Glasgow (pictured), in the 1990s. She was later moved to Lea Valley Marina, Harlow to be converted, but her current use and whereabouts are unknown.

651 • Samuel Oakes

40' x 11' Watson motor • Summers & Payne/Saunders • SP 66/S 16
Built 1918 • Spurn Point 1919-23, Weymouth 1924-29, Shoreham Harbour 1929-33 • Sold 1.1933 • Esmee/ Grey Gull

651 was sold in 1933 to a Hove-based owner and she was used at Dunkirk by the Navy. She was kept in the Chatham area and later at Rochester and Sheerness (pictured). Restoration work started in 1984 at Medway Bridge Marina. She was later moved to Cuxton, where she was burnt out.

653 • William Evans

45' x 12'6" Watson motor • Summers & Payne/Saunders • SP 68/S 30
Built 1921 • Wexford No.1 1921-25, Rosslare Harbour 1925-27, Galway Bay 1927-39 • Sold 11.1940 • unknown

After service at Wexford (pictured) and Galway Bay, 653 was sold out of service in November 1940 to Haulbowline Ship Repair Company, at Cobh. However, details of her subsequent use and whereabouts are unknown.

654 • Joseph Adlam

45' x 12'6" Watson motor • Saunders • S 27
Built 1921 • Blyth 1921-48, Reserve 1948-51
Sold 2.1952 • unknown

After service at Blyth (pictured) and in the Reserve Fleet, 654 was sold out of service in February 1952 to a Troon-based owner. However, details of her subsequent use and whereabouts are unknown.

655 • Priscilla Macbean

35' x 8'6" Self-righting motor • J. S. White • W 1578
Built 1921 • Eastbourne 1921-27, Kirkcudbright 1928-31, Maryport 1931-34 • Sold 9.1934 • Laurita

655 was sold in 1934 and was converted into a yacht. During 1939-45 she was at Ulverston, and was taken to Lake Windermere in 1947 as a pleasure boat. She remained there until being taken to Eastbourne (pictured). By 2000 she had been moved and was being stored at Hellingly, East Sussex.

657 • Frederick H. Pilley

38' x 9'9" Self-righting motor • Summers & Payne/Saunders • SP72/S31
Built 1920 • Lizard 1920-34, Islay 1934-35, Fleetwood 1935-39
Sold 1939 • Anzac/ Seaspell/ Natalie/ Ladybird

657 was sold in 1939 and operated out of Sunderland for 30 years. She was sold to Hartlepool owners, and kept near the lifeboat station there. She was not well maintained, and sank at her moorings, but was refloated and was used as a fishing boat at Stockton-on-Tees (pictured) in the 1980s and 90s.

658 • Dunleary (Civil Service No 7)

45' x 12'6" Watson motor • Saunders • S 17
Built 1919 • Dun Laoghaire 1919-38, Lytham 1939-51
Sold 5.1951 • Dunleary

658 was sold in 1951 and, after conversion to a motor sailer with a cabin added, was kept on the Tyne. In the 1990s she was at Friars Goose Marina and was re-engined with a Gardner 6LXB engine during the 1990s. By 2004 she had been moved to Amble (pictured) where she has been stored ashore.

659 • Frederick and Emma

45' x 12'6" Watson motor • Saunders • S 25
Built 1921 • Wick 1921-38, Amble 1939-50
Sold 8.1950 • Stadats

659 was sold in 1950 and has been based at Woodbridge ever since. She was used as a fishing vessel until 1966 after which she was converted into a houseboat, which included the fitting of a new 100hp engine. Since the 1990s she has been at Woodbridge (pictured) in a mud berth as Stadats.

663 • John and Mary Meiklam of Gladswood/ Agnes Cross

46'6" x 12'9" Norfolk & Suffolk motor • Saunders • S 26
Built 1921 • Gorleston No.1 1921-21, Lowestoft 1921-39, Reserve 1939-40 & 1941-52, Dover 1940-41 • Sold 10.1952 • Wimp

663 was sold out of service in October 1952 and was sent to Aden after being bought by Wimpey, and renamed Wimp. The bottom of her hull was coppered and she was used as an inspection craft. She was last reported being in Aden in 1955, and details of her whereabouts since are unknown.

667 • Margaret Harker Smith

40' x 10'6" Self-righting motor • Saunders • S 23
Built 1918 • Whitby 1919-38
Sold 4.1938 • unknown

After service at Whitby (pictured) as the station's first motor lifeboat, 667 was sold out of service in April 1938 for £250 to the Chelsea Yacht & Boat Company, London. However, details of her use and whereabouts since being sold are unknown.

668 • Duke of Connaught

45' x 12'6" Watson motor • Saunders • S 24
Built 1921 • Peterhead No.2 1921-39, Reserve 1939-51
Sold 10.1951 • King John II

668 was sold in 1951 and used as a workboat in Dover (pictured). In 1989 she was sold and became a yacht at Zuider Zee, Holland. By the late 1990s she had been sold and was at Uppsala, near Stockholm, as a pleasure boat. In 2009 she was for sale, stripped out, with original fittings and an engine.

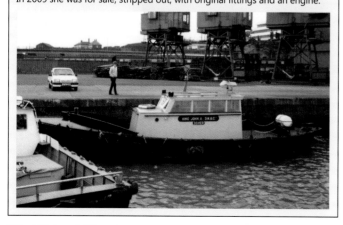

670 • H. F. Bailey/John & Mary Meiklam of G'wood

46'6" x 12'9" Norfolk & Suffolk motor • J. S. White • W 1566
Built 1923 • Cromer No.1 1923-24, Gorleston 1924-39, Reserve 1939-52
Sold 10.1952 • Pen Cw/ John and Mary Meiklam of Gladswood

670 was sold in 1952 and used as a workboat at Fishguard (pictured) from then, with a wheelhouse added, by British Rail to disembark pilots. In the 1980s she was found in poor condition and taken by road to Gorleston in July 1986. Housed in the old lifeboat house, she was restored for display.

671 • The Brothers

45' x 12'6" Watson motor • J. S. White • W 1567
Built 1922 • Penlee 1922-31, Falmouth 1931-34, Reserve 1934-48,
Workington 1948-52 • Sold 8.1952 • Admiral Douglas

671 was sold in 1952 to Dover Harbour Board and was used as a work boat
until the 1980s, altered by the addition of an enclosed wheelhouse. After
several years out of the water, by 2000 she was in use as a diving support
boat at Wellington Basin, Dover (pictured), for Dover Subaqua Club.

672 • Alfred and Clara Heath

40' x 10'6" Self-righting motor • J. S. White • W 1574
Built 1922 • Torbay 1922-30, Salcombe 1930-38, Reserve 1938-40,
St Peter Port 1940-45 • Sold 10.1945 • Moby Dick SH543

672 was sold in 1945 to an Esher-based owner and became a yacht at Beccles,
Norfolk. She had several other owners and was later based in Southampton
before going to King's Lynn and St Ives, Hunts. In 1985 she left St Ives for
Gibraltar (pictured). She was broken up at Marina Bay, Gibraltar, in 2009.

673 • Jane Holland

40' x 10'6" Self-righting motor • J. S. White • W 1575
Built 1922 • Selsey 1922-29, Eastbourne 1929-49, Reserve 1949-53
Sold 3.1953 • Reporter

After service at Selsey (pictured) and Eastbourne, 673 was sold in 1953 to
Sir Alfred McAlpine & Son Ltd who renamed her Reporter and operated her
out of Birkenhead. She was last reported as a yacht at Birkenhead Dock in
1960, and details of her subsequent use and whereabouts are not known.

674 • The Newbons

40' x 10'6" Self-righting motor • J. S. White • W 1576
Built 1922 • Sennen Cove 1922-48, Port St Mary 1949-50
Sold 3.1951 • Fair Lady

After service at Sennen Cove, 674 was sold to a Warrington-based owner
and was converted into a fishing boat. In 1965 she was at Caernarfon and
in 1969 at Hoylake as a fishing boat. In 1974 she was at Morpeth Dock,
Birkenhead (pictured) as a yacht, but her recent whereabouts are not known.

675 • V. C. S.

40' x 10'6" Self-righting motor • J. S. White • W 1577
Built 1922 • Appledore 1922-38, Reserve 1938-45
Sold 9.1945 • Fiducia

After service at Appledore, 675 was sold in 1945 and became the yacht
Fiducia at Axmouth. She was at Seaton (pictured) in April 1954 having had
a small cabin added, and was last reported as a yacht at Axmouth in 1960.
Details of her subsequent use and whereabouts are unknown.

676 • Langham

40' x 10'6" Self-righting motor • J. S. White • W 1573
Built 1922 • Bembridge 1922-39, Reserve 1939-50
Sold 11.1950 • Freedom/ Langham

676 was sold in 1950 and lay derelict at Teignmouth until 1969 when she
was converted into a motor yacht at Bristol. She was later at Largs where her
owner was keen to restore her. By the 1990s she was on the Isle of Wight for
restoration, at Newport and then Arreton Barns Craft Village (pictured).

677 • Prince David

40' x 11' Watson motor • J. S. White • W 1571
Built 1922 • Barry Dock 1922-37
Sold 12.1937 • unknown

After service at Barry Dock (pictured), 677 was sold out of service in 1937 for £275 to a Sevenoaks-based owner. However, nothing more is known of her, and details of her current whereabouts are lacking.

678 • Edward, Prince of Wales

45' x 12'6" Watson motor • J. S. White • W 1568
Built 1924 • Mumbles 1924-47
Wrecked on service 23.4.1947

After more than 20 years of service at Mumbles, 678 was capsized and wrecked on service to the steamship Santampa on 23 April 1947 with the loss of eight lifeboatmen. She was destroyed by fire where she lay (pictured).

679 • Elizabeth Newton

45' x 12'6" Watson motor • J. S. White • W 1569
Built 1923 • Hartlepool 1924-39, Berwick 1939-40, Reserve 1940-53
Sold 5.1953 • Viking

679 was sold in 1953 to 20th Century Fox Productions and converted into a Viking ship for the film Prince Valiant. She later became a pilot boat at Caernarvon and from the mid-1970s was an angling boat at Rhyl, but sank in 1981 at the entrance to Rhyl Harbour and was scrapped.

680 • City of Bradford I

45' x 12'6" Watson motor • J. S. White • W 1570
Built 1923 • Humber 1923-29, Reserve 1929-30; Humber No.2 1930-32, Reserve 1932-52 • Sold 10.1952 • Hammer

After service in the Reserve Fleet (pictured), 680 was sold in 1952 to George Wimpey & Co of Hammersmith and used as a work boat named Hammer. By the 1980s she was owned by a Rothesay-based owner, who resold her to an owner on Arran. Details of her subsequent whereabouts are not known.

681 • K. B. M.

40' x 11' Watson motor • J. S. White • W 1572
Built 1922 • Buckie 1922-49, Reserve 1949-52
Sold 9.1952 • Striker/ K B M

681 was sold in 1952 to a Blakeney-based owner and was in East Anglia as a fishing boat. By the 1980s she was at Clonakilty, Ireland, used as a fishing boat with a cabin added. She was also based at Union Hall, Ring and Kinsale (pictured) and in 2012 was in Dublin before moving to Ireland's west coast.

682 • William and Kate Johnston

60' x 15' Barnett • J. S. White • W 1586
Built 1923 • New Brighton 1923-50
Sold 12.1950 • Jymphany/ Nexus/ William and Kate Johnston

682 was sold in 1950 and converted into a yacht at Dartmouth. In the 1980s and 1990s she was at Hartlepool for refurbishment. She was sold in 2000 and has since moved around a lot, being based at Ipswich, Chatham, Faversham, Ostend, then Ramsgate (pictured) and Dover in 2012.

683 • Herbert Joy

35' x 8'9" Self-righting motor • Saunders • S 35
Built 1923 • Scarborough 1923-31, Reserve 1931-37
Sold 3.1937 • Swallow

683 was sold in 1937 and was at Portsmouth for a number of years. She was used by the Admiralty on war service, but by the 1960s was at Old Portsmouth being used for fishing. Having been laid up at the Camber, Portsmouth (pictured), she was broken up there in November 1995.

684 • John R. Webb/ 684 RM/ Hearts of Oak

45' x 12'6" Watson motor • J. S. White • W 1594
Built 1923 • Tenby 1923-30, Barra Is 1931-32, Yarmouth 1934-36 and 1937-38, Res 1936-55 • Sold 2.1955 • William Bradley/ Hearts of Oak

684 was sold in 1955 and used for piloting and general duties in the Thames Estuary, based at Southend. During the 1980s she was in a mud berth at Leigh-on-Sea (pictured) gradually deteriorating. In 2003 was taken to St Denis Les Sens, France, by Simon Evans, and later moved to Migennes.

685 • J. W. Archer

45' x 12'6" Watson motor • J. S. White • W 1601
Built 1924 • Teesmouth 1924-50, Amble 1950-54, Reserve 1954-56
Sold 7.1956 • Brighter Hope

685 was sold in 1956 and fished out of Hartlepool and Seaham until 1970, when she was sold to an owner in Essex. By the late 1980s she was at Potton Island, river Crouch, where she steadily deteriorated. In 2010 she was towed to Rochford, and taken by road to Middlesborough to be restored (pictured).

686 • T. B. B. H.

45' x 12'6" Watson motor • J. S. White • W 1602
Built 1924 • Portrush 1924-49, Reserve 1949-53
Sold 1.1953 • Moonraker/ Hamptonian/ Juno

686 was sold in 1953 and was converted into a motor yacht, being re-engined with a Gardner diesel and with extensive accommodation. She has always been based around the Southampton area, first moored near Northam Bridge, then at Smiths Quay, Woolston (pictured).

687 • B. A. S. P.

45' x 12'6" Watson motor • J. S. White • W 1610
Built 1924 • Yarmouth 1924-34, Falmouth 1934-40, Reserve 1940-47, Valentia 1947-51, Res 1951-55 • Sold 2.1955 • Valencia/ B. A. S. P.

687 was sold in 1955 and had various owners, being used for bombing range work and contracted to the oil industry. In 1980 she was recovered from the Thames and restored at the National Lifeboat Museum, Bristol. She was moved to the Historic Lifeboat Collection at Chatham in 1994 (pictured).

688 • The Lord Southborough (Civil Service No.1)

45' x 12'6" Watson motor • Saunders • S 36
Built 1924 • Margate 1925-51, Reserve 1951-55
Sold 1.1955 • Lord Southborough

After service at Margate (pictured), 688 was sold in 1955 to the Crown Agents for the Colonies for use in Cyrenaica, a district of Libya once under British administration. However, what happened to her is not known and in 2002 she was reported as a yacht belonging to a Southampton-based owner.

689 • Manchester and Salford

45'x 12'6" Watson motor • Saunders • S 37
Built 1924 • Douglas 1924-46, Reserve 1946-54
Sold 10.1954 • Alison Jane/ Jean Louise

689 was sold in 1954 and converted on Clydeside, being fitted with a 120hp Perkins 56M diesel. She was based in North Wales and visited Scotland. By the 1990s she was at Bangor and later Deganwy (pictured), where she was abandoned. In 2001 a new owner took her to Hesketh Bank to be restored.

690 • C. and S.

45'x 12'6" Watson motor • Saunders • S 38
Built 1925 • Dunmore East 1925-40, Pwllheli 1940-43, Reserve 1943-46, Valentia 1946-47 • Sold 11 1947 • Caradoc

After a varied service career starting at Dunmore East, 690 was sold out of service in November 1947 to an owner based in Kingston-upon-Hull. She was converted into the yacht Caradoc and was reported at Victoria BC, Canada, in the mid-1980s, and she was also reported there in 1995.

691 • Mary Scott

46'6" x 12'9" Norfolk & Suffolk motor • J. S. White • W 1608
Built 1925 • Southwold 1925-40, Reserve 1940-53
Sold 3.1953 • Atanua/ Mary Scott

691 was sold in 1953 and became the ketch Atanua with a Lister Blackstone diesel engine. She was at Poole in the 1960s, Christchurch in the 1970s and by the late 1980s had moved to Gillingham pier. In 2009 she was at Hoo Marina, but was at Ramsgate (pictured) in 2010 for a Dunkirk Little Ships rally.

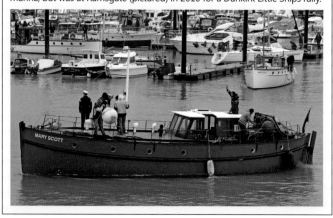

692 • Milburn

45'x 12'6" Watson motor • Saunders • S 39
Built 1925 • Holy Island 1925-46, Reserve 1946-55
Sold 9.1955 • Asmara/ Rosanaed

692 was sold in 1955 and used as a pleasure boat with a cabin added, based at Fareham and West Itchenor, Chichester. In the 1990s she was at Smiths Quay, Woolston, Southampton, but in 1998 moved to Brighton Marina. In 2000, heavily converted, she was at Denton Island, Newhaven (pictured).

693 • Emma Constance

60' x 15' Barnett • Saunders • S 40
Built 1926 • Aberdeen 1926-51
Sold 3.1951 • Southern Cross/ Griselda/ Achileus

693 was sold in 1951 and has had a series of owners. In 1966 she was converted into a yacht by Morris & Lorimer, Sandbank and was based at Gosport. In 1987 she was taken from Southampton to Hartlepool by road and on to Keils, Tayvallich, Argyll (pictured); she has since deteriorated.

694 • H. F. Bailey/ J. B. Proudfoot

45' x 12'6" Watson motor • J. S. White • W 1603
Built 1924 • Cromer No.1 1924-28 & 1929-35, Res 1935-41, Southend 1941-45, Dover 1947-49, Res 1949-56 • Sold 9.1956 • Anatura/ Gramarie

694 was sold in March 1953 to Herd & Mackenzie boatyard, Buckie who rebuilt her as a single screw yacht fitted with a single 94bhp Gardner diesel. After further sales, she moved to Newcastle but by 1978 was at Puerto Pollensa, Majorca (pictured) as Gramarie, and by 2007 in Marbella, Spain.

695 • M. O. Y. E.

45' x 12'6" Watson motor • J. S. White • W 1611
Built 1925 • Porthdinllaen 1926-49, Reserve 1949-56
Sold 4.1956 • Unknown

After service at Porthdinllaen (pictured) and then at various stations while in the Reserve Fleet, 695 was sold out of service in April 1956 for £350 to a Holyhead-based owner. However, details of her subsequent use, any changes of name and whereabouts are unknown.

696 • Robert and Marcella Beck

60' x 15' Barnett • J. S. White • W 1626
Built 1926 • Plymouth 1926-43 & 1947-52
Sold 6.1952 • Melaka/ Blaskbeg/ Idle Hours

696 was sold in 1952 and was used as a tender by the Commissioners of Irish Lights. Sold again in 1956, she was kept at Dun Laoghaire before a further sale took her to Weymouth, where she was heavily converted. In 1994 she was sold from Lymington (pictured) and by 1996 was at Hamburg, Germany.

697 • Prudential

48' x 13' Ramsgate motor • Saunders • S 41
Built 1925 • Ramsgate 1926-53
Sold 11.1953 • Trimilia

697 was sold in 1953 and was converted in the 1950s, being renamed Trimilia. By the 1980s she was a houseboat at Woodbridge, based at a number of locations, including the Tide Mill Marina in 2009. In 2011 she moved to Ipswich Haven Marina and was at Harwich (pictured) in 2012.

698 • K. T. J. S.

45'6" x 12'6" Watson motor • Saunders • S 42
Built 1926 • Longhope 1926-33, Aith 1933-35, Arranmore 1935-50, Reserve 1950-52 • Sold 5.1952 • Alton BM 160/ LO 511

698 was sold in 1952 and was converted for stern trawling, being used as a fishing boat out of Lowestoft in the mid-1950s. By 1980 she had become BM.160, and was fishing out of Brixham. She was put up for sale in 1980, but broke her moorings and was swept onto the beach at Seaton, where she was broken up.

699 • John Russell

45'6" x 12'6" Watson motor • Saunders • S 43
Built 1926 • Montrose No.1 1926-39, Reserve 1939-55
Sold 7.1956 • Athena/ John Russell

699 was sold in 1956 and, converted, cruised the Western Isles, becoming a houseboat at Lochgilphead. In the 1990s she was sold to an Inverness owner and refitted near Drumnadrochit. By 2002 she was at Middlesbrough, but in 2011 she moved to Ocean Village Marina, Southampton (pictured).

700 • K. E. C. F.

45'6" x 12'6" Watson motor • J. S. White • W 1630
Built 1927 • Rosslare Harbour 1927-39, Galway Bay 1939-52, Res 52-56
Sold 12.1956 • Taob Ruo/ P'teuchi IV/ P'teuchi

700 was sold in 1956 and became a fishing boat at Girvan and Portpatrick. By the 1990s she was on the river Tyne (pictured), having had a cabin added, in use as a pleasure boat at Davey Bank. She has been kept at various locations on the Tyne, and in 2012 was at C. & J. Marina, near the Tyne Tunnel.

701 • N. T.

45'6" x 12'6" Watson motor • J. S. White • W 1629
Built 1927 • Barrow 1927-51, Workington 1952-53, Reserve 1953-56
Sold 12.1956 • Diana Victoria

After service at Barrow and Workington (pictured), 701 was sold in 1956 to Roy Edward Cook Ltd, York, who converted her into the work boat Diana Victoria and kept her on the river Ouse near York. The last reported sighting of her was in 1987 since when no details of her whereabouts are known.

702 • J. J. K. S. W.

51' x 13'6 Barnett • Saunders • S44
Built 1928 • Stromness 1928-55, Reserve 1955-64
Sold 1.1965 • Jon Dee BS 19

702 was sold in 1965 to a Bangor-based owner in North Wales, where she was altered with a small wheelhouse. She was used as the work boat John Dee based at Port Penrhyn, and was laid up. In 2000 she was moved to Dickie's boatyard, Bangor (pictured), where she was reported broken up.

703 • L. P. and St Helen

35' x 8'10" Self-righting motor • Saunders • S 45
Built 1927 • Eastbourne 1927-29, Boulmer 1931-37, Newcastle 1937-49
Sold 11.1949 • unknown

703 was one of the first motor lifeboats to be designed and built for carriage-launching. After service at Eastbourne, Boulmer and Newcastle, she was sold out of service in 1949 to a Morecambe-based owner. However, details of her subsequent use and whereabouts are unknown.

704 • Greater London (Civil Service No.3)

48'6" x 13' Ramsgate • J. S. White • W 1648
Built 1928 • Southend 1928-41 & 1945-55, Reserve 1941-45 & 1955-57
Sold 9.1957 • ADES 1, Captain Francisco Alvarez

704 was sold in 1957 to Montevideo, Uruguay for use as a lifeboat, renamed Captain Francisco Alvarez, with the operational number ADES I (pictured). After serving there until 1991, she was placed on display in a dry dock at Colonia, Montevideo where she has been ever since.

705 • E. M. E. D.

48'6" x 13' Ramsgate • J. S. White • W 1649
Built 1928 • Walton and Frinton 1928-53, Reserve 1953-56
Sold 1.1956 • Capitan Christianson

705 was sold in 1956 to the lifeboat service at Valparaiso, Chile and was used as a lifeboat renamed Capitan Christianson. After service in Chile until 1998, she became a demonstration lifeboat. Since 2000 she has been on display on the quayside at Valparaiso (pictured).

706 • Thomas Markby

40'x 10'6" Self-righting motor • Saunders • S 46
Built 1928 • Swanage 1928-49, Whitehills 1949-52, Reserve 1952-57
Sold 5.1957 • Ambler

After service at Swanage (pictured) and elsewhere, 706 was sold out of service in 1957 to a German owner. After she had been converted into the yacht Ambler, she was kept in Tonga. Little is known about her subsequent use or whereabouts, other than a last reported sighting which was in 1995.

707 • Edward Z. Dresden

45'6"x 12'6" Watson motor • Saunders • S 47
Built 1929 • Clacton-on-Sea 1929-52, Stronsay 1952-55, Res 1955-68
Sold 12.1968 • St Peter

After service at Clacton and Stronsay (pictured), 707 was sold in 1968 and had a couple of owners who used her as a yacht, renamed St Peter. She was kept at Strangford, Co Down until the mid-1970s. In September 1984 she sank a few miles off Scotland's west coast, with Troon lifeboat going to her.

708 • H. C. J.

45'6"x 12'6" Watson motor • J. S. White • W 1656
Built 1928 • Fowey 1928, Holyhead 1928-29, Thurso 1929-56, Reserve 1956-62 • Sold 12.1962 • Mary Dolan/ Seawitch

708 was sold in 1962 to a Holyhead-based owner. Converted into a pleasure boat, she was based at Severn Motor Boat Club, Worcester during the 1980s and 90s. She moved to Arran in about 2002, and in 2004 went to the Isle of Man, being kept at Peel, Castletown and Derbyhaven (pictured) as Seawitch.

709 • City of Bradford II

45'6"x 12'6" Watson motor • Saunders • S 48
Built 1929 • Humber 1929-53, Amble 54-57, Res 57-59 & 60-65, Broughty Fy 1959-60 • Sold 12.1968 • Freida/ Spurn/ Freida/ City of Bradford II

709 was sold in 1968 and has been based in Northern Ireland ever since. Kept at Carnlough and Coleraine, she was converted into a pleasure yacht with a cabin added. She was at Cushendall in the 1990s, at Bangor Marina (pictured) in 2002, and by 2005 was at Ringhaddy Pier, Strangford Loch.

710 • White Star

45'6"x 12'6" Watson motor • J. S. White • W 1657
Built 1930 • Fishguard 1930-57, Reserve 1957-68
Sold 6.1968 • Outward Bound/ Kurt Hahn/ White Star/ Tunnara II

710 was sold in 1968 and was used by the Outward Bound Sea School at Aberdovey. She moved to Fishguard in the 1990s as a fishing boat, much altered. In the 1990s she moved to Pembroke and about 2005 to Milford Haven. By 2012 she was on a pontoon mooring off Dunleavey Drive, Cardiff (pictured).

711 • James Macfee

45'6"x 12'6" Watson motor • J. S. White • W 1662
Built 1928 • Cromarty 1928-55, Reserve 55-56 & 57-59, Thurso 1956-57
Sold 9.1959 • Macfee

711 was sold in 1959 and was converted into a private motor yacht, being re-engined in 1959 and again in 1972. She was at Grimsby and Woodbridge, but has travelled to Malta and Portugal. By the 1990s she was a houseboat near Laggan Locks on the Caledonian Canal, and later Loch Oich (pictured).

712 • C. D. E. C.

45'6"x 12'6" Watson motor • J. S. White • W 1663
Built 1928 • Fowey 1928-54, Reserve 1954-59
Sold 11.1959 • Thameserver

712 was sold in 1959 and, renamed Thameserver, was used for pilotage and supplying vessels in the Thames Estuary, operating from Southend and Leigh-on-Sea. She had a wheelhouse added, but this was later removed. By the 1990s she was laid up at Leigh and has since become semi-derelict.

713 • Elizabeth Elson

45'6"x 12'6" Watson motor • J. S. White • W 1664
Built 1929 • Angle 1929-57, Reserve 1957-68
Sold 12.1968 • Elizabeth E/ Elizabeth Elson

713 was sold in 1968 and was at Carrickfergus in the 1990s being converted.
She was then moved to Larne Lough and kept at Millbay and Islandmagee
until sold in 2000 to a Kerry-based owner. She went to Sneem on the Kerry
peninsula, and then to Kilmakilloge (pictured) on the Beara Peninsula.

714 • H. F. Bailey II/ Canadian Pacific

45'6"x 12'6" Watson motor • S. E. Saunders • S 49
Built 1928 • Cromer No.1 1928-29, Selsey 1929-37
Destroyed in fire at the Groves & Guttridge yard, 18.6.1937

714 was stationed at Cromer (pictured) for a short while before being
reallocated to Selsey. But after just eight years at Selsey, she was destroyed
by fire while undergoing overhaul at Groves & Guttridge yard, Cowes, on 18
June 1937. The fire also destroyed 787 and a lifeboat in build for Cloughey.

715 • Princess Mary

61'x 15' Barnett • Saunders • S 50
Built 1929 • Padstow 1929-52
Sold 6.1952 • Aries B

715 was sold in 1952 and was rebuilt by Tough Bros, Teddington Wharf for
a transatlantic crossing; she made a double crossing of the Atlantic in 1954.
Since 1957 she has been a private motor yacht, kept at St Jean, Cap Ferrat,
Southern France (pictured), cruising to Corsica, Sardinia and Italy.

716 • Sarah Ward and William David Crossweller

45'6"x 12'6" Watson motor • J. S. White • W 1666
Built 1929 • Courtmacsherry 1929-58; Res 1958-59, Whitehills 1959-61
Sold 9.1961 • Lady Leigh IV/ Court McSherry/ Courtmacsherry

716 was sold in 1961 and, renamed Lady Leigh IV, was converted into a
yacht at Leigh-on-Sea, re-engined with two 100hp Parsons diesels. She was
taken to France and Holland and moored at St Katharine Docks, London.
Since the 1990s she has been in Guernsey, often at St Peter Port (pictured).

717 • A. E. D.

51' x 13'6" Barnett • J. S. White • W 1669
Built 1929 • Holyhead 1929-50, Valentia 1951-57
Sold 12.1957 • Morning Star PH76

717 was sold in 1957 and was used as a fishing boat operating out of Sutton
Harbour, Plymouth. She was at Swansea in 1975 and in May 1991 was at St
Ives (pictured) on passage from Barry Dock to Weymouth. In 1992 she was
at Fuengirola, Spain and details of her whereabouts since are unknown.

718 • William and Harriot

51' x 13'6" Barnett • J. S. White • W 1670
Built 1929 • Stornoway 1929-54, Reserve 1954-59
Sold 9.1959 • W and H

After service at Stornoway and in the Reserve Fleet, 718 was sold out
of service for £1,000 in 1959 to a Leicester-based owner. Details of her
subsequent use and whereabouts were not recorded, but in 1976 she was
reportedly broken up at Barry Dock.

719 • Queen Victoria

51' x 13'6" Barnett • J. S. White • W 1671
Built 1929 • St Peter Port 1929-40 and 1945-54, Reserve 1940-41 and 1954-58, Killybegs 1941-45 • Sold 5.1958 • Queen Victoria

After service in Guernsey (pictured), 719 was sold out of service in 1958 to a Poole-based owner. She was at Berthon Boat Co, Lymington, in 1967, being used as a yacht. However, in 1978 she was burnt on the river Hamble after excessive rot had been found during conversion.

720 • City of Glasgow

51' x 13'6" Barnett • J. S. White • W 1672
Built 1929 • Campbeltown 1929-53, Reserve 1953-58
Sold 11.1959 • Hubberstone/ Elfred

720 was sold in 1959 and used by Milford Haven Harbour Commissioners and made their pilot craft no.2. She was sold to a Penarth owner, and while moored in Barry Dock suffered fire damage; she was last reported as a yacht at Barry Dock, but was possibly destroyed in the 1970s.

721 • Lady Kylsant

40'6" x 11'8" Watson motor • J. S. White • W 1673
Built 1929 • Weymouth 1929-30, Howth 1930-37, Wicklow 1937-56
Sold 8.1956 • Kylsant

721 was sold in 1956 to the Isle of Man Harbour Board. She was renamed Kylsant in 1981 and used at Douglas (pictured) as a Harbour Board tender with a wheelhouse. She was sold to the Peel Viking Association Longboat Committee in the 1990s, but was damaged and then broken up in 2003.

722 • J. and W.

40'6" x 11'8" Watson motor • J. S. White • W 1674
Built 1929 • Portpatrick 1929-37, Reserve 1937-40, Berwick 1940-57
Sold 5.1957 • LN68/ Amethyst/ J. and W.

722 was sold in 1957 and used as a fishing vessel with a wheelhouse at Wells and in Essex. By the 1990s she was at West Mersea and then taken out of the water at Canvey Island (pictured). After being moved to South Benfleet, she was taken to SWP Engineering, Berwick in 2011 to be restored.

723 • Sir David Richmond of Glasgow

40'6" x 11'8" Watson motor • J. S. White • W 1675
Built 1929 • Troon 1929-55
Sold 6.1955 • Aber Girl AB52

723 was sold out of service in June 1955 to an owner from Minsterley, Shropshire. She was renamed Aber Girl and used as a fishing boat at Aberystwyth during the 1960s. Her last reported location was Aberystwyth (pictured) in December 1969, but her whereabouts since are unknown.

724 • G. W.

40'6" x 11'8" Watson motor • J. S. White • W 1676
Built 1929 • Moelfre 1930-56
Sold 5.1956 • Storm Siren

724 was sold in 1956 from Moelfre and, fitted with a wheelhouse in 1976, was based at Teignmouth as a pilot boat. From 1994 she was kept on the river Exe (pictured). In about 2002 she went to North Woolwich before being taken to Northwich, and in 2012 was taken to Donaghadee to be restored.

725 • Sir William Hillary

64' x 14' Fast lifeboat • Thornycroft • T 2126
Built 1929 • Dover 1930-40
Sold 11.1941 • Isle of Colonsay

After service at Dover (pictured), the unique fast lifeboat 725 was sold to the Navy who, in 1946, sold her on and she became a privately-owned motor yacht. She was re-engined and based on the west coast of Scotland. On 31 October 1980 she was involved in a collision off Sardao, Portugal and sank.

726 • City of Nottingham

35'6" x 8'10" Self-righting motor • Saunders-Roe • S 51
Built 1929 • Hythe 1930-36, Clovelly 1936-49
Sold 9.1950 • Margaret Rose/ Dauntless LT214/ City of Nottingham

726 was sold in 1950 and was used as a Lundy Mail Packet. She was then used as a fishing boat out of Lowestoft until being sold and taken to Port Penrhyn, Bangor in the 1980s. She was sold and moved to Wareham in the 1990s, later going to Chepstow to be restored and in 2012 was at Oxwich.

727 • Westmorland

35'6" x 8'10" Self-righting motor • Saunders-Roe • S 52
Built 1930 • Berwick-upon-Tweed 1930-40, Cullercoats 1940-51
Sold 6.1951 • Swallow

After service at Berwick and Cullercoats, 727 was sold out of service in June 1951 to an owner based at Whitley Bay and she was renamed Swallow. She was later owned in Portsmouth, but any details of her use and subsequent whereabouts are not known.

728 • Cunard

45'6"x 12'6" Watson motor • Saunders-Roe • S 53
Built 1930 • St Marys 1930-55, Reserve 1955-69
Sold 10.1969 • Henry Joy

728 was sold in 1969 to a Belfast owner, and she has been in Northern Ireland since. She was renamed Henry Joy during the 1970s but work on a conversion at Dundrum Harbour was never completed. Semi-derelict, she was beached at Coney Island (pictured) between Killough and Ardglass.

729 • John R. Webb

45'6"x 12'6" Watson motor • Saunders-Roe • S 54
Built 1930 • Tenby 1930-55; Reserve 1955-69
Sold 9.1969 • Rairewa III

After an RNLI career lasting almost 40 years, 729 was sold out of service in September 1969 to a London-based owner and converted into the yacht Rairewa III (pictured). She was reportedly taken to Poland and used as a yacht, but her exact use and whereabouts are unknown.

730 • Cecil and Lilian Philpott

45'6"x 12'6" Watson motor • J. S. White • W 1694
Built 1930 • Newhaven 1930-59, Reserve 1959-69
Sold 10.1969 • Stenoa

730 was sold in 1969 and was used as a pleasure boat based at Thorpe le Soken near Walton-on-the-Naze. Her name Stenoa is an anagram of the initials of the family who own her. She has participated in anniversaries of the Dunkirk evacuation, including the 70th (pictured leaving Ramsgate).

Part 3
Motor Lifeboats 1930-1945

Lifeboat developments during the inter-war years centred on the motorisation of the lifeboat fleet, with motor lifeboats taking over from pulling and sailing craft. But the phasing out of the pulling lifeboat took time, and the RNLI's fleet in 1931 still included 76 pulling lifeboats out of a total of 183 lifeboats on station, while of the 23 boats in the Reserve Fleet just three were motor lifeboats.

Probably the most significant design of the era was the 51ft Barnett, which was the largest and most powerful type. With its introduction, together with that of the 45ft 6in Watson cabin motor type, new stations could be established at more remote places, such as Shetland, the west coast of Ireland and the Channel Islands,

where pulling lifeboats could not be operated as they were not powerful enough to cope with the heavy seas and long distances that often had to be travelled.

A carriage-launched motor lifeboat was also developed in the form of a small 35ft self-righting type. Motorisation came to the beach as well, with the motor tractor, first used in the 1920s to take lifeboats across the sand and to the sea, being further developed to take over the work previously done by horses, and by 1931 seventeen tractors were in service.

The RNLI's lifeboats faced the dangers and difficulties of another world war between 1939 and 1945, during which they undertook some outstanding rescues, earning many Coxswain

and crews RNLI medals of gallantry. The war tested lifeboats and lifeboat crews to the limit, lifeboat construction virtually halted, and several lifeboats were destroyed by bombs dropped by the enemy, in build, undergoing refits or when in their boathouses at the coast.

The challenge of the post-war years was to phase out the pulling lifeboat completely and continue to develop the motor lifeboat. By 1950 only one pulling lifeboat remained in service, at Whitby, out of a total fleet of 154 craft. The last sailing lifeboat had been replaced in 1948, at New Quay, in Wales. In 1950 no fewer than twelve new lifeboats entered service, indicative of the rapid building programme then being undertaken.

The 45ft 6in Watson motor lifeboat Charlotte Elizabeth (ON-774) at Port Askaig, Islay. She served at Islay for 24 years and saved 162 lives.

731 • Lady Jane and Martha Ryland

51' x 13'6" Barnett • J. S. White • W 1695
Built 1930 • Lerwick 1930-58; Reserve 1958-69
Sold 3.1969 • Cambrae/ Lady Jane

731 was sold in 1969 and became the pleasure boat Cambrae. She was re-engined in 1981 with two 90hp Gardner 6LW diesels and cruised to Scotland, Orkney and Holland. In 1985 she was sold and taken to Brighton and Chichester. By 2000 she was moored at Torpoint, Plymouth (pictured).

732 • Catherine

45'6" x 12'6" Watson motor • J. S. White • W 1696
Built 1930 • Built for Bombay Port Trust, commissioned 3.7.1930
Sold 1935

732 was released from the RNLI's building programme in 1930 for service in India with the Bombay Port Trust. However, after decaying she was sold in 1935 to Khilji & Sons, Bombay for scrapping.

733 • Mary Stanford

51' x 13'6" Barnett • Saunders-Roe • S55
Built 1930 • Ballycotton 1930-59, Reserve 1959-68
Sold 2.1969 • Mary Stanford

733 was sold in 1969 and was used as a pilot boat at Limerick. In 1987 she was taken to Crosshaven where she was partially restored with the intention of display at Ballycotton. However, the work was not finished, and she ended up at Alexandra Basin, Dublin (pictured), where she is deteriorating.

734 • George Shee

51' x 13'6" Barnett • Saunders-Roe • S56
Built 1930 • Torbay 1930-58, Reserve 1958-58
Sold 12.1958 • George Shee

After service at Torbay (pictured), 734 was sold out of service in December 1958 to the Guatemalan lifeboat service. She was shipped to South America and, together with 781 and 799, was used as a lifeboat. Nothing is known about her career in Guatemala or her current whereabouts.

735 • William and Clara Ryland

51' x 13'6" Barnett • Saunders-Roe • S57
Built 1930 • Weymouth 1930-57
Sold 1.1958 • William and Clara/ Ryland

735 was sold in 1958 to a Kent-based owner, and was kept at Gillingham pier and on the Medway during the 1970s. In the 1980s she was at Strood, and by the 1990s was at Hoo, Kent, as a pleasure boat. She has been used as a houseboat at Whitton Marine, Hoo (pictured), since about 1994.

736 • W. and S.

45'6" x 12'6" Watson motor • J. S. White • W 1705
Built 1930 • Penlee 1931-60, Buckie 1960-61, Reserve 1961-69
Sold 3.1970 • Early Mist/ Atlantic

736 was sold in 1970 and converted into a ketch-rigged motor cruiser, cruising to Gibraltar and the Mediterranean. By the 1990s, renamed Atlantic, she was used as a pleasure boat and kept in Carrickfergus Marina. In about 2001 she moved to Falmouth (pictured), and later to Trelew, near Mylor Bridge.

737 • Louisa Polden

35'6" x 8'10"' Self-righting motor • Saunders-Roe • S58
Built 1931 • Redcar 1931-51
Sold 7.1951 • Louisa Polden

After service at Redcar (pictured), 737 was sold in 1951 to the Sea Cadets at Stockton-on-Tees, and she was kept on the river Tees at Stockton for a number of years. Information about her usage or any alterations made to her is not known. In the 1980s she was broken up at Stockton.

738 • J. H. W.

35'6" x 8'10" Self-righting motor • J. S. White • W 1708
Built 1931 • Lytham St Annes 1931-39, Padstow No.2 1939-47
Sold 4.1948 • Follie/ Navette

738 was sold in 1948 and was converted into the single screw ketch Follie registered at Maldon. By the early 1970s she was at Thames Ditton, near Kingston-on-Thames, and was later renamed Navette at Birdham Pool (pictured). However, by the 1990s her whereabouts was unknown.

739 • Lily Glen – Glasgow

35'6" x 8'10" Self-righting motor • Saunders-Roe • S59
Built 1931 • Girvan 1931-51
Sold 5.1952 • Ivydale/ Seeker II

739 was sold in 1952 to a London owner and converted into the yacht Ivydale. She was used as a houseboat with one end box removed and a cabin added at Itchenor. By the 1990s she had moved to Rye Town Quay (pictured), and later became derelict between Rye Town and Rye Harbour.

740 • Cyril and Lilian Bishop

35'6" x 8'10" Self-righting motor • J. S. White • W 1709
Built 1931 • Hastings 1931-50
Sold 11.1950 • Lindy Lou/ CN180/ Thekla

740 was sold in 1950 to Wallasea Yacht Club, but after a further sale she became a fishing boat on the west coast of Scotland. In the 1990s she was found in poor condition at Port Askaig and taken to France by Simon Evans for restoration at St Denis les Sens (pictured), moving to Migennes in 2012.

741 • Morison Watson

35'6" x 8'10" Self-righting motor • Saunders-Roe • S60
Built 1931 • Kirkcudbright 1931-53
Sold 5.1953 • Scauronian

741 was sold in 1953 and was returned to Kirkcudbright and Kippford as a pleasure boat. By the early 1990s she was under restoration at Kingholm Quay, Dumfries, and her shelter was removed. She was later taken to Terregles, west of Dumfries (pictured), where she was broken up in 1998.

742 • Herbert Joy II

35'6" x 8'10" Self-righting motor • J. S. White • W 1710
Built 1931 • Scarborough 1931-51
Sold 2.1951 • Viking Raumur

742 was sold in 1951 and had several different owners during the 1950s and 1960s. Registered in London, she was renamed Viking Raumur and fitted with a single 24hp Petter engine. She was based in Goole in the 1970s, but during the 1980s she was broken up at Acouter Boatyard, York.

743 • John and Sarah Eliza Stych

35'6" x 8'10" Self-righter motor • Saunders-Roe • S 61
Built 1931 • Padstow (Hawker's Cove) 1931-38, St Ives 1938-39
Wrecked on service 23.1.1939

743 was wrecked on 23 January 1939 on service to the steamer Wilston. Off Clodgy Point, a tremendous wave struck the boat and capsized her. She capsized two more times, and although she righted, only one man survived. She was then hurled onto rocks at Gwithian (pictured) where she was burnt.

744 • Laurana Sarah Blunt

35'6" x 8'10" Self-righter motor • J. S. White • W 1711
Built 1931 • Youghal 1931-52
Sold 10.1952 • Laurana

744 was sold in 1952 to the west coast of Scotland where, with the addition of a small wheelhouse, she became the fishing boat Laurana at Ullapool. By the early 1980s she had been abandoned on a beach about a mile west of Ullapool near Morefield (pictured). She was broken up in about 2005.

745 • Lady Harrison

35'6" x 8'10" Self-righter motor • Saunders-Roe • S62
Built 1931 • Ramsey 1931-48, Aberystwyth 1949-51
Sold 3.1952 • Neula/ Merch-y-Mor/ Isle of Skomer/ Lady Harrison

745 was sold in 1952 and became the fishing boat Neula at Aberystwyth. By the 1980s she was at Pembroke (pictured) with a wheelhouse as the fishing boat Isle of Skomer. In 2000 she went to Marchwood, Southampton to be restored, but this never happened and she was burnt there in April 2005.

746 • William Maynard

35'6" x 8'10" Self-righter motor • J. S. White • W 1712
Built 1931 • Cloughey 1931-39, Reserve 1939-41 and 1949-53, Ferryside 1941-48, Whitehills 1948-49 • Sold 2.1953 • Endora

746 was sold in 1953 to an Essex-based owner. She became the yacht Endora and visited Penarth (pictured), Cardiff, Paignton and Weymouth during her time. She was lost off Dungeness in December 1970 while cruising in the English Channel.

747 • Stanhope Smart

35'6" x 8'10" Self-righter motor • Saunders Roe • S63
Built 1931 • Bridlington 1931-47, Padstow (Hawker's Cove) 1947-51
Sold 10.1951 • Unknown

After service at Padstow (pictured), 747 was sold out of service in October 1951 to the rescue service of Liberia for use as a lifeboat. However, information about her subsequent history or service there is not known, and details of her use and location, or her current whereabouts are missing.

748 • Mary Ann Blunt

35'6" x 8'10" Self-righter motor • J. S. White • W 1713
Built 1931 • Clogher Head 1931-50
Sold 3.1951 • Unknown

After spending her whole service career at Clogher Head (pictured), 748 was sold out of service in March 1951 for £200 to Father McCooey, who sold her on to the Sea Scouts at Balbriggan. However, no further information about her subsequent history or location is known, or if she remains in existence.

749 • George and Sarah Strachan

45'6" x 12'6" Watson motor • J. S. White • W 1718
Built 1931 • Dunbar 1931-59; Res 1959-60 & 63-69, Exmouth 1960-62
Sold 3.1969 • George and Sarah Strachan

749 was sold in 1969 to a Fraserburgh owner, who sold her on in 1972 to an Inverness-based owner. She was at Inverary in the late 1970s, where a cabin was added and she was a work boat. By the 1990s she was at Inverary Quay (pictured), and has since been used as a work boat just north of Dunoon.

750 • Oldham

35'6" x 10' Liverpool motor • Groves & Guttridge • G&G 175
Built 1931 • Hoylake 1931-52
Sold 3.1952 • Grey Lass

After service at Hoylake, 750 was sold out of service in March 1952 to a Hoylake based owner for use as a fishing boat (pictured). She was renamed Grey Lass but is thought to have been broken up at Hoylake in November 1955. Further information about her use and conversion is not known.

751 • Abdy Beauclerk

41' x 12'3" Watson motor • J. S. White • W 1726
Built 1931 • Aldeburgh No.1 1931-58
Sold 1.1959 • St Ita

751 was sold in 1959 to Cork Harbour Commissioners for use as a pilot boat and has been in Ireland ever since. By the 1990s, renamed St Ita, she was at Galway Docks (pictured) in a neglected state. In about 2000 she moved from Galway to Rusheen Bay and was reportedly used as a houseboat.

752 • John and William Mudie

35'6" x 8'10" Self-righting motor • Thornycroft • T 2245
Built 1932 • Arbroath 1932-50
Sold 6.1951 • unknown

After just service at Arbroath (pictured), 752 was sold out of service in June 1951 to an owner based in Ambleside, in the Lake District. But no further information about her use or whereabouts has been found, and whether she remains in existence is not known.

753 • Civil Service No.5

45'6" x 12'6" Watson motor • J. S. White • W 1732
Built 1932 • Donaghadee 1932-50, Port St Mary 1950-56, Reserve 1956-58 • Sold 2.1958 • Donaghadee/ Loe Trout/ Silver Sea/ Silver Bay/ Lorelei/ White Star

753 was sold in 1958 and has had a number of owners. She was in Cornwall from the 1960s to the 1990s, when she moved to Ireland and was at Arklow, Kilmore and New Ross. In 2001 she went to the Caledonian Canal (pictured), and sank, but was recovered and is out of the water at Muirtown, Inverness.

754 • Lloyd's

51' x 13'6" Barnett • Groves & Guttridge • G&G 180
Built 1932 • Barra Island 1932-57, Reserve 1957-69
Sold 1.1970 • Jersey Gleaner/ Causeway Gleaner/ Lloyds

754 was sold in 1970 and was used as a workboat. She was on the south coast in the 1980s, before moving to Northern Ireland in the 1990s. In about 2003 she was repaired at Padstow, and ended up at Shoreham (pictured) soon after. In 2010 she was taken to Sandwich Marina, with her engines removed.

755 • Peter and Sarah Blake

51' x 13'6" Barnett motor • J. S. White • W 1732
Built 1932 • Fenit 1932-58; Reserve 1958-72
Sold 10.1972 • New Providence/ Peter and Sarah Blake

755 was sold in 1972 and, with a wheelhouse added, became the trip boat New Providence. By 1983 she had moved to Bangor, North Wales, then went to Port Amlwch in 1986, and in 1997 to Davey Bank. In 2005 she was at Slaughden Quay, Aldeburgh (pictured), moving to Great Wakering in 2009.

756 • Civil Service No.4

35'6" x 8'10" Self-righting motor • J. S. White • W 1734
Built 1932 • Whitehills 1932-48
Sold 6.1948 • M. G. M./ Sandy K.

After service at Whitehills (pictured), 756 was sold in 1948 but her subsequent history is somewhat vague. She was converted into the yacht M. G. M., and registered in Buckie. Sometime after 1970 she was sold to an owner in St Johns, Newfoundland where she was last reported, as Sandy K.

757 • Frederick Angus

35'6" x 8'10" Self-righting motor • J. S. White • W 1735
Built 1932 • Aberystwyth 1932-49
Sold 8.1949 • Yr-Ystwyth

757 was sold in 1949 to an owner in Kingston on Thames who converted her into a motor yacht. By 1980 she was at Aberaeron (pictured) in Wales, renamed Yr Ystwyth. In the early 2000s she was swept away in a storm and holed, and has since laid in a field at Oakford about a mile off the A487.

758 • Rosa Woodd and Phyllis Lunn

41' x 11'8" Watson motor • Groves & Guttridge • G&G 181
Built 1933 • Shoreham Harbour 1933-63, Reserve 1963-73
Sold 3.1973 • Dowager

758 was sold in 1973 to a Canvey Island owner and was heavily converted into the cruising yacht Dowager at Halcon Marine, Essex. She is maintained at Canvey Island and based at Allington Lock on the Medway. She was taken to Dunkirk (pictured) in 2010 and is a well-known Dunkirk Little Ship.

759 • Thomas McCunn

45'6" x 12'6" Watson motor • Groves & Guttridge • G&G 182
Built 1933 • Longhope 1933-62, Reserve 1962-72
Sold 8.1972 • Pentland Speir/ Thomas McCunn

759 was sold in 1972 to a Walton-on-the-Naze owner and, unaltered, became the yacht Pentland Speir. She moved to Buckler's Hard in the 1980s, and later to Hayling Island. In 2000 she went back to Longhope (pictured) to be displayed in the old lifeboat house from which she is occasionally launched.

760 • Anne Allen

35'6" x 10' Liverpool motor • Thornycroft • T2255
Built 1932 • Skegness 1932-53
Sold 1953 • LN 175/ Golden Fleece II/ Anne Allen

760 was sold in 1953 and became the whelk boat LN175 at Wells-next-the-Sea. By the 1980s she was the pleasure boat Golden Fleece II at Blakeney with a wheelhouse added. In 2002 a restoration began at Sutterton, near Boston (pictured). This was due to be completed in 2013.

761 • Charles Cooper Henderson

41' x 12'3" Watson motor • Groves & Guttridge • G&G 183
Built 1933 • Dungeness 1933-57, Reserve 1957-74
Sold 1.1976 • Elizabeth and Marie Spencer/ Caresana

761 was sold in 1976 and became the yacht Elizabeth and Marie Spencer. She was renamed Caresana in 1977 and was then based in Guernsey, then France and Guernsey again. After a short period at Leigh on Sea she was rescued by the Dunkirk Little Ships Restoration Trust and is to be restored.

762 • Charles Dibdin (Civil Service No.2)

41' x 12'3" Watson motor • Groves & Guttridge • G&G 184
Built 1933 • Walmer 1933-59
Sold 1959 • Channel Rover

After service at Walmer (pictured), 762 was sold in 1959 to an owner in Kingsdown, Kent, where she was converted into the motor yacht Channel Rover. She was kept at Dover and was used as a pilot boat in 1980. Information about her current whereabouts is not known.

763 • Caroline Parsons

35'6" x 9'3" Self-righting motor • J. S. White • W 1745
Built 1933 • St Ives 1933-38
Wrecked on service 1.1938

763 was wrecked on 31 January 1938 on service to the steamer Alba. Having saved 23 people, 763 was capsized by a large wave. She righted, but then ran aground on rocks, where she was completely wrecked (pictured). The lifeboat crew got ashore safely, but five of the rescued were lost.

764• Nellie and Charlie

35'6" x 10' Liverpool motor • J. S. White • W 1746
Built 1933 • Anstruther 1933-50
Sold 4.1951 • Frogmans Miss/ Nellie/ Nellie and Charlie

764 was sold in 1951 and became the work boat Frogmans Miss at Felixstowe Ferry. By the 1980s she had been heavily converted as a yacht and renamed Nellie. In 2006 she moved to Woodbridge, and in 2010 went to Sharpness Marina (pictured) and was restored to her lifeboat colours.

765 • Fifi and Charles

35'6" x 10' Liverpool motor • J. S. White • W 1747
Built 1933 • Weston-super-Mare 1933-62
Sold 10.1962 • Wyvern

765 was sold in 1962 and was converted at Kimbers, Devon. She was based at Cowes from the 1960s, and was further altered on the Isle of Wight in 1995, and then moored in the Medina. She was at Poole in 1999 for the RNLI's 175th anniversary (pictured). She went to Redon, Brittany, France in 2008.

766 • Robert Patton - The Always Ready

35'6" x 10' Liverpool motor • J. S. White • W 1748
Built 1933 • Runswick 1933-54
Sold 5.1954 • Alaska II; The Always Ready

766 was sold in 1954 to Sharpness Docks where she was used as the pilot boat Alaska. In the 1980s, in private ownership, she remained at Sharpness and toured the canals. By 1997 she was at Saul Junction (pictured), where, under new ownership, she was restored and renamed The Always Ready.

767 • Catherine Harriet Eaton

35'6" x 9'3" Self-righting motor • J. S. White • W 1749
Built 1933 • Exmouth 1933-53
Sold 1953 • Sharon

767 was sold in 1953 and became a ferry between Marloes and Skomer Island, Wales. By the 1980s she had moved to Lochans, Dumfries, and by 1990 was out of the water at Kingholme Quay, Dumfries (pictured). By 2002 she had been removed and her current whereabouts are unknown.

768 • Thomas and Annie Wade Richards

35'6" x 9'3" Self-righting motor • J. S. White • W 1750
Built 1933 • Llandudno 1933-53
Sold 1953 • Craiglais/ Will Ifan/ Dolphin AB6

768 was sold in 1953 and converted into a fishing boat. She was named Craiglais and Will Ifan before being renamed Dolphin at Aberystwyth. She moved to Rhyl (pictured) in about 1983 before moving to Coburgh Marina in 1995. She was damaged off Rock Point in 2001 and broken up in 2004.

769 • Duke of York

41' x 11'8" Watson motor • Groves & Guttridge • G&G 185
Built 1934 • The Lizard (Polpeor) 1934-61
Sold 1961 • Lizzie Doy

769 was sold in 1961 to a Cornwall owner. An aft cabin was added and she was used as a pleasure boat based at Mylor. By 1990 she had been moved to the Shannon Estuary, later moving to Arklow. By 1996 she was at Wexford (pictured) where she is kept in the summer, going to Castlebridge for winter.

770 • Harriot Dixon

35'6" x 10'3" Liverpool motor • Groves & Guttridge • G&G 194
Built 1934 • Cromer No.2 1934-64
Sold 12.1964 • Sareter

770 was sold in 1964 and was heavily converted into the motor yacht Sareter, based at Blakeney. She has remained at Blakeney and was, during much of the 1980s and 1990s, stored in a boatyard (pictured) above the village. She has since been in the water at Blakeney Pit during the summer.

771 • The Three Sisters

35'6" x 10' Liverpool motor • J. S. White • W 1771
Built 1934 • Coverack 1934-54
Sold 1954 • Gay Dawn 2/ Patricia Mary/ Coverack/ Silent Waters

771 was sold in 1954 and became the pleasure boat Gay Dawn 2 at St Ives, before becoming the trip boat Coverack in Padstow. In the 1980s she became the fishing boat Silent Waters, and was at Rhyl, Deganwy and Rhos on Sea (pictured). In 2009 she was destroyed by Harbour Authorities there.

772 • Elizabeth and Albina Whitley

35'6" x 10' Liverpool motor • Groves & Guttridge • G&G 195
Built 1934 • Flamborough 1934-48, Reserve 1948-52
Sold 1. 1953 • Albina

772 was sold in 1953 to a Shoreham owner, but moved to the west coast of Scotland and was converted into the yacht Albina. She was based on Loch Etive but moved to Port Appin (pictured) in the 1980s and stayed there until 2011, when she was sold. She is now reported to be in the Oban area.

773 • Joseph Braithwaite

35'6" x 10' Liverpool motor • J. S. White • W 1772
Built 1934 • Maryport 1934-49, Reserve 1949-52
Sold 1952 • Joseph Braithwaite/ Seahawk

773 was sold in 1952 to Aberdovey Outward Bound School, and in 1960 was sold to Barry Dock Sea Scouts. In 1962-3 she was converted into a yacht. The Scouts sold her in 1980 and the new owner took her into his back garden in Borough Avenue, Barry, where she has slowly deteriorated.

774 • Charlotte Elizabeth

45'6" x 12'6" Watson motor • Alexander Robertson • R201
Built 1935 • Islay (Port Askaig) 1935-59, Reserve 1959-61
Sold 8.1961 • Corgarth/ Dale Queen

774 was sold to Dale in South Wales where a small wheelhouse was added and she was renamed Corgarth, and then Dale Queen, By 1980 she was a work boat at Scrabster harbour, later becoming a fishing boat at Thurso. By 1995 she was out of the water there (pictured) and has gradually broken up.

775 • Mona

45'6" x 12'6" Watson motor • Groves & Guttridge • G&G 196
Built 1935 • Broughty Ferry 1935-59
Wrecked on service 8.12.1959

775 was wrecked on service to the North Carr Light Vessel on 8 December 1959. While heading into St Andrews Bay in extreme weather, she capsized and was later found washed up at Buddon Sands (pictured) with all eight crew drowned. She was salvaged, but was burnt at Cockenzie in March 1960.

776 • The Rankin

51' x 13'6" Barnett • Groves & Guttridge • G&G 197
Built 1935 • Aith 1935-61, Reserve 1961-69
Sold 3.1970 • Penny Dragon/ Perseverance

776 was sold in 1970 and taken to Carnlough as the pleasure boat Penny Dragon. By 1987 she had moved to Emsworth, Hampshire and been renamed Perseverance. She remained on the south coast, and has been based at Fareham and, from 2011, Tipner Boating and Angling Club (pictured).

777 • H. F. Bailey

46' x 12'9" Watson motor • Groves & Guttridge • G&G 204
Built 1935 • Cromer 1935-45; Helvick Head 1946-60; Reserve 1960-72
Sold 6.1973 • H. F. Bailey

777 was sold to Leisure Sport Ltd, Feltham, and displayed at Thorpe Park, but before 1990 she was stored afloat at Leigh on Sea. In 1991 she returned to Cromer for display in the old boathouse. In 2009 she was moved into the new Henry Blogg Museum to become the centrepiece (pictured).

778 • Edward and Isabella Irwin

46' x 12'9" Watson motor • Groves & Guttridge • G&G 205
Built 1935 • Sunderland 1935-63; Reserve 1963-69
Sold 4.1971 • Lady Clare C; Edward and Isabella Irwin

778 was sold in 1971 and became the yacht Lady Clare C in Essex. She was based at Stamford Mill until 1983 when she moved to Benfleet. By 1989 she was at Wrexham being stripped down. She moved to Vickers yard, Birkenhead in 2000 and in 2009 went to Liverpool Sailing Club (pictured).

779 • Rosabella

32' x 9' Surf motor • J. S. White • W 1790
Built 1935 • Ilfracombe 1936-45
Sold 1946 • Rosabella

779 was one of two lifeboats given by the RNLI to the Netherlands lifeboat service, KNZHRM, for use as a lifeboat. She was needed due to the shortage of lifeboats following the Nazi occupation. She was stationed at Terschelling 1946-55 and sold in 1955, being restored as a pleasure boat at Aalsmeer.

780 • Royal Silver Jubilee 1910-1935

32' x 9' Surf motor • Groves & Guttridge • G&G 206
Built 1935 • Wells 1936-45
Sold 1946 • Rosilee

780 was one of two lifeboats given by the RNLI to the Netherlands lifeboat service, KNZHRM, for use as a lifeboat following the wartime occupation by the Nazis. She was re-engined in 1953 with a single 42hp Perkins PM4 diesel and a conventional propeller, and was sold by the KNZHRM in 1959.

781 • W. R. A.

35'6" x 10'3" Liverpool motor • J. S. White • W 1803
Built 1936 • North Sunderland 1936-54, Reserve 1954-58
Sold 8.1958 • W. R. A.

After service at North Sunderland (pictured) and in the Reserve Fleet, 781 was sold out of service in August 1958 to Guatemala for use as a lifeboat with the country's lifeboat organisation, together with 734 and 799. How long she remained in service and her current status are not known.

782 • Margaret Dawson

35'6" x 10'3" Liverpool motor • J. S. White • W1804
Built 1936 • Gourdon 1936-52, Reserve 1952-55
Sold 1.1956 • LL 23/ Storm/ Viking II/ Viking

782 was sold in 1956, minus her engine and gearbox, for use by Hoylake Coxswain Jack Bird as a fishing boat. A wheelhouse was added and she was at Rhyl (pictured) and Holyhead in the 1990s. In 2001 she was driven on to rocks adjacent to the old lifeboat house where only her hull remains.

783 • The Viscountess Wakefield

41'x 12'3" Watson motor • Groves & Guttridge • G&G 207
Built 1936 • Hythe 1936-40
Lost on war service 5.1940

783 was lost on the beaches of Dunkirk helping to evacuate troops on 31 May 1940. She had been at Hythe (pictured) for four years when, manned by naval personnel, she was taken across the Channel to Dunkirk. She had to be abandoned after going aground on the shoals off the French coast.

784 • Swn-Y-Mor (Civil Service No.6)

46'x 12'9" Watson motor • Groves & Guttridge • G&G 208
Built 1936 • St Davids 1936-63, Eyemouth 1964-67, Reserve 1967-72
Sold 2.1973 • Swn-Y-Mor

784 was sold in 1973 and converted into a motor yacht by Harrison, Amble, being re-engined and fitted with a deckhouse. She was kept at Amble until 1980, when she was sold. She has since been around the world and travelled almost 100,000 miles, with her owners Warren and Jill Scott living on board.

785 • Sir Heath Harrison

35'6" x 9'6" Self-righting motor • J. S. White • W 1810
Built 1936 • Port St Mary 1936-49, Reserve 1949-55
Sold 1.1956 • King John III

After 19 years of service, at Port St Mary and then in Reserve, 785 was sold in January 1956. She was bought by John Walker, a marine engineer and pilot in Dover, and used as a work boat during the 1960s. She was last reported as a pilot boat at Dover's Western Docks (pictured) in the 1970s.

786 • Foresters Centenary

35'6" x 10'3" Liverpool motor • Groves & Guttridge • G&G 210
Built 1936 • Sheringham 1936-61
Sold 9.1961 • Seal Morning/ RNLB Foresters' Centenary

786 was sold in 1961 and became a fishing boat, with a wheelhouse, at Wells before being moved to Benfleet Creek by 1990. In 1995 she was fishing at Maldon. In 1996 she was moved to Sheringham for restoration and was eventually placed on display at The Mo Museum (pictured).

787 • S. G. E.

46' x 12'9" Watson motor • Groves & Guttridge • G&G 213
Built 1936 • Yarmouth 1936-37
Destroyed at boatyard 6.1937

The first lifeboat to be fitted with a diesel engine, 787 had been in service at Yarmouth for less than a year when she was destroyed by fire at Groves & Guttridge's yard, Cowes on 18 June 1937 (pictured). She had been built by the yard and had returned for maintenance work.

788 • Jeanie Speirs

46' x 12'9" Watson motor • Alexander Robertson & Sons • R211
Built 1936 • Portpatrick 1937-61
Sold 4.1961 • Unnamed

788 served at Portpatrick, on Scotland's south-west coast (pictured), for well over 20 years and was sold out of service in April 1961 to a Colchester-based owner. Her subsequent whereabouts are unknown, and it was reported that she had been lost at Largs in 1974.

789 • R. P. L.

46' x 12'9" Watson motor • Groves & Guttridge • G&G 215
Built 1937 • Howth 1937-62
Sold 9.1962 • Blue Gannet/ Southern Cross/ Maid of Sker

789 was sold in 1962 and was used as a workboat, helping as a safety boat during speedboat racing in the Bristol Channel. She was mostly based in South Wales and in the early 1990s was semi-derelict at Barry Dock (pictured). She was destroyed by fire at Grangetown, Cardiff in April 1999.

790 • John and Charles Kennedy

46' x 12'9" Watson motor • Groves & Guttridge • G&G 216
Built 1937 • Fraserburgh 1937-53
Wrecked on service in 2.1953

790 had been on station at Fraserburgh (pictured) for almost 16 years when she capsized while returning from service on 9 February 1953, and six of her crew of seven were lost in the tragedy. She was damaged beyond repair in the incident and was subsequently broken up.

791 • Elizabeth Wills Allen

35'6" x 10'3" Liverpool motor • J. S. White • W 1817
Built 1936 • Seaham 1936-50, Reserve 1950-53
Sold 2.1953 • Elizabeth

791 was sold in 1953 to Wells where she was used as a fishing boat, later moving to Lowestoft. By 1983 she was at Port Penrhyn, Bangor. Altered with a wheelhouse in the 1980s, she operated from there and Caernarfon. Since 2006 she has been ashore at Port Penrhyn (pictured) and may be broken up.

792 • Annie Ronald and Isabella Forrest

35'6" x 10'3" Liverpool motor • J. S. White • W 1818
Built 1936 • St Abbs 1936-49, Reserve 1949-52, Bridlington 1952-53, Reserve 1953-56 and 58-59, Scarborough 1956-58, Llandudno 59-64
Sold 7.1965 • Petomi/ Ocean Wanderer

792 was sold in 1965 to Solihull and, with the addition of a wheelhouse, was kept at Barmouth as the yacht Petomi. By 1980 she was on the river Blackwater. In 2003 she went to Sutterton, Boston before being sold to Walton on the Naze in 2007 and renamed Ocean Wanderer (pictured).

793 • Clarissa Langdon

35'6" x 10'3" Liverpool motor • J. S. White • W 1822
Built 1937 • Boulmer 1937-62, Seaham 1962-63, Reserve 1963-65
Sold 4.1965 • Westering Homewards/ Homewards

793 was sold in 1965 to the Department of Agriculture and Fisheries for Scotland for use as a work boat, named Westering Homewards, in Shetland usually based at Foula. Later renamed Homewards, she became a trip and post delivery boat but by 2009 she was out of the water (pictured).

794 • Richard Silver Oliver

35'6" x 10'3" Liverpool motor • J. S. White • W 1823
Built 1937 • Cullercoats 1937-39, Newquay 1940-45, Ilfracombe 45-52, Criccieth 1953-61, Reserve 61-63 • Sold 1963 • Valperaiso II/ Talcahuano

794 was sold in 1963 to the Chilean lifeboat service at Valperaiso, where she was used as the lifeboat Valperaiso II. She was later sold by the service and became the pleasure boat Talcahuano at Port of Lirquén. Unfortunately ,she was wrecked there on 13 July 1978 and became a total loss.

795 • Frank and William Oates

35'6"x 10'3" Liverpool motor • Groves & Guttridge • G&G 218
Built 1937 • Eyemouth 1937-51, Girvan 1952-55, Reserve 1955-63, Hastings 1963-64
Sold 11.1964 • Seren-y-Mor

795 was sold in 1964 to become the trip boat Seren-y-Mor at Tenby (pictured). A small wheelhouse was added and she was used to take visitors to nearby Caldy Island. She has performed this service for almost 50 years.

796 • [Herbert John]

35'6"x 10'3" Liverpool motor • Groves & Guttridge • G&G 219
Built 1937 • Allocated to Cloughey
Destroyed at builder's yard, 6.1937

796 was destroyed while she was being built when a fire engulfed the builders yard at Cowes on 18 June 1937. The Cloughey station (boathouse pictured as it is today) therefore continued to operate 746 until 1939, when another new Liverpool class lifeboat, 825, was placed on station.

797 • Howard D

35'6" x 10'3" Liverpool motor • Saunders-Roe • S 64
Built 1937 • St Helier 1937-48, Flamborough 1948-53, Arbroath 1953-56, Reserve 1956-62, Seaham 1962-63, Reserve 1963-64
Sold 10.1964 • Spero II/ Howard D

797 was sold in 1964 to Wells where she was used as a fishing boat. By 1985 she had moved to Great Yarmouth where she was used for fishing. In 1999 she went to Jersey where she was restored to her original condition.

798 • Ann Isabella Pyemont

35'6" x 10'3" Liverpool motor • Groves & Guttridge • G&G 220
Built 1937 • Kilmore Quay 1937-65
Sold 3.1966 • Ann Isabella

798 was sold in 1966 to Wells next the Sea where, unaltered, she was used as a fishing boat. By 1983 she had moved to Gorleston, and by 1998 to Lowestoft (pictured), where she was given a transom stern and wheelhouse. She is one of six boats that rotate work, and is sometimes on Oulton Broad.

799 • Helen Sutton

35'6" x 10'3" Liverpool motor • Saunders-Roe • S65
Built 1937 • Peel 1937-52, Reserve 1952-58
Sold 12.1958 • Helen Sutton

After service at Peel, Isle of Man (pictured) and in the Reserve Fleet, 799 was sold out of service in 1958 to the government of Guatemala where, from 1959, she operated as a lifeboat under her original name. However, there is no record of her current whereabouts or current use.

800 • Sarah Ann Austin

35'6" x 10'3" Liverpool motor • Groves & Guttridge • G&G 221
Built 1937 • Blackpool 1937-61, Reserve 1962-65
Sold 8.1965 • SAA/ Fly by Night/ Valhalla/ Sarah Ann Austin

800 was sold in 1965 and became a pleasure boat at Lowestoft. A wheelhouse was added and she was renamed SAA and then Fly by Night. By 1984 she had joined the fishing fleet at Hamilton Dock, Lowestoft as Valhalla. By 2002 she had moved to Gorleston (pictured) but moved to St Olaves in 2011.

801 • Sir Arthur Rose

46' x 12'9" Watson motor • Alexander Robertson • R219
Built 1938 • Tobermory 1938-47, Mallaig 1948-57, Courtmacsherry Harbour 1958-69, Res 1969-72 • Sold 2.1973 • Belmura/ Rose Marion

801 was sold in 1973 to a Bristol owner and she was heavily converted as the yacht Belmura. By 1985 she had been renamed Rose Marion and was at Bristol Floating Dock. By 1993 she had been rebuilt with a revised superstructure, and is now kept at Limekiln Quay, Woodbridge (pictured).

802 • City of Edinburgh

46' x 12'9" Watson motor • Alexander Robertson • R218
Built 1938 • Wick 1938-68, Reserve 1968-76
Sold 7.1976 • Stadab/ Saltire

802 was sold in 1976 and, renamed Stadab, was converted and kept at Loch Ness Marina. By 1988 she was rebuilt ashore at Peterhead, renamed Saltire and by 1996 had moved to Dochgarroch, Inverness. By 2003 she was at Caley Marina, Inverness, then moved to Lock 14 on the Crinan Canal (pictured).

803 • Canadian Pacific

46' x 12'9" Watson motor • Alexander Robertson • R 217
Built 1938 • Selsey 1938-69; Reserve 1969-77
Sold 2.1978 • Scrabster Pilot/ Kelmar/ Tusack/ Canadian Pacific

803 was sold in 1978 to the Scrabster Harbour Trust and used as a pilot boat until 1985. She then became the diving boat Kelmar, and later the fishing boat Tusack, based at Scrabster. She then moved to Scotland's west coast and became a pleasure boat at Dornie, near the Kyle of Lochalsh.

804 • S. G. E.

46' x 12'9" Watson motor • J. S. White • W 1831
Built 1938 • Yarmouth 1938-43 and 1945-63; Reserve 1943-45
Sold 4.1964 • John Dutton

After service at Yarmouth (pictured) and Reserve, 804 was sold out of service with engines in April 1964 to the Government of St Helena, via the Crown Agents in London. She was taken to St Helena in 1964 where she became a work boat, but in 2001 was reported to have been lost there.

805 • Samuel and Marie Parkhouse

46' x 12'9" Watson motor • J. S. White • W 1832
Built 1938 • Salcombe 1938-62
Sold 9.1963 • Oniros

805 was sold in 1963 without engines and in 1972 was bought by Anthony Merriman, who left her unaltered externally and used her as a private yacht based at the Hamble until 2009. She then moved to Old Mill Creek boatyard near Dartmouth, and has been based at Salcombe since 2011.

806 • Rachel and Mary Evans

41' x 11'8" Watson motor • Groves & Guttridge • G&G 226
Built 1937 • Barry Dock 1937-68; Reserve 1968-69
Broke from moorings

806 served at Barry Dock (pictured) for more than 30 years with distinction. After being replaced in 1968 and then transferred to the Reserve Fleet, she was sent to Weston-super-Mare on temporary duty but broke from her moorings there on 12 April 1969 and was wrecked.

807 • Inbhear Mor

41' x 11'8" Watson motor • Groves & Guttridge • G&G 227
Built 1938 • Arklow 1938-68, Reserve 1968-73
Sold 3.1974 • The Lady Ann/ Arklow

807 was sold in 1974 and was used as a fishing boat until being damaged. In 1985 she was restored and rebuilt at Maylandsea as the pleasure boat Arklow. She was based in Essex, moved to Wells, then went to Hartlepool in 2002. Since 2007 she has been ashore at Aber Tewi, near Borth (pictured).

808 • Mary Ann Hepworth

41' x 11'8" Watson motor • Groves & Guttridge • G&G 228
Built 1938 • Whitby 1938-74
Sold 7.1974 • Mary Ann Hepworth

808 was sold out of service in 1974 to a Norfolk-based owner and was used as a pleasure boat on the Broads. Following a change of ownership in the 1990s, she returned to Whitby (pictured), where she was restored to her lifeboat appearance and operated as a trip boat out of the harbour.

809 • Helen Blake

28' x 8' Harbour • Groves & Guttridge • G&G 234
Built 1938 • Poolbeg 1938-59
Sold 11.1959 • Sea Call/ Helen Blake

809 was sold in 1959 and, renamed Sea Call, was used as a fishing boat at Walmer. Following a change of owner she was taken to Scotland, and in 1971 was bought by Walter Hume. Following restoration by apprentices, she was displayed at Bristol and, from 1995, at Chatham Dockyard (pictured).

810 • Augustus and Laura

32'x 9'3" Surf motor • Groves & Guttridge • G&G 235
Built 1938 • Newbiggin 1938-50
Sold 10.1950 • Betsy Lyn

After service at Newbiggin (pictured), 810 was sold by the RNLI in October 1950 and was used to take men and stores to Coquet lighthouse off Amble. She was later converted for fishing. By the early 1990s she was reported at Ouseburn Quay, Newcastle, where she was broken up.

811 • Thomas Kirk Wright

32'x 9'3" Surf motor • Groves & Guttridge • G&G 236
Built 1939 • Poole 1939-62
Sold 9.1964 • Thomas Kirk Wright

811 was sold in 1964 to a Poole owner, who used her as a yacht until 1974, when she was acquired by the National Maritime Museum and moved to Poole for display in the old lifeboat house on Poole Quay (pictured). In 2002 she was placed on the National Register of Historic Vessels.

812 • Edmund and Mary Robinson

41'x 11'8" Watson motor • Groves & Guttridge • G&G 237
Built 1938 • New Brighton No.2 1938-50; Reserve 1950-64
Sold 3.1964 • Yoko/ Maid of Troy

812 was sold in 1964 and was converted into the pleasure boat Yoko, later renamed Maid of Troy. She was used as a rescue boat for Swansea Diving Club on the river Taw, but later moved to Worcester and Gloucester before ending up at Saul Junction (pictured), and having her wheelhouse removed.

813 • Ann Letitia Russell

41'x 11'8" Watson motor • Groves & Guttridge • G&G 238
Built 1939 • Fleetwood 1939-76, Troon 1976
Sold 4.1977 • Angela/ Olive

813 was sold in 1977 to the Southern Ireland Fisheries Board who used her as a fisheries protection vessel renamed Angela. In 1984 she was sold again and moved to Swansea. She stayed around the Bristol Channel, including Barry Dock (pictured), until being taken to Lowestoft by road in 2005.

814 • Dunleary II

46'x 12'9" Watson motor • J. S. White • W 1839
Built 1938 • Dun Laoghaire 1938-67; Lochinver 1967-69; Res 1969-72; Dunmore East 1972-73 • Sold 8.1974 • Dunleary II

814 was sold in 1974 and was stripped down in Bristol before being sailed down to Appledore for her conversion to be completed. She has been kept at Bristol City Docks more or less ever since, and is usually berthed at Princess Wharf, Bristol Floating Dock (pictured) used as a pleasure boat.

815 • Violet Armstrong

46' x 12'9" Watson motor • J. S. White • W 1840
Built 1938 • Appledore 1938-62
Sold 10.1962 • Violet/ Violet Armstrong

815 was sold in 1962 to a Penarth owner and had a wheelhouse added. By 1985 she had moved to Rothesay and renamed Violet. By 1994 she was at Appledore but in 1997 she had moved to Bristol Floating Dock (pictured). In 2009 a rebuild was started at Albion Yard, Bristol.

816 • Kate Greatorex

32' x 9'3" Surf motor • Groves & Guttridge • G&G 250
Built 1939 • Minehead 1939-51
Sold 3.1952 • Suann/ Gannet/ Kate Greatorex

816 was sold in 1952 and, with a large cabin added, was renamed Suann. By 1997 she was at Macgruers boatyard, Clynder as Gannet. The owner gave her away on the understanding she would be restored. She was at St Denis Les Sans, France (pictured), until 2012, and was then moved to Migennes.

817 • Lawrence Ardern, Stockport

32' x 9'3" Surf motor • Groves & Guttridge • G&G 251
Built 1939 • Barmouth 1939-49, Reserve 1949-51
Sold 12.1951 • Lawrence Ardern/ The Lady Godiva/ Godiva II

817 was sold in 1951 to the Coventry Diesel Eng Co in Coventry. Although they kept her lifeboat name, she was later renamed The Lady Godiva, having been converted into a yacht at Saundersfoot (pictured), and subsequently Godiva II. There is no record of her subsequent use or whereabouts.

818 • Mabel Marion Thompson

46' x 12'9" Watson motor • J. S. White • W 1871
Built 1939 • Rosslare Harbour 1939-52, Galway Bay 1952-68, Res 68-74
Sold 4.1975 • Carstiona

818 was sold in 1975 to Stranraer, where she was converted into the motor yacht Carstiona. In 1997 she was at Galway Docks (pictured), and throughout the 1990s at East Pier, Ballyvaughan. In 2005 she moved to Kinvarra, near Galway, where she was to be restored.

819 • Julia Park Barry of Glasgow

46' x 12'9" Watson motor • Alexander Robertson • R222
Built 1939 • Peterhead 1939-69, Reserve 1969-79
Sold 3.1979 • Savell O. Hicks/ Julia Park Barry/ Julia Barry

822 was sold in 1979 and became the fisheries patrol boat Savell O. Hicks at Coleraine and sometimes at Portrush, with a wheelhouse added. By 2000 she was out of the water at Seaton's Boatyard. She moved to Fahan Marina, Lough Swilly (pictured) in about 2002 and was renamed.

820 • Louise Stephens

46' x 12'9" Watson motor • J. S. White • W 1872
Built 1939 • Great Yarmouth and Gorleston 1939-67, Eyemouth 1967-74
Sold 8.1974 • Mid Tyne Mariner/ Tyne Star/ Louise/ Louise Stephens

820 was sold in 1974 and was used as a work boat on the river Tyne named Mid Tyne Mariner, having had a large cabin added. She moved to Teignmouth and then to Wivenhoe, but by 1989 she was based at Port Ellen, Islay (pictured), but she may return to Gorleston for display.

821 • The Good Hope

46' x 12'9" Watson motor • Alexander Robertson • R223
Built 1939 • Montrose 1939-72; Reserve 1972-80
Sold 6.1981 • Myra Jane/ Soraya

821 was sold in 1981 to a Barry Dock owner where she was kept, little altered, as the yacht Myra Jane until 2007. She then moved to Cardiff Bay Yacht Club. In 2010, renamed Soraya, she moved up the river Ely a short distance to a pontoon mooring off Dunleavey Drive, Cardiff (pictured).

822 • Jesse Lumb

46' x 12'9" Watson motor • J. S. White • W 1873
Built 1939 • Bembridge 1939-70; Reserve 1970-80
Sold 7.1981 • Jesse Lumb

822 was sold in 1981 to the Imperial War Museum at Duxford, where she was displayed outside one of the hangars. In 1988 she was refurbished at Crescent Marine Services, Otterham Quay, and then displayed inside the museum (pictured). She was removed from display in 2013.

823 • Matthew Simpson

41' x 11'8" Watson motor • Groves & Guttridge • G&G 255
Built 1939 • Port Erin 1939-72, Reserve 1972-75
Sold 2.1976 • Christine Bradley/ Christine/ Penros

823 was sold in 1976 and was based at Leigh on Sea as the work boat Christine Bradley with a shelter added. By 1999 she had been renamed Penros and moved to the south coast, where she was based at Yarmouth (pictured), Chichester Harbour and most recently at Hayling Island.

824 • John Pyemont

41' x 11'8" Watson motor • Groves & Guttridge • G&G 256
Built 1939 • Tynemouth 1939-41
Destroyed in service 1941

One of only a handful of lifeboats completed during World War II, 824 served at Tynemouth (pictured) for only two years. On 9 April 1941 she was destroyed when an air raid on Newcastle completely devastated the area, with her boathouse also being damaged beyond repair.

825 • Herbert John

35'6" x 10'3" Liverpool motor • Groves & Guttridge • G&G 257
Built 1939 • Cloughey 1939-52, Youghal 1952-66
Sold 4.1966 • Sea Drift/ Paua/ Alexis/ Herbert John

825 was sold in 1966 and became the work boat Sea Drift. By the late 1980s she was based at Carrickfergus where she was the workboat Paua. She moved around the Belfast area until 2005. She was taken to Donaghadee to be restored and in 2012 was delivered to Restronguet, Cornwall (pictured).

826 • Guide of Dunkirk

35'6" x 9'10" Self-righting motor • Rowhedge Ironworks • S570
Built 1940 • Cadgwith 1941-63
Sold 1963 • Girl Guide/ Ex RNLB Guide of Dunkirk

826 was sold in 1963 to a boatbuilder in Mevagissey (pictured) where, unaltered, she was used as the pleasure boat Girl Guide. By 1990 she was under survey there and since then has spent time on public display. Still out of the water, she is now named Ex RNLB Guide of Dunkirk.

827 • George and Elizabeth Gow

35'6"x 10'3" Liverpool motor • Morgan Giles • M9
Built 1939 • Aberdeen No.2 1939-44 and 1947-62, Reserve 1962-64
Sold 1.1965 • The Gow/ RNLB George and Elizabeth Gow

827 was sold in 1965 to the Outward Bound School, Burghead, Moray. By the 1990s she was on the Isle of Skye, where she sank at her moorings. In 1997 she was purchased by Simon Evans, and taken to France. In original condition apart from an 80hp Ford diesel, she was renovated at St Denis les Sens (pictured), and moved to Migennes in 2012.

828 • The Princess Royal (Civil Service No.7)

46' x 12'9" Watson motor • J. S. White • W 5004
Built 1939 • Hartlepool 1939-68, Humber No.2 1968-69, Res 1968-76
Sold 9.1976 • La Rochelle/ The Princess Royal (Civil Service No.7)

828 was sold in 1976 and was heavily converted with a large cabin, and during the 1990s was kept at Barry Dock in use as a fishing boat. In 2000 she was returned to Hartlepool (pictured) and was restored by volunteers as a working exhibit in memory of the brave men who served in her.

829 • Crawford and Constance Conybeare

46' x 12'9" Watson motor • J. S. White • W 5005
Built 1940 • Falmouth 1940-68, Reserve 1968-74
Sold 8.1974 • Three Seas/ Bilitis/ Connie

829 was sold in August 1974 and heavily converted with a cabin added, and was used as a pleasure boat based on the Hamble, named Three Seas. She was sold several times and was based in the Southampton area (pictured) in the 1990s. In January 1997 she was shipped to Singapore.

830 • Annie Blanche Smith

46' x 12'9" Watson motor • J. S. White • W 5006
Built 1940 • Dunmore East 1940-70, Reserve 1970-71
Sold 7.1971 • Dunmore East Lifeboat/ Annie Blanche Smith

830 was sold in 1971 and remained unaltered while at Dartmouth in the 1980s. By 1989 she was at Rolle Quay, Barnstaple, and was offered for sale. By the mid-1990s she was at Barnstaple as a trip boat. By 2000 she was at Bideford (pictured) where she deteriorated until being broken up in 2011.

831 • Caroline Oates Aver and William Maine

35'6"x 10'3" Liverpool motor • Groves & Guttridge • G&G 262
Built 1940 • St Ives 1940-48, Ferryside 1948-60
Sold 7.1960 • Caroline and William

After service at St Ives and Ferryside, 831 was sold in 1960 to the Outward Bound School, Aberdovey, who used her as a work boat. She was later used as a fishing boat at Barmouth (pictured) in the late 1960s with a cabin added, but details of her whereabouts since then are not known.

832 • Lucy Lavers

35'6"x 10'3" Liverpool motor • Groves & Guttridge • G&G 263
Built 1940 • Aldeburgh No.2 1940-59, Reserve 1959-68
Sold 11.1968 • P2/ L'Esperance/ Lucy/ Lucy Lavers

832 was sold in 1968 and used as a pilot boat at Sark and St Helier, with a wheelhouse added. In the late 1990s efforts were made to restore her and she was stripped. She then went to Husbands yard, Marchwood (pictured), before going to Keyhaven. In 2010 she went to George Hewitt's at Stiffkey.

833 • The Cuttle

35'6"x 10'3" Liverpool motor • Groves & Guttridge • G&G 264
Built 1940 • Filey 1940-53, Skegness 1953-64, Reserve 1964-66
Sold 8.1966 • The Cuttle

After service at Skegness (pictured), 833 was sold in August 1966 from Robinsons Boatyard, Oulton Broad, Lowestoft to a London-based owner and was used as a yacht. However, while bound from London for Gibraltar on 6 October 1967, she caught fire and sank off the Ile d'Oleron, France.

834 • Jose Neville

35'6"x 10'3" Liverpool motor • Groves & Guttridge • G&G 265
Built 1941 • Caister 1941-63, Reserve 1963-66
Sold 8.1966 • Concorde LT267/ Valas

834 was sold in 1966 and became a pilot boat at Lowestoft. In 1972 she was sold for fishing out of Southwold and Walberswick. In the early 1990s she was converted and had a whaleback cabin added at Slaughden (pictured). She was moored in the river Alde, until taken out of the water at Slaughden Quay.

835 • The Gordon Warren

32' x 9'3" Surf motor • J. S. White • W 5007
Built 1939 • Rhyl 1939-49, Reserve 1949-51
Sold 1.1952 • Welsh Maid CO332

835 was sold in January 1952 and, re-engined with Gardner 3LW engines in 1959, was converted into a fishing boat named Welsh Maid. She has been based at Conwy (pictured) ever since her sale. With her hull painted black and her original shelter removed, she works the mussel beds at Conwy.

836 • Norman Nasmyth

32' x 9'3" Surf motor • Alexander Robertson • R225
Built 1940 • Montrose No.2 1940-50, Reserve 1950-66
Sold 1966 • Montrose

836 was sold in 1966 and used for a spell on the Fens, then she was moved to Harwich, and was later taken to Burnham-on-Crouch. She became the motor yacht Montrose at Lamlash, Isle of Arran (pictured). By 1986 she was ashore, sheeted over, but details of her whereabouts since are unknown.

837 • John Ryburn

32' x 9'3" Surf motor • Alexander Robertson • R224
Built 1941 • Newburgh 1941-65
Sold 1966 • unknown

After service at Newburgh, 837 was sold in April 1966 to an owner based in Lurgen, County Armagh, Northern Ireland for £800. She was rebuilt as a half-decker fishing boat, later becoming a planter at the Manor House Hotel in Enniskillen (pictured), but in 2010 was removed and broken up.

838 • Michael Stephens

46' x 12'9" Watson motor • J. S. White • W 5015
Built 1939 • Lowestoft 1939-63, Exmouth 1963-68, Reserve 1968-75
Sold 1.1976 • Michael Stephens

838 was sold in 1976 to a Bristol owner who kept her unaltered at Bristol Floating Dock. By 1987 she had been sold to a Devon owner who kept her at Ilfracombe. She later moved to Newton Ferrers, on Devon's south coast, where she remains although she tours extensively along the south coast.

839 • 842 • 843

ON-839 • 35'6" x 10'8" Liverpool motor • Groves & Guttridge • G&G 275 • Built 1942 • Unallocated

839 was to be named W. and B., but she was destroyed during construction by an enemy bomb, which hit the builder's yard on 4 May 1942. She was to have been the first twin-screw 35'6" Liverpool motor class lifeboat.

ON-842 • 46' x 12'9" Watson motor • Groves & Guttridge • G&G 275 • Built 1942 • Unallocated

842 was destroyed during construction by an enemy bomb which hit the builder's yard on 4 May 1942. She was to have been named Millie Walton, and this name was reallocated to a later lifeboat.

ON-843 • 46' x 12'9" Watson motor • Groves & Guttridge • G&G 310 • Built 1942 • Unallocated

843 was destroyed during construction by an enemy bomb which hit the builder's yard on 4 May 1942. She was to have been named Charles Henry Ashley, and this name was reallocated to a later lifeboat.

840 • Millie Walton/ 1947- Henry Blogg

46' x 12'9" Watson motor • Sussex Yacht Co • SS 58
Built 1945 • Cromer No.1 1945-66; Reserve 1966-76
Sold 4.1977 • Blogg of Cromer

840 was sold in 1977 to Swansea where she was converted with a large cabin and renamed Blogg of Cromer. She was at Neyland Marina, on the river Bure and at Dickies, Bangor. By 1999 she was at Upton-on-Severn (pictured), but in 2010 was taken out of the water and is now in a field.

841 • Manchester and Salford XXIX

46' x 12'9" Watson motor • J. S. White • W 5111
Built 1943 • Pwllheli 1943-53, Workington 1953-72, Relief 1972-74
Sold 1974 • Maureen Mary/ Paul David II/ Frederick William/ Manchester & Salford XXIX RNLI O.N.-841

841 was sold in 1974 and became the yacht Maureen Mary. By 1980 she was the pilot boat Paul David II at Sheerness, with a wheelhouse added. By 1985 she had been sold and renamed Frederick William at Canvey Island (pictured). In 2012 she was a work boat at A. W. Marine, Canvey Island.

844 • Jean Charcot

13m x 3.96m • Chantiers Augustin Normand • AND 165
Built 1938 • [Came from Île-Molène, France] Reserve 1941-45
Returned to France 1945

844 was a French lifeboat which had managed to escape the German occupation from the Île-Molène station, taking 23 of the island's inhabitants on board, going to the Isles of Scilly. She was used as a reserve lifeboat during her time with the RNLI and was returned to France after the war.

845 • Minister Anseele

14m x 3.82m Watson motor • Henri Oltmanns Bootwerft, Bremerhaven
Built 1926 • Ostende, Reserve 1941-43, Plymouth 1943-46
Returned to Belgium 1947

845 was a Belgian lifeboat which was found drifting in the English Channel during World War II. While in RNLI service she was used as a Reserve boat at Pwllheli and Holyhead before a spell at Plymouth. After an overhaul, she was returned to the Belgian government in April 1947.

846 • Field Marshall and Mrs Smuts

46' x 12'9" Watson motor • Morgan Giles • MG 456
Built 1945 • Beaumaris 1945-77, Relief 1977-79
Sold 8.1979 • Kenanda/ Llas-Sah-D/ Beaumaris

846 was sold in 1979 to an Isle of Man owner where, after conversion to a motor yacht, she was based at Castletown named Kenanda. By 1990 her cabin had been extended and she was based at Conwy. In 2007, renamed Beaumaris, she returned to Castletown, Isle of Man (pictured).

Part 4

Motor Lifeboats 1945-1980

At the end of the Second World War, the RNLI's fleet was in need of rebuilding, as new construction had more or less stopped during the conflict, and so an ambitious building programme was embarked upon. The new lifeboats all had twin engines and twin propellers, and new motor boats were soon completed and entered service with more than 30 new lifeboats being built between 1945 and 1950. The pulling and sailing lifeboat was phased out completely during the 1950s, and the last such boat, Robert and Ellen Robson (ON-669), was withdrawn from Whitby in November 1957.

The 46ft 9in Watson was the first new post-war lifeboat type and, fitted with twin 40bhp four-cylinder diesel engines, was also the first to be diesel-powered. Diesel engines were not only more economical to operate, but diesel was less flammable than petrol so its use reduced the risk of

fire aboard the lifeboat.

The next Watson type, slightly larger at 47ft, also had midship steering as did the 52ft Barnett type, first built in 1950, and these boats became the mainstay of the fleet for many years. Subsequently, the cockpit on these designs was enclosed to provide a degree of shelter. Many of the Watsons and Barnetts of this size were slipway launched, while others were kept afloat at moorings, and many of these large lifeboats remain in existence, thriving in private ownership.

Following a series of disasters in the 1950s and 1960s, when a number of lifeboats capsized with lifeboat crews being drowned, the RNLI reviewed its policy on self-righting and increased efforts to find a design of lifeboat with a self-righting capability. This resulted in the Oakley design in 1957, which used a water ballast transfer system to right

in the event of a capsize. Designers then realised that self-righting could be achieved by having a wheelhouse and superstructure which was buoyant and made a boat unstable when capsized, and this method of righting has been employed in every lifeboat design since.

Further significant advances in lifeboat design came in the 1960s with the introduction of the American steel-hulled 44ft lifeboat, which became the Waveney class. The boat was faster than the traditional designs used hitherto, and pointed the way ahead in terms of speed, crew protection and self-righting. The Arun class, developed during the 1970s, was larger and faster than the Waveney, with better crew protection. After giving good service in British and Irish waters, many of the Aruns and Waveneys sold by the RNLI went abroad where they continued to serve as lifeboats.

The first 52ft Arun lifeboat Arun (ON-1018), pictured when stationed at Barry Dock, was ground-breaking in many ways and incorporated into the design were many features which are still used in 21st century lifeboat types.

847 • Gertrude

46' x 12'9" Watson motor • Rowhedge Iron Works • R 622
Built 1946 • Holy Island 1946-68, Exmouth 1968-70, Sheerness 1970-74, Relief 1974-80, Fowey 1980-81
Sold 10.1982 • Gertrude/ Ex RNLB Gertrude

847 was sold out of service in 1982 to a Mevagissey owner. She has been a pleasure boat at Mevagissey ever since, moored in the harbour, unaltered and maintained in her lifeboat colours, sometimes visiting Fowey (pictured).

848 • Millie Walton

46' x 12'9" Watson motor • Groves & Guttridge • G&G 390
Built 1946 • Douglas 1946-56; Relief 1956-57; Amble 1957-74; Relief 1974-77 • Sold 10.1977 • Tyne Winder/ Millie Walton

848 was sold in 1977 and became the work boat Tyne Winder on the Tyne. By 1987 she had been sold to Campbeltown, renamed Millie Walton. A 1991 refit at Arklow saw her bulwarks raised and an aft cabin was added. She subsequently moved to Charlotte Quay, Grand Canal, Dublin (pictured).

849 • William Gammon – Manch. and Dist. XXX

46'9" x 12'9" Watson motor • Groves & Guttridge • G&G 391
Built 1947 • Mumbles 1947-74, Relief 1974-82
Sold 3.1983 • William Gammon-Manchester and District XXX

849 was sold in March 1983 to the Swansea Maritime Museum, where she was initially kept afloat in the dock. When the museum closed in 2005, she was moved to the Swansea Museums Collection Centre at Landore. The Centre is open and can be visited on Wednesdays from 1000 to 1600.

850 • Cecil Paine

35'6" x 10'8" Liverpool motor • Groves & Guttridge • G&G 418
Built 1945 • Wells 1945-65, Kilmore Quay 1965-72, Relief 1972-73
Sold 7.1973 • Patreo-Joao-Rangel

850 was sold out of service in July 1973 to Portuguese Institute for Lifesaving who renamed her Patreo-Joao-Rangel and stationed her at Sesimbra (pictured). Although she has been retired from service, she is still displaying her lifeboat livery as a local fishing boat.

851 • Tillie Morrison, Sheffield

35'6" x 10'8" Self-righting motor • J. S. White • W 5381
Built 1948 • Bridlington 1947-52, Llandudno 1953-59
Sold 11.1959 • Imshi/ Elizabeth

851 was sold in 1959 and became the yacht Imshi at Bristol. By 1984 she had moved to Rhyl and was converted into a fishing boat. By 1994 she was at Walker Quay on the Tyne. In 2011 she was the fishing boat Elizabeth at St Peter's Marina (pictured), Tyne, but moved to Hartlepool Marina in 2012.

852 • Tynesider

46'9" x 12'9" Watson motor • J. S. White • W 5395
Built 1947 • Tynemouth 1947-79, Relief 1979-83
Sold 2.1984 • Tynesider

852 was sold out of service in 1984 to a Chesterfield owner, who kept her unaltered as a pleasure boat, but converted internally. She was moored off Whitstable during the summer and Oare Creek in winter until 1997. She was then moved to Iron Wharf, Faversham (pictured), where she remains.

853 • Winston Churchill (Civil Service No.8)

46'9" x 12'9" Watson motor • J. S. White • W 5399
Built 1948 • Blyth 1948-79, Relief 1979-82
Sold 7.1983 • Watson Explorer

853 was sold in 1983 to a North Wales owner. She was initially moored in the river Foryd at Rhyl, but by 1985 had been moved to Beaumaris and, until about 2005, she was often moored out in the Menai Straits. Since 2005 she has been ashore at Gallows Point Boatyard, Beaumaris (pictured).

854 • Sarah Tilson

46'9" x 12'9" Watson motor • Alexander Robertson • AR 255
Built 1949 • Baltimore 1950-78, Relief 1978-79
Sold 8.1979 • The Sarah/ Sarah Tilson

854 was sold in 1979 to a Cork-based owner for use as a dive boat. In 1986 she was moved to the river Medway as the unaltered pleasure boat The Sarah. She was later renamed Sarah Tilson and was taken to a berth at Medway Bridge (pictured), in original RNLI configuration, under restoration.

855 • W. M. Tilson

46'9" x 12'9" Watson motor • Alexander Robertson • AR 256
Built 1949 • Arranmore 1950-69
Sold 8.1970 • Un-named/ W. M. Tilson

855 was sold in 1970 and taken to Portavogie, where she was used as a work boat. By the late 1980s she was ashore, holed in two places. By 1993 she had been moved to Magerascourse Road, Comber, Ulster (pictured) where she was stripped for restoration, but this has not been completed.

856 • Susan Ashley

41' x 11'8" Watson motor • Groves and Guttridge • G&G 481
Built 1948 • Sennen Cove 1948-72, Barry Dock No.2 1973-79
Loaned for display 1982 • Susan Ashley

856 was taken out of service in 1981 and loaned to the Lifeboat Museum, Bristol in 1982. When that museum closed, she was transferred to the Lifeboat Collection at Chatham Historic Dockyard (pictured), where she has been on static display since April 1996, in her original condition.

857 • Glencoe, Glasgow

41' x 11'8" Watson motor • Morgan Giles • MG509
Built 1949 • Buckie 1949-60, Girvan 60-61, Res 61-65, Portavogie 65-78
Sold 3.1979 • Glencoe/ Vagrant

857 was sold in 1979 to a Loch Awe owner in western Scotland where, renamed Glencoe, she was converted into a pleasure boat. By 1988 she was at Toward Point as a workboat with a small cabin. By 1993 she had been converted into the pleasure boat Vagrant (pictured) at Burghead Harbour.

858 • R. L. P.

41' x 11'8" Watson motor • Sussex Yacht Company • SS94
Built 1949 • Swanage 1949-75, Relief 1975-81
Sold 8.1981 • Beya

858 was sold out of service in 1981 from Poole (pictured) to Millport Harbour Authority, Great Cumbrae. She sailed from Poole in June 1983 to Millport where, unaltered she was used as the workboat Beya. Details of her subsequent whereabouts are uncertain, but she was lost some time ago.

859 • Beryl Tollemache

41' x 12'3" Watson motor • Sussex Yacht Company • SS100
Built 1949 • Eastbourne 1949-77, Relief 1977-79
Sold 9.1979 • St Boisel/ Steadfast/ Ex Eastbourne Lifeboat

859 was sold in 1979 to Berwick-upon-Tweed harbour authority to became the pilot boat St Boisel. By 1987 she had been sold and was a fishing boat on the Tyne based at Royal Quays Marina and later Friars Goose Marina. In 2010 she was sold and became a trip boat based at Amble (pictured).

860 • Southern Africa

51'x 13'6" Barnett motor • Rowhedge Iron Works • S 681
Built 1949 • Dover 1949-67, Relief 1967-81
Sold 7.1980 • Valparaiso III (B.S.05)/ Southern Africa

860 was sold to Cuerpo de Volantarios de los Botes Salvavidas de Valparaiso, Chile and operated as the lifeboat Valperaiso III until 2002. She was then sold and brought back to England on board a cargo ship. She was at Mashford's yard, Cremyll (pictured), and moved to Torpoint in 2007.

861 • Edgar, George, Orlando and Eva Child

35'6"x 10'8" Liverpool motor • Groves & Guttridge • G&G 485
Built 1948 • St Ives 1948-68, Res 1968-70, Blackpool 70-75, Relief 75-82
Sold 7.1983 • Eileena Anne LT283/ Eileena Anne LT317/ Edgar George Orlando and Eva Child

861 was sold in 1983 to become the fishing boat Eileena Anne at Great Yarmouth but by 1985, after a survey at Bure Marine, she went to Lowestoft (pictured). In 2010 she was acquired by a lifeboat trust at Stiffkey, Norfolk and is to be restored. In 2011 she was moored in Blakeney Pit.

862 • Thomas Corbett

35'6"x 10'8" Liverpool motor • Groves & Guttridge • G&G 486
Built 1948 • Ramsey 1948-70, Hoylake 1970-74, Clogher Head 1974-81
Sold 11.1981 • Thomas Corbett

862 was sold in 1981 and was a pleasure boat at Crosshaven. She had a wheelhouse added as a fishing boat in the 1990s. She was sold to Hoylake in 2002 and was partially restored at Cammell Laird, Birkenhead. In 2011 she was moved to Hoylake (pictured) for display at Hoylake Lifeboat Museum.

863 • St Albans

35'6"x 10'8" Liverpool motor • Groves & Guttridge • G&G 487
Built 1948 • New Quay 1948-70
Sold 12.1970 • Roadstone Pilot/ Lorraine

863 was sold in 1970 and became the pilot boat Roadstone Pilot at Arklow. By the 1980s she had been sold but remained at Arklow (pictured) as the fishing boat Lorraine. She was rebuilt with an aft wheelhouse but by 2002 she was on the quayside where she deteriorated and was broken up in 2005.

864 • The Chieftain

35'6"x 10'8" Liverpool motor • Groves & Guttridge • G&G 488
Built 1948 • Barmouth 1949-82
Sold 4.1982 • The Chieftain

864 was sold in 1982 to Portmadoc Museum for display. By 1993 she was in private hands at Bangor and by 2000 had moved to Wells in Norfolk. In 2004 she was restored at Caldicott and taken Bristol in her original livery in 2010. She took part in the Jubilee Pageant (pictured) in June 2012.

865 • Elizabeth Rippon

46'9" x 12'9" Watson motor • J. S. White • W 5405
Built 1948 • St Helier 1948-74, Relief 1974-77
Sold 10.1977 • Star of Helier/ Elizabeth Rippon

865 was sold in 1977 and became the fishing boat Star of Helier, being based in North Wales. Following a refit at Hesketh Bank in 1997 she was moored in the Menai Straits. In 2004 she went to Stourport on Severn, renamed Elizabeth Rippon. In 2011 she was taken to Barmouth (pictured).

866 • Charles Henry Ashley

46'9" x 12'9" Watson motor • J. S. White • W 5406
Built 1949 • Porthdinllaen 1949-79, Relief 1979-86, Lowestoft 1986
Sold 3.1987 • Charles Henry Ashley/ Sidney/ Charles Ashley

866 was sold in 1987 and was used as a work boat at Southampton. She was renamed Sidney in 1992 and by 1993 was based at Penton Hook Marina, near Chertsey, as the pleasure boat Charles Ashley. By 1999 she had been moved to France, near Creteil, and in 2011 she was for sale.

867 • Lady Scott (Civil Service No.4)

46'9" x 12'9" Watson motor • J. S. White • W 5407
Built 1949 • Portrush 1949-81, Relief 1981-86
Sold 7.1987 • Marjorie Rae/ Janet Rae

867 was sold in 1987 and became the pleasure boat Marjorie Rae at Bembridge; in 1988 she was renamed Janet Rae. She operated out of Bembridge harbour (pictured) as a rescue/work boat until 2010 when she was re-engined and altered with a large aft cabin, used for pleasure only.

868 • John and Lucy Cordingley

46'9" x 12'9" Watson motor • Sussex Yacht Company • SS 101
Built 1949 • Teesmouth 1950-60, Helvick Head 1960-69, Reserve 69-81
Sold 11.1981 • Jaybee/ Tempo

868 was sold in 1981 to Clynder on Gare Loch, Argyll where, unaltered, she was used as work boat Jaybee. By 1990 she had moved to Great Yarmouth (pictured) and been renamed Tempo. Her aft cabin was removed and she became a fishing boat kept at Berth 26 with additions to her superstructure.

869 • Anthony Robert Marshall

35'6"x 10'8" Liverpool motor • Groves & Guttridge • G&G 500
Built 1949 • Rhyl 1949-68, Reserve 1968-72, Pwllheli 72-79, Relief 79-80
Sold 4.1980 • Ellen B YH126/ Anthony Robert Marshall

869 was sold in 1980 and became the fishing boat Ellen B, number YH126, based at Great Yarmouth (pictured), and having had a small wheelhouse added. In 2010 she was acquired by a lifeboat trust at Stiffkey, Norfolk, and she was taken to George Hewitt's boatyard to be restored there.

870 • William and Laura

35'6"x 10'8" Liverpool motor • Groves & Guttridge • G&G 501
Built 1949 • Newcastle 1949-80
Sold 9.1980 • William and Laura

870 was acquired in 1980 for display at Ulster Folk and Transport Museum, Cultra, Co Down. She is in store there (pictured) and can only be seen by arrangement. In June 1984 she was transported to Liverpool and placed on display for the Liverpool Garden Festival, and then was returned to Cultra.

871 • William Cantrell Ashley

35'6"x 10'8" Liverpool motor • Groves & Guttridge • G&G 502
Built 1949 • Clovelly 1949-68
Sold 9.1968 • St Cedd/ William Cantrell Ashley

871 was sold in 1968 to Essex County Council who used her at Bradwell. She remained there until about 1990, when she was sold to becoem a trip boat at Scarborough. She was sold in 2005 and moved to Looe, still in use as a trip boat. In 2011 another sale took her to Albert Dock, Liverpool (pictured).

872 • J. B. Couper of Glasgow

35'6"x 10'8" Liverpool motor • Groves & Guttridge • G&G 503
Built 1949 • St Abbs 1949-53, Kirkcudbright 1953-65, Youghal 1966-71, Poole 1971-74, Relief 1974-75
Sold 1.1976 • Etoile du Nord GU45

872 was sold in January 1975 and became the fishing boat L'Etoile Du Nord in Guernsey, remaining largely unaltered. She was kept at La Grande Havre (pictured) for many years, but in 2011 was put up for sale.

873 • George Elmy

35'6"x 10'8" Liverpool motor • Groves & Guttridge • G&G 504
Built 1950 • Seaham Harbour 1950-62, Reserve 1963-69, Poole 1969-72
Sold 9.1972 • Gabrielle K/ Samantha H/ Ellen Louise/ Miza/ George Elmy

873 was sold in 1972 and became the fishing boat Gabrielle K at Great Yarmouth in the 1980s. By 1990 she was at Wells, and by 2000 at Holyhead as Ellen Louise. In 2011 she was taken to South Shields, and by March 2013 she had been restored (pictured) for display in the old lifeboat house at Seaham.

874 • Robert Lindsay

35'6"x 10'8" Liverpool motor • Groves & Guttridge • G&G 505
Built 1950 • Arbroath 1950-53, Res 53-55, Girvan 1955-60, Reserve 60-61, Criccieth 61-68 • Sold 9.1972 • Taupo/ BEB 505/ Zephyr LT165/ Robert Lindsay

874 was sold in 1968 and became the pleasure boat Taupo. She later carried the number BEB 505 and by 1991 she was on Oulton Broad. In 1992 she became fishing boat Zephyr at Lowestoft (pictured). In 2001 she moved to Wells and in 2005 to George Hewitt's yard at Stiffkey to be restored.

875 • Richard Ashley

35'6"x 10'8" Liverpool motor • Groves & Guttridge • G&G 511
Built 1950 • Newbiggin 1950-66
Sold 1967 • Kirstey of Luing

875 was sold in 1967 to an owner based at Ballymena, Co Antrim, and became the yacht Kirstey of Luing. She was reported at Red Bay in 1980, but exact details of her use are not known, although she spent many years on Lough Neagh before she was wrecked in Dun Laoghaire harbour.

876 • James and Ruby Jackson

35'6"x 10'8" Liverpool motor • Groves & Guttridge • G&G 512
Built 1950 • Anstruther 1950-65, Reserve 1965-67
Sold 12.1968 • Galore B42

876 was sold in 1968 to an owner based at Killough, Co Down and an aft cabin was added when she was used as a fishing boat Galore (pictured) based at Portrush and Craigavon. She was later at Howth having been converted into a yacht, but moved to Dun Laoghaire and sank there in 1999.

877 • George and Caroline Ermen

35'6" x 10'8" Liverpool motor • J. S. White • W 5416
Built 1950 • Clogher Head 1950-74
Sold 7.1974 • Boreas

877 was sold in 1950 to an Inverness owner, but nothing is known of her until she was found in a semi derelict state adjacent to the Kyle of Lochalsh golf course in the early 1990s renamed Boreas. She was taken from there to Camuscross, Isleornsey for survey in 2000, but she has since deteriorated.

878 • M. T. C.

35'6" x 10' Self-righting motor • Groves and Guttridge • G&G 506
Built 1950 • Hastings 1950-63
Sold 9.1964 • Good Fortune/ John Stuart BH 211

878 was sold in 1963 and operated out of Aberystwyth as the fishing boat Good Fortune. She went to Barmouth by 1978 and by 1988, with her aft end box removed and a cabin added, was the fishing boat John Stewart. She moved to Bridlington in 1996 and by 2001 was in a field near Bridlington.

879 • E. C. J. R.

35'6" x 10' Self-righting motor • Groves & Guttridge • G&G 507
Built 1950 • Scarborough 1951-55, Reserve 1956-63
Sold 3.1963 • Tyne Trident/ Can-Y-Don AB115

879 was sold in 1963 to the Scouts in Newcastle upon Tyne who renamed her Tyne Trident. By 1990 she was on the shores of Loch Harport by the cemetery at Merkedale, heavily sheeted over but largely unaltered. She remains there, slowly deteriorating, with the sheeting having rotted away.

880 • Isaac and Mary Bolton

35'6" x 10' Self-righting motor • Groves & Guttridge • G&G 508
Built 1950 • Cullercoats 1951-63
Sold 12.1964 • R. A. J./ Isaac and Mary Bolton

880 was sold in 1964 and became the trip boat R. A. J. By 1970 she was at Great Yarmouth and by 1988 at Fencehouses, where she was restored and renamed Isaac and Mary Bolton prior to operating as a trip boat out of river Tyne. In 1999 she went to Blyth and soon afterwards went to Holland.

881 • City of Leeds

35'6" x 10' Self-righting motor • Groves & Guttridge • G&G 510
Built 1951 • Redcar 1951-65
Sold 6.1965 • Sea Ilex LO 283

881 was sold in 1965 to a North Wales owner who converted her with a small wheelhouse and she was operated as the fishing boat Sea Ilex out of Rhyl. By 1996 she had moved to Walney Channel (pictured). By 2000 she was no longer there and no record of her current whereabouts exists.

882 • B. H. M. H.

35'6" x 10'8" Liverpool motor • Rowhedge Iron Works • R 721
Built 1951 • Minehead 1951-73, Relief 1973-81, Clogher Head 1981-84
Sold 1.1985 • Kingfisher/ Jensa/ The Queen Eileen

882 was sold in 1985 and operated as the pleasure boat Kingfisher. By 1988 she had moved to Kinlochbervie and been renamed Jensa. By 2000 she was at Tayinloan, where she was renamed The Queen Eileen. Having been fully restored at Tayinloan, she moved to Bray Marina, Windsor in 2006.

883 • Norman B. Corlett

52' x 13'6" Barnett • J. S. White • W 5418
Built 1950 • New Brighton 1950-73, Relief 1973-81
Sold 2.1982 • Hannah/ Norman B. Corlett

883 was sold out of service in 1982 to Crosshaven to be used as a work boat. By 2000 she had been sold to Carrickfergus and, renamed Hannah, was extensively converted to a houseboat/yacht. By 2007 she had moved to Bangor and in 2011 she was taken, minus engines, to Coalisland, Tyrone.

884 • St Cybi (Civil Service No.9)

52' x 13'6" Barnett • J. S. White • W 5419
Built 1950 • Holyhead 1950-80, Relief 1980-85
Sold 1986 • St Cybi (Civil Service No.9)

After being taken out of service, 884 was loaned to Scottish Maritime Museum, Irvine in 1986 for display. She was kept afloat in a dock adjacent to the museum until 1995, when she was transferred to Chatham Historic Dockyard (pictured). She has been a static display there since April 1996.

885 • Sir Samuel Kelly

46'9"x 12'9" Watson motor • J. S. White • W 5420
Built 1950 • Donaghadee 1950-76, Relief 1976-79
Sold 6.1980 • Sir Samuel Kelly

885 was sold to the Ulster Folk Museum, Holywood, Co Down, in 1980. By the mid-1980s she was on permanent display in the open in a car park (pictured) adjacent to Donaghadee Harbour, protected by a fence. She remains on display about 100 yards away from the local lifeboat station.

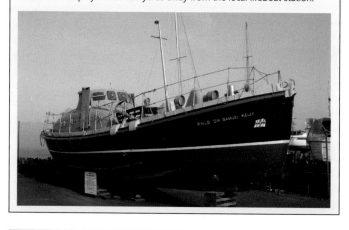

886 • Sarah Townsend Porritt

46'9"x 12'9" Watson motor • Sussex Yacht Company • SS 105
Built 1951 • Lytham 1951-78, Relief 1978-82
Sold 10.1982 • Sarah

886 was sold to a Newcastle owner who renamed her Sarah, shortened her aft cabin and used her as a fishing charter boat based at Davey Bank. With the closure of the Davey Bank moorings in 2005 she moved down the Tyne to Royal Quays Marina, North Shields (pictured), where she remains.

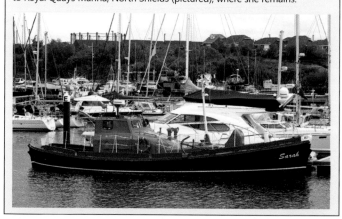

887 • Sir Godfrey Baring

46'9"x 12'9" Watson motor • J. S. White • W 5423
Built 1951 • Clacton 1952-68, Wick 1968-70, Workington 1972-82, Reserve 70-72 and 82-6 • Sold 7.1986 • Duchess of Cornwall/ Sir Baring

887 was sold in 1986 and taken to Gweek, Cornwall, her cabin was raised and a flying bridge was added. She moved to Restronguet Creek, Mylor by the Pandora Inn as a pleasure boat in 1987. By 2003 she had been sold to Friedeburgh, Germany, where she is used as trip boat named Sir Baring.

888 • North Foreland (Civil Service No.11)

46'9"x 12'9" Watson motor • J. S. White • W 5424
Built 1951 • Margate 1951-78, Relief 1978-81
Loaned to Bristol 1982 • North Foreland (Civil Service No.11)

888 was not sold out of service, but was loaned to the Lifeboat Museum, Bristol, in 1982. When that museum closed, the boat was transferred to the Lifeboat Collection at Chatham Historic Dockyard (pictured), where she has been on static display by the entrance since April 1996.

889 • Hilton Briggs

52' x 13'6" Barnett • J. S. White • W 5425
Built 1951 • Aberdeen 1951-58, Fenit 1959-69, Longhope 1970, Relief 1970-74, Invergordon 1974-75
Sold 7.1976 • Tartan Prince/ Hilton Briggs

889 was sold in 1976 and was renamed Tartan Prince. By 1984 she was at Bristol Floating Dock, where she was converted into a houseboat and renamed Hilton Briggs. In 1989 the owner took her to Ilfracombe but by 1990 she was back at Bristol in the Floating Dock (pictured).

890 • Thomas Forehead and Mary Rowse

52' x 13'6" Barnett • J. S. White • W 5426
Built 1952 • Plymouth 1952-74; Relief 1974-79
Sold 12.1982 • Lynda II/ Isle Ornsay

890 was sold in 1982 and became a work boat, renamed Lynda II, having been altered by the addition of an enlarged aft cabin. In 1999 she was taken to Millbay, Larne Loch and renamed Isle Ornsay. After a refit in Carrickfergus from 2002 to 2005 she returned to Larne as a pleasure boat. In 2010 she moved to Amlwch, Anglesey and in 2011 was at Port Penrhyn (pictured).

891 • Bassett-Green

35'6" x 10'8" Liverpool motor • Groves & Guttridge • G&G 515
Built 1951 • Padstow No.2 1951-62; Poole 1962-69
Sold 1969 • RYV/ Aqua Nomad/ Bassett Green

891 was sold in 1969 to joint owners in Ayr and Luing. She was at Gourdon in 1985 as RYV with a cabin added. By 1988 she was at Tayport, renamed Aqua Nomad. By 2000 a large wheelhouse had been fitted and, renamed Bassett Green, she was based at Crinan and Adrishaig.

892 • Aguila Wren

35'6" x 10'8" Liverpool motor • Groves & Guttridge • G&G 516
Built 1951 • Aberystwyth 1951-64; Redcar 1965-72
Sold 12.1972 • Aguila Wren

892 was sold in 1972 and became a sea cadet boat in Scunthorpe. An aft wheelhouse was added to her before she was laid up at Keadby in 1985. She was taken to South Shields and became a fishing boat. By 2004 she was at Amble from where she was moved to Donaghadee to be restored (pictured).

893 • Clara and Emily Barwell

35'6" x 10'8" Liverpool motor • Groves & Guttridge • G&G 517
Built 1951 • Eyemouth 1951-63; Reserve 1963-68
Sold 2.1969 • Mor Forwyn/ Wellwyn/ Julia Helen LT 546

893 was sold in 1969 to become the fishing boat Mor Forwyn at Pwllheli. In 1984 she had moved to Fletcher's yard, Oulton Broad as the fishing boat Julia Helen. Although she operates as fishing boat LT546 out of Hamilton Dock, Lowestoft (pictured), she has been at Oulton Broad and Southwold.

894 • Oldham IV

35'6" x 10'8" Liverpool motor • Groves & Guttridge • G&G 518
Built 1952 • Hoylake 1952-70
Sold 10.1970 • unknown

894 was sold in 1970 to Holyhead Boatyard Ltd but it is not certain whether they used her as a work boat or sold her on. The only sighting of her was on the Isle of Muck in 1987 (pictured) when she was unaltered from her lifeboat days. Since then there is no information about her whereabouts.

895 • Edith Clauson-Thue

35'6" x 10'8" Liverpool motor • Groves & Guttridge • G&G 519
Built 1952 • Gourdon 1952-69
Sold 9.1969 • Rambler SO 299

895 was sold in September 1969 and became a fishing boat at Arklow Harbour, with a wheelhouse added. She was later moved to Courtown Harbour, where she was kept for a few years before being taken to Crosshaven, Co Cork (pictured), in the late 1990s.

896 • Douglas Hyde

46'9"x 12'9" Watson motor • Camper & Nicholson • 765
Built 1952 • Rosslare Harbour 1952-69, Dunmore East 1970-72
Sold 2.1973 • Rima/ Douglas Hyde

896 was sold in 1973 and became a pleasure boat at Bromborough Dock, but she deteriorated and by the 1990s was at Port Penrhyn, Bangor, in a semi-derelict condition. In 2001 she was sold and taken to the Isle of Man, being towed to Peel (pictured), where she was rebuilt as a houseboat.

897 • St Andrew (Civil Service No.10)

41' x 11'8" Watson motor • William Osborne • WO 897
Built 1952 • Whitehills 1952-59, Reserve 1959-61, Girvan 1961-68, Arklow 1968-73, Relief 1973-76, Girvan 1976-77, Relief 1977-82;
Sold 11.1982 • Norlands/ Girl Jan/ St Andrew

897 was sold in 1982 and used as a pilot boat at Wick renamed Norlands. She was then stored in a field at Staxigoe until 2003, when she was taken to Glasson Dock. In 2004 she was taken to Restronguet Creek, Mylor, where she was restored. In 2011 she was moved to the BRS yard, Falkirk.

898 • Joseph Hiram Chadwick

52' x 13'6" Barnett • J. S. White • W 5427
Built 1952 • Padstow 1952-67, Galway Bay 1968-77, Relief 1977-79
Sold 4.1980 • Julia Clare/ Forceful/ Joseph Hiram Chadwick

898 was sold out of service in April 1980 and was kept in the Solent area named Julia Clare, little altered and used as a pleasure boat. In the early 1990s she was renamed Forceful and moved to the river Waveney, at Beccles (pictured). In 2008 her owner began a complete restoration at Burgh Castle.

899 • City of Glasgow II

52' x 13'6" Barnett • J. S. White • W 5428
Built 1953 • Campbeltown 1953-79
Sold 4.1980 • Pisces/ City of Glasgow II

899 was sold in 1980 and kept at Kip Marina, later moving to Barry Dock and the Hamble being used as a pleasure boat. She was sold in the 1990s and kept at Woodbridge before moving to Titchmarsh Marina and Harwich (pictured) as a trip boat. In 2010 she went to Orkney but returned to Walton.

900 • Herbert Leigh

46'9" x 12'9" Watson motor • J. S. White • W 5429
Built 1951 • Barrow 1951-82; Relief 1982-88
Sold 2.1989 • Herbert Leigh

900 was sold in 1989 to Furness Maritime Trust and placed on display at Barrow in 1990. She was officially accepted by the great nephew of the original donor, Brian Leigh-Bramwell. She has been on display at the Dock Museum (pictured) ever since, and is now in a cradle outside the museum.

901 • Michael and Lily Davis

46'9" x 12'9" Watson cabin motor • J. S. White • W 5430
Built 1953 • Ramsgate 1953-76, Relief 1976-79
Sold 1979 • Viceroy/ Coastal Waters

901 was sold out of service in 1979 to a Stockport owner, who renamed her Viceroy and kept her at Falmouth. The original Ferry engines were retained, but she was much neglected. In the mid-1990s she was renamed Coastal Waters and moved to Swansea Marina, where she has been ever since.

902 • Constance Calverley

35'6" x 10'8" Liverpool motor • Groves & Guttridge • G&G 520
Built 1952 • Cloughey 1952-65, Reserve 1965-69
Sold 1.1970 • Sea Rover

902 was sold out of service in 1970 and had a wheelhouse added for use as a fishing boat based at East Ferry, Co Cork in the early 1990s. In 2000, when moored in Youghal Harbour, she sank to the seabed on 6 November and it is not known whether she was ever raised.

903 • Helena Harris – Manchester & District XXXI

35'6" x 10'8" Liverpool motor • Groves & Guttridge • G&G 521
Built 1952 • Peel 1952-72
Sold 9.1972 • Helena Harris

903 was sold in 1972 and was used as a tender to a marine surveying team at Portishead Dock. From 1978 she operated out of Ramsgate as a work boat with a wheelhouse added, but in the late 1980s was taken to St Denis Les Sens, France (pictured) by Simon Evans, moving to Migennes in 2012.

904 • Robert and Phemia Brown

35'6" x 10'8" Liverpool motor • Groves & Guttridge • G&G 522
Built 1952 • Ilfracombe 1952-66
Sold 9.1967 • Un-named

904 was sold out of service in September 1967 to a private owner from Haverfordwest in south-west Wales, and she was last reported to be in use as a yacht at Weymouth in 1971. Her subsequent whereabouts and usage are unknown.

905 • Katherine and Virgoe Buckland

35'6" x 10'8" Liverpool motor • Groves & Guttridge • G&G 523
Built 1953 • Pwllheli 1953-72
Sold 9.1972 • Lord Hurcomb/ James Noel

905 was sold out of service in September 1972 and, re-engined with two Perkins 4.108 (M) diesels, used for taking students to Grassholm, Skomer, Skokholm, and Ramsey until 1980. She was then sold, renamed James Noel, and operated out of Tenby (pictured) as a trip boat to Caldy Island.

906 • W. Ross MacArthur of Glasgow

35'6" x 10'8" Liverpool motor • Groves & Guttridge • G&G 524
Built 1953 • St Abbs 1953-64, Reserve 1965-68
Sold 2.1969 • Viking of Wells/ Shirley Jean Adye/ Mariners Friend

906 was sold in 1969 to become a fishing boat out of Wells, before being bought by the Caister Volunteer Rescue Service and used as a lifeboat until 1991. She was sold to Pembroke Dock Authority in July 1992, but later bought by Alan Baker, who gave her back to Caister VRS for display.

907 • William Taylor of Oldham

42' x 12' Watson motor • William Osborne • WO 907
Built 1954 • Coverack 1954-72, Relief 1972-73, Arklow 1973-86
Sold 8.1986 • William Taylor/ Gipsy Moth

907 was sold in August 1986 from Bangor and taken to Pembroke Dock as a pleasure and work boat. At the end of 1987 she was shipped by Geest Line from Barry in Wales to St Vincent and Petite Martinique (pictured) in the West Indies, for fishing, but may now be broken up.

908 • Duchess of Kent

46'9"x 12'9" Watson motor • Groves & Guttridge • G&G 549
Built 1954 • Fraserburgh 1954-70
Capsized on service 21.1.1970, broken up at Buckie 1970

908 was operated as a lifeboat for 16 years before capsizing on 21 January 1970 after being swamped by a huge wave and overturned on service to the Danish fishing vessel Opal. Five of her crew were lost. The lifeboat was salvaged and towed to Buckie (pictured), where she was broken up.

909 • James and Barbara Aitken

42' x 12' Watson motor • William Osborne • WO 909
Built 1954 • Troon 1955-68, Girvan 1968-76
Sold 4.1977 • Cape Lorna

909 was sold in April 1977 to a Peterhead owner and had a wheelhouse added. She was used as a pleasure boat out of Aberdeen and Peterhead in the 1990s. In 1998 she was taken to Paris and ended up at Simon Evans' yard at St Denis les Sens (pictured); he moved her to Migennes in 2012.

910 • Edian Courtauld

46'9"x 12'9" Watson motor • J. S. White • W 5431
Built 1953 • Walton and Frinton 1953-77, Relief 1977-81
Sold 8.1981 • Scapa Agent/ Juno

910 was sold out of service in August 1981 and became the dive boat Scapa Agent based at various ports around Scapa Flow, Orkney. In summer 2003 she left Scapa and was taken to Dartmouth, but in 2008 went to Milford Haven for survey, and then went to Cardiff Bay Marina on the river Ely.

911 • City of Bradford III

46'9"x 12'9" Watson motor • J. S. White • W 5432
Built 1954 • Humber 1954-77, Lytham St Annes 1978-85
Sold 7.1985 • City of Bradford III

911 was sold out of service in 1985 to a Newquay-based owner and remained unconverted at Restronguet Creek, on the river Fal (pictured). She was sold in 2008 and was taken to Cardiff Bay Marina on the river Ely. A year later, a former Salcombe coxswain acquired her and took her to Salcombe.

912 • Euphrosyne Kendal

52'x 13'6" Barnett • J. S. White • W 5433
Built 1954 • St Peter Port 1954-72, Dunmore East 1973-75, Rel 1975-83
Sold 5.1983 • Beatrice Mary/ Euphrosyne Kendal

912 was sold out of service in 1983 and, renamed Beatrice Mary but largely unaltered, was used as a fishing and pleasure boat based at Kilmore Quay (pictured). She moved in about 2006 to Cork Dockyard, in Rushbrooke, Cobh, for a complete survey and she remains in use as a fishing boat.

913 • James and Margaret Boyd

52'x 13'6" Barnett • J. S. White • W 5434
Built 1954 • Stornoway 1954-73, Relief 1973-74, Macduff 1974-75, Invergordon 1975-84 • Sold 11.1985 • Grey Goose/ Sea Terror

913 was sold in November 1985 and was used as a pleasure boat in the Devon area until 1994, when she was sold to a new owner who increased her fuel capacity to take her to the Bijagos archipelago off Guinea Bissau, then headed for the Canaries. In 2009 she was in Antigua up for sale.

914 • Tillie Morrison, Sheffield II

35'6" x 10'8" Liverpool motor • Groves & Guttridge • G&G 525
Built 1953 • Bridlington 1953-67, Reserve 1967-68
Sold 1969 • Rescue III

914 was sold out of service in 1969 to the Sumner Lifeboat Institution, New Zealand, and was used as a lifeboat named Rescue III. By the early 1990s she was working as a trip boat (pictured) housed in a boathouse with a slipway at New Plymouth, where visitors could experience a slipway launch.

915 • Friendly Forester

35'6" x 10'8" Liverpool motor • Groves & Guttridge • G&G 526
Built 1953 • Flamborough 1953-83
Sold 7.1984 • Friendly Forester

After serving at Flamborough for 30 years, 915 was sold out of service in July 1984 to Blackgang Saw Mills, Ventnor, Isle of Wight. She was placed on display outside at Blackgang Chine Land of Imagination (pictured), a major tourist attraction located on the Isle of White's south coast.

916 • Maria Noble

35'6" x 10'8" Liverpool motor • Groves & Guttridge • G&G 527
Built 1953 • Exmouth 1953-60, Blackpool 1961-70, Relief 1970-75
Sold 9.1975 • Endurance/ CA49/ Sula/ Valerie Marilyn YH231/ Jack Sam

916 was sold in 1975 and used as a workboat at Dale Fort Field Centre. In the 1990s she went to Wells as a fishing boat and was moved again in the late 1990s, going to Holyhead (pictured). In 2007 she became the fishing boat Jack Sam at Kilrush, and in 2010 went to Limerick for restoration.

917 • Isa and Penryn Milsted

35'6" x 10'8" Liverpool motor • Groves & Guttridge • G&G 528
Built 1953 • Filey 1954-68
Sold 12.1968 • Achievable YH15

917 was sold out of service in December 1968 to a Norfolk owner and was converted into a fishing vessel, with an enclosed wheelhouse aft. During the early 1990s she operated out of Lowestoft but by the mid-1990s she had moved to Gorleston from where she operates angling trips.

918 • The Elliott Gill

35'6" x 10'8" Liverpool motor • Groves & Guttridge • G&G 529
Built 1953 • Runswick 1954-70, Reserve 1970-74
Sold 8.1974 • Gill of London/ Santana/ Wendy and Barbara

918 was sold in August 1974 to a Poole-based owner. She was sold again in the 1980s and moved to Lancaster where she was used as a fishing boat, renamed Wendy and Barbara. She then moved to Sunderland Point, Lancaster, and in 2012 went to R. W. Davis boatyard, Saul Junction (pictured).

919 • Deneys Reitz

46'9" x 12'9" Watson motor • Groves & Guttridge • G&G 550
Built 1954 • Fowey 1954-80
Sold 9.1980 • Joy M/ Daniel Arthur/ Deneys Reitz

919 was sold out of service in September 1980 and used as a houseboat at Falmouth during the 1980s before becoming a pilot boat at Sheerness. After a spell at Halcon Marine, Canvey Island, she was rebuilt at Burgh Castle into a cabin cruiser and cruised extensively around Britain and Europe.

920 • Dunnet Head (Civil Service No.31)

47' x 13' Watson motor • William Osborne • WO 920
Built 1955 • Thurso 1956-56
Accidentally burnt in boathouse, 10.12.1956.

920 arrived at Thurso in January 1956 and was officially named at Scrabster by HM The Queen Mother on 18 August 1956. Unfortunately, she was completely destroyed when the lifeboat house at Scrabster accidentally caught fire on 10 December 1956.

921 • Greater London II (Civil Service No.30)

46'9" x 12'9" Watson motor • Groves & Guttridge • G&G 551
Built 1955 • Southend-on-Sea 1955-76, Beaumaris 1977-89
Sold 2.1991 • Gallichan

921 was sold out of service in February 1991 and became a pleasure boat at Penton Hook Marina, Staines. In the late 1990s she moved to Cobbs Quay Marina, Poole, and soon afterwards to Brixham Marina. She was converted to a long distance cruiser and kept at Puerto Ginestra Marina, Barcelona.

922 • Watkin Williams

42' x 12' Watson motor • William Osborne • WO 922
Built 1956 • Moelfre 1956-77, Oban 1978-81, Relief 1982-83
Sold 5.1983 • Watkin Williams

922 was sold out of service in May 1983 to Cardiff Maritime Museum, Bute Street, Cardiff. She was displayed outside the Museum for a number of years (pictured) but was later stored at Nantgarw, near Cardiff, after the museum had been closed and the exhibits placed in storage.

923 • John Gellatly Hyndman

52' x 13'6" Barnett • J. S. White • W 5435
Built 1955 • Stronsay 1955-72, Relief 1972-84
Sold 8.1985 • Stronsay/ John Gellatly Hyndman

923 was sold in August 1985 and used as a fishing boat at Hartlepool before moving to Littleport near Ely in the early 1990s. She was rejuvenated in 2002 following purchase by a new owner, who stripped her down and repainted her at Mashford's yard. She is kept at Old Mill Creek, Dartmouth.

924 • Archibald and Alexander M. Paterson

52' x 13'6" Barnett • J. S. White • W 5436
Built 1955 • Stromness 1955-84, Arranmore 1985-86, Lowestoft 1986-87 • Sold 5.1989 • St Issey/ Archibald and Alexander M. Paterson

924 was sold in May 1989 and, renamed St Issey, kept at Padstow as a pleasure boat. She was later moved to Maldon, and was at Cork in the mid-1990s. She broke from her moorings at Fishguard in 2003, but was repaired at Portishead. She went to Loughor and then Watermouth Bay in 2010.

925 • Henry Comber Brown

46'9" x 12'9" Watson motor • J. S. White • W 5437
Built 1955 • Tenby 1955-86
Sold 3.1987 • Manxman/ Henry Comber Brown

925 was sold in March 1987 to the Isle of Man Sea Cadet Unit who renamed her Manxman and used her as a training vessel based in Peel. She was converted internally and repainted with a blue hull. She was sold again in 2006, fitted with twin Ford diesels, and moved to Amlwich, Anglesey.

926 • Guy and Clare Hunter

46'9" x 12'9" Watson motor • J. S. White • W 5438
Built 1955 • St Mary's 1955-81, Fowey 1981-82, Relief 1981-88, Penlee 1982-83 • Sold 6.1988 • Ex RNLB Guy and Clare Hunter

926 was sold in June 1988 to a Worcester-based owner, at Redstone Wharf, Stourport in 1989 and Creek Point in 1991. In the early 1990s she was sold again and moved to Donaghadee under the ownership of Quinton Nelson. She was moved to moorings at Ringhaddy Pier, Strangford Lough, in 2004.

927 • Grace Darling

35'6" x 10'8" Liverpool motor • Groves & Guttridge • G&G 530
Built 1954 • North Sunderland 1954-67, Res 1967-71, Youghal 1971-84
On sale list 1985 • Grace Darling

927 was placed on the sale list in 1985, but ended up being loaned to the National Lifeboat Museum, Bristol, where she arrived in October 1985 for permanent exhibition. In 1994 she was moved to Chatham Historic Dockyard (pictured) for display as part of the Lifeboat Collection.

928 • Lilla Marras, Douglas and Will

46'9" x 12'9" Watson motor • Groves & Guttridge • G&G 552
Built 1955 • Cromarty 1955-68, Falmouth 1968-71 and 1972-74, Relief 1974-78, Donaghadee 1978-79, Relief 1979-82
Sold 10.1982 • Adriana of Loosdrecht • Happy • Lilla Marras

928 was sold in October 1982 and used as a private pleasure boat in North Devon during the 1980s. She moved to the Netherlands in 2000 and became a one-bedroom hotel facility based in Harlingen (pictured).

929 • R. A. Colby Cubbin No.1

46'9" x 12'9" Watson motor • J. S. White • W 5439
Built 1956 • Douglas 1956-88
Sold 1989 • Redundant Hero/ Colby Cubbin

929 was sold out of service in 1989 to an Isle of Wight-based owner, who used her as a charter boat based at Yarmouth but travelling extensively. In the mid-1990s she was sold and her new owner moved her to France, where she was based at Honfleur. She moved to Saint-Valéry-sur-Somme in 2008.

930 • R. A. Colby Cubbin No.2

46'9" x 12'9" Watson motor • J. S. White • W 5440
Built 1956 • Port St Mary 1956-76, Relief 1976-77
Sold 10.1977 • Southport Girl

930 was sold out of service on 24 October 1977 to a Southport owner and, renamed Southport Girl, was kept moored in the river Ribble as a pleasure boat, remaining largely unaltered. In the mid-1990s she was moved to the Menai Straits, where she is moored at Pwllfanogl, not far from Beaumaris.

931 • Richard Vernon & Mary Garforth of Leeds

46'9" x 12'9" Watson motor • J. S. White • W 5441
Built 1957 • Angle 1957-87, Wicklow 1987-88
Sold 6.1989 • Scubie Doo/ Spirit of Angle

931 was sold in 1989 to an Oban-based owner and was taken to Scotland. After being sold again, she spent the 1990s at Hartlepool. Then, renamed Spirit of Angle, she went to Milford Haven (pictured). In 2009 she moved to Neyland, and in 2012 was sold again and taken to Saul Junction.

932 • Howard Marryat

46'9"x 12'9" Watson motor • J S White • W 5442
Built 1957 • Fishguard 1957-81, Barrow 1982-86, Moelfre 1987-88
Sold 9.1989 • North Foreland

932 was sold out of service in September 1989 and taken to west Wales, being initially based at Dale Fort Field Centre during the summer. She remained unaltered externally, and by the mid-1990s was kept at Neyland Marina and used as a private pleasure boat.

933 • J. W. Archer

42' x 12' Watson motor • William Osborne • WO 933
Built 1956 • Wicklow 1956-87
Sold 3.1989 • Irish Rose/ Irma Dewi

933 was sold out of service in March 1989 and has been kept at Port Penrhyn (pictured), near Bangor in North Wales, unaltered, as a private pleasure boat ever since. She has cruised to Scotland, Ireland and the Isle of Man and has been painted in lifeboat colours, with internal modifications.

934 • The Duke of Montrose

42' x 12' Watson motor • Groves & Guttridge • G&G 563
Built 1956 • Arbroath 1956-82; Relief 1982-84
Sold 1.1985 • ADES2 Sudelmar

934 was sold out of service in January 1985 to ADES, the Uruguay Lifeboat Society, and she was used as a lifeboat based at Colonia, river Plate. She remained unaltered, apart from a change of livery, with other former RNLI lifeboats in Uruguay. She was retired in 1995 and is now on display.

935 • R. A. Colby Cubbin No.3

52'x 13'6" Barnett • J. S. White • W 5466
Built 1957 • Barra Island 1957-84
Sold 11.1984 • Colby Cubbin No.3/ Colby

935 was sold out of service in November 1984 and taken from Edinburgh to Nottingham, where she was converted into a houseboat named Colby and moored on the river Trent. In the late 1990s she was sold to a buyer in the Netherlands and has been based at City Marina, Rotterdam (pictured).

936 • E. M. M. Gordon Cubbin

52'x 13'6" Barnett • J. S. White • W 5467
Built 1957 • Mallaig 1957-82, Relief 1982-85
Sold 5.1985 • Scrabster Pilot/ Gordon Cubbin

936 was sold out of service on 9 May 1985 and became a pilot boat at Scrabster, near Thurso. In the early 1990s a change of ownership saw her move to Hartlepool (pictured) for use as a charter boat. By 2006 she was moored at Dents Wharf Marina near the Tees barrage in Middlesborough.

937 • Mabel E. Holland

42' x 12' Watson motor • William Osborne • WO 937
Built 1957 • Dungeness 1957-79, Relief 1979-83
Sold 1.1983 • Mabel E. Holland

937 was sold in 1983 and went to Woodbridge Marina before moving to Newcastle in 1990. She travelled through the North West Passage, becoming stuck in ice for over a year, before going to Bridport, then Bow Creek on the Thames (pictured) by 2000. In 2006 she moved to South Wales.

938 • Rowland Watts

52' x 14' Barnett • Groves & Guttridge • G&G 568
Built 1957 • Valentia 1957-83, Relief 1983-85
Sold 7.1985 • Rowland Watts

938 was sold in 1985 and became a work boat in south-west Ireland, mainly at Derrynane. In 2000 she was acquired for possible display, had her lifeboat name restored, and was moved to Murphy Marine, Valentia (pictured) where funds are still being sought to complete her restoration.

939 • Frank Spiller Locke

52' x 14' Barnett • Groves & Guttridge • G&G 569
Built 1957 • Weymouth 1957-76, Galway Bay 1977-85, Relief 1985-86
Sold 10.1986 • Louise/ Resolution/ Frank Spiller Locke

939 was sold in 1986 and became the work boat Louisa at Barry Dock. By 1995 she had moved to the Thames and, by 2001, was a house boat at Oulton Broad. In 2002 she moved to Old Mill Creek, Dartmouth where she was restored and based. She often visits Fowey (pictured) for the ex lifeboat rally there.

940 • Pentland (Civil Service No.31)

47' x 13' Watson motor • J. S. White • W 5468
Built 1957 • Thurso 1957-70, Relief 1970-74, Mumbles 1974-85, Workington 1986-90 • Sold 3.1991 • Pentland

940 was sold in 1991 and was moored in the Menai Straits before moving into Penrhyn Dock, Bangor, in 1994. In 2006 she was taken to Silverstone for survey prior to going to Plymouth. After spending winter 2009-10 at Mashfords, Plymouth, she moved to Portishead Quays Marina (pictured).

941 • William and Mary Durham

42' x 12' Watson motor • William Osborne • WO 941
Built 1957 • Berwick 1957-76; Girvan 1977-83
Sold 10.1983 • Ron Meadhonach

941 was sold out of service in 1983 to become fishing/pleasure boat Ron Meadhonach (Middle Seal) at Portree, Isle of Skye (pictured). Following the death of her owner in about 2006, she was brought ashore for survey and, under new local ownership, she will be again taken afloat at Portree.

942 • J. G. Graves of Sheffield

37' x 11'6" Oakley • William Osborne • WO 942
Built 1957 • Scarborough 1958-78, Relief 1978-88, Clogher Head 1989-91, Relief 1991-92, Newcastle 1992-93, stored 1993-94
Loaned out for display 1994 • J. G. Graves of Sheffield

942 was not sold because, as a pioneering design, she was deemed worthy of preservation so was placed on display at Chatham Historic Dockyard (pictured) as part of the RNLI Historic Lifeboat Collection.

943 • Claude Cecil Staniforth

52' x 14' Barnett • Groves & Guttridge • G&G 570
Built 1958 • Lerwick 1958-78; Arranmore 1978-85
Sold 11.1985 • Claude Cecil Staniforth/ Lady Sarah/ Naomh Seasamh

943 was sold in 1985 and kept at Itchenor, then taken to Crosshaven, Co Cork, as an angling boat. She was sold again and taken to Howth, near Dublin, renamed Lady Sarah. She was moved again in about 2000, this time to Ireland's south coast, being kept at Fethard and Waterford (pictured).

944 • Ramsay-Dyce

52' x 14' Barnett • Groves & Guttridge • G&G 591
Built 1958 • Aberdeen 1958-76; Relief 1976-78; Lochinver 1978-85
Sold 8.1985 • Ramsay Dyce

944 was sold in August 1985 and was used as a pleasure boat touring the Scottish coast, including a visit to her old station at Aberdeen. By the late 1990s she was a diving boat having been altered internally. In 2007 she was sold to new owners who took her to Glasson Dock Marina (pictured).

945 • Princess Alexandra of Kent

52' x 14' Barnett • J. S. White • W 5469
Built 1958 • Torbay 1958-75; Relief 1975-79 & 80-83; Tynemouth 79-80
Sold 2.1984 • Audreys/ Princess

945 was sold in 1984 and used as a fishing boat on the Tyne. By 1990 she had been renamed Princess, and was unaltered at Davey Bank. In 1999 she was sold and taken to St Peters Marina (pictured), being heavily converted. In 2012 she was wrecked off the Fife coast while on passage to Peterhead.

946 • Alfred and Patience Gottwald

42' x 12'3" Watson (Beach) motor • J. S. White • W 5470
Built 1959 • Aldeburgh 1959-79; Relief 1979-80
Sold 8.1980 • Lord Hurcomb/ Patience

946 was sold out of service in 1981 to the Field Studies Council for use at Dale Fort Field Centre, near Milford Haven. In 1987 she was sold again and kept unaltered at Ilfracombe (pictured) and Portway Village Marina, Penarth. By 1997 she had been sold again, and was taken to Nieuwport, Belgium.

947 • Margaret

47' x 13' Watson motor • Groves & Guttridge • G&G 576
Built 1959 • Dunbar 1959-86
Sold 2.1987 • Hallowstell/ Theo

947 was sold out of service in 1987 to Berwick Harbour Commissioners and was used as the pilot boat Hallowstell. She was sold in 1997 to the owner of the Gortahork Hotel, Donegal, who kept her unaltered at Portnalach, just east of Gortahork (pictured), named Theo. She sank at Rathmullen in 2006.

948 • Charles Dibdin (Civil Service No.32)

42' x 12'3" Watson motor • William Osborne • WO 948
Built 1959 • Walmer 1959-75, Relief 1975-77, Eastbourne 1977-79, Aldeburgh 1979-82, Relief 1982-88 • Sold 10.1988 • Charlie Dee

948 was sold out of service in 1988 from Crescent Marine to a Lincolnshire-based owner, who had her converted into a cruiser at Grimsby leaving her unrecognisable as a lifeboat. During the late 1990s she was taken to London and she toured the Med. In 2011 she was in Brighton Marina (pictured).

949 • Ethel Mary

52' x 14' Barnett • Groves & Guttridge • G&G 578
Built 1959 • Ballycotton 1959-85, Relief 1985-87, Baltimore 1987-88
Sold 1988 • Helen Christina/Catriona/Ethel Mary

949 was sold in 1988 and, unaltered externally, was kept at Canvey Island as the pleasure boat Helen Christina, before moving to Southampton. She was renamed Catriona at Castletown, IOM, and in 1999 went to Hull Marina. In 2006 she moved to Aberdeen on her way to Craignure on Mull.

950 • Kathleen Mary

47' x 13' Watson motor • William Osborne • WO 950
Built 1959 • Newhaven 1959-77, Relief 1977-79, Porthdinllaen 1979-87, Appledore 1987-88
Sold 1988 • Kathleen Mary/ Katie May/ C. Fury/ Katie May

950 was sold in 1988 to become the pleasure boat Kathleen Mary based in Bristol Docks. In 2002 she went to Plymouth, spending much time in Mashfords yard, Cremyll. In 2010 she was sold and went to Liverpool Marina (pictured), and is scheduled to sail the French canals from Cherbourg.

951 • Francis W Wotherspoon of Paisley

47' x 13' Watson motor • William Osborne • WO 951
Built 1959 • Islay 1959-79, Relief 1979-81, Fishguard 1981, Workington 1982-86 • Sold 10.1986 • Kimros Man/ Francis W. Wotherspoon

951 was sold in 1986 and became the work boat Kimros Man at Ramsey, Isle of Man, remaining largely unaltered. By 1999 she had moved to Douglas (pictured), later went to Peel and then to Ramsey in 2012. In 2008 she was renamed Francis W. Wotherspoon following a change of ownership.

952 • The Duke of Cornwall (Civil Service No.33)

52' x 14' Barnett • Groves & Guttridge • G&G 583
Built 1959 • Lizard-Cadgwith 1960-84, Padstow 1984, Relief 1984-89
Sold 1989 • The Duke/ Ex RNLB Duke of Cornwall

952 was sold in 1989 to become the work boat The Duke on the Tyne at Davey Bank. She later moved to Milford Haven, and was sold when in Poole in 1999. She moved to her current home at Old Mill Creek, Dartmouth in 1999, where she has been completely restored to her lifeboat condition.

953 • Sarah Jane and James Season

47' x 13' Watson motor • Groves & Guttridge • G&G 584
Built 1960 • Teesmouth 1960-86, Shoreham Harbour 1986-88
Sold 1989 • Manx Voyager

953 was sold out of service in 1989 and, remaining largely unaltered, became the work boat Manx Voyager at Douglas, IOM, although she also operated out of Ramsey. She moved to Peel (pictured) in 2004, and went to Ramsey shipyard for repairs in 2010, remaining there afterwards.

954 • Solomon Browne

47' x 13' Watson motor • William Osborne • WO 954
Built 1960 • Penlee 1960-81
Wrecked on service 12.1981

954 was tragically lost with her crew of eight from Penlee when on service to the coaster Union Star on 19 December 1981. Only small fragments of the boat were recovered following the disaster, and these were taken to Poole to form part of the investigation into the events.

955 • The Robert

47' x 13' Watson motor • William Osborne • WO 955
Built 1960 • Broughty Ferry 1960-78, Baltimore 1978-84, Lytham St Annes 1985-88, Beaumaris 1989-91
Sold 2.1992 • Harriet Claire/ Former RNLB The Robert

955 was sold in 1992 and operated out of Bacton Oil Terminal as a rescue boat. She moved to Bordeaux before becoming a trip boat in Sovereign Harbour, Eastbourne (pictured). She was at Fords Wharf, Allington from 2009 before moving to St Margaret's Hope, Orkney in 2011 as a charter boat.

956 • John and Frances Macfarlane

52' x 14' Barnett • J. S. White • W 5495
Built 1960 • Aith 1961-86 • Sold 10.1986 • Ruthstan/ Iris O Faith/ True Grit/ John and Frances Macfarlane

956 was sold out of service in October 1986 and remained unaltered while passing through the hands of several owners. She was based at Hartlepool, Cowes, Great Yarmouth, Oban, Holyhead, and Heybridge Basin, where she has been based. She took part in the Diamond Jubilee Pageant (pictured).

957 • The Jeanie

47' x 13' Watson motor • Groves & Guttridge • G&G 587
Built 1961 • Portpatrick 1961-86
Sold 6.1987 • Jeanie Brandon

957 was sold out of service June 1987 and taken to Brighton Marina having been renamed Jeanie Brandon (pictured). She was later moved to Strood Yacht Club on the Medway and then to Rochester. By the mid-1990s she had been converted with a large cabin, and was on the river Danube.

958 • Laura Moncur

47' x 13' Watson motor • Groves & Guttridge • G&G 588
Built 1961 • Buckie 1961-84, Relief 84-86 and 87-88, Appledore 1986-87
Sold 11.1988 • Chizz/ Laura Moncur

958 was sold in 1988 and was a pleasure boat on the river Hamble, renamed Chizz. In the 1990s she moved to the Isle of Wight where she was used as a trip boat out of Yarmouth and Cowes. Sold in 2005, she went to Lowestoft Haven Marina (pictured) and was sold again in 2012 to be restored.

959 • Helen Wycherley

47' x 13' Watson motor • Groves & Guttridge • G&G 589
Built 1961 • Whitehills 1961-69, Courtmacsherry Harbour 1969-87
Sold 12.1988 • Helen Wycherley/ Parachinar

959 was sold out of service in 1988 and kept at Aquastar Workboats, at Carigaline, in County Cork during the 1990s, unaltered. In 1999 she moved to Coates Marine at Whitby, where she was restored, and taken to Dents Wharf on river Tees in 2008. In 2010 she returned to Whitby (pictured).

960 • Manchester Unity of Oddfellows

37' x 11'6" Oakley • William Osborne • WO 960
Built 1960 • Sheringham 1961-90
Left service 10.1990 • Manchester Unity of Oddfellows

960 was replaced in October 1990 and taken to the Muckleburgh Collection, Weybourne, in Norfolk for display. By the late 1990s she was being stored at Aylsham, ready to go on display at Sheringham. In May 2009 she became the centrepiece of The Mo Museum (pictured) on Sheringham seafront.

961 • Calouste Gulbenkian

37' x 11'6" Oakley • J. S. White • W 5496
Built 1961 • Weston-s-Mare 1962-69, Relief 69-90, New Quay 1990-91
Sold 11.1991 • Calouste Gulbenkian

After being sold in 1991, 961 went to Marine and Port Services, Pembroke Dock, in RNLI colours on a carriage (pictured). Her condition deteriorated and in 2004 a new owner had her taken to Donaghadee, where work on her restoration was undertaken for possible future display at Weston.

962 • T. G. B.

47' x 13' Watson motor • J. S. White • W 5520
Built 1962 • Longhope 1962-69, Arranmore 1970-78, Relief 1978-85
Sold 7.1986 • T. G. B.

962 was sold in July 1986 and exhibited outside at the Scottish Maritime Museum, Irvine. By 2000 she had been moved inside the Linthouse Engine Shop, as the centrepiece of a display about the Longhope lifeboat disaster. In 2002 she was placed on the National Register of Historic Vessels.

963 • A. M. T.

47' x 13' Watson motor • J. S. White • W 5521
Built 1962 • Howth 1962-86, Relief 1986-89
Sold 6.1989 • Crack O Dawn/ AMiTy

963 was sold in June 1989 to a Barnstaple owner and was used as a pleasure boat at Rolle Quay, Barnstaple, remaining unaltered but renamed Crack O Dawn. She was sold in 2003 and moved along the coast to Watermouth Bay, Combe Martin (pictured), and renamed AMiTy to reflect her lifeboat name.

964 • The Baltic Exchange

47' x 13' Watson motor • J. S. White • W 5522
Built 1962 • Salcombe 1962-88
Sold 1989 • Baltic Exchange/ Baltic Air

964 was sold in 1989 and has remained in her original condition externally while based at several different locations, including Birdham Quay, Ramsholt and Levington. In 2003 she was sold and taken to Southwold, before going to Cowes, Plymouth and Falmouth. Since 2009 she has been at Blyth.

965 • Louisa Anne Hawker

47' x 13' Watson motor • Groves & Guttridge • G&G 594
Built 1962 • Appledore 1962-86
Sold 8.1987 • Lord Hurcomb/ Louisa Ann Hawker

965 was sold in August 1987 to the Field Studies Council and, after minor alterations, was used for trips from Dale Fort, Milford Haven, taking students to offshore islands. In 2003 she was sold from Tenby (pictured) and taken by cargo ship from Southampton to Malaysia to be used as a pleasure boat.

966 • Robert and Dorothy Hardcastle

37' x 11'6" Oakley • Groves & Guttridge • G&G 595
Built 1962 • Boulmer 1962-68, Filey 1968-91, Relief 1991-93
Sold 4.1993 • Robert and Dorothy Hardcastle

966 was sold to Nuclear Electric for display at the Hartlepool Information Centre and she has been at Hartlepool ever since. She was used at a number of fund-raising events around the north-east of England. She was sold into private hands in 2010 and was surveyed at Middleton Road.

967 • Dorothy and Philip Constant

42' x 12' Watson motor • Groves & Guttridge • G&G 600
Built 1962 • Shoreham Harbour 1963-81, Oban 1981-82, Relief 1982-88
Sold 3.1988 • Constance of Blakeney/ Constance /Pentlandssker

967 was sold in 1988 and was a pleasure boat at Blakeney, then a training boat named Constance of Blakeney. In 2007 she moved to Lowestoft Marina (pictured) from where she was sold in 2009. She was taken to St Margaret's Hope in Orkney, where, unaltered externally, she is used as a trip boat.

968 • The Earl and Countess Howe

48'6" X 14' Oakley • William Osborne • WO 968
Built 1963 • Yarmouth 1963-77, Walton and Frinton 1977-84
Unsuitable for sale, so placed on display at RNLI Depot, Poole

968 was deemed unsuitable for private sale and so was placed on display outside at the RNLI's Depot, Poole (pictured), in January 1984 where she remained until 2003. With space needed at the Depot, she was taken to Portishead Quays Marina in March 2003 and broken up.

969 • William Myers and Sarah Jane Myers

47'x 13' Watson • J. S. White • W 5531
Built 1963 • Sunderland 1963-90, Relief 1990-92
Sold 2.1992 • Blue Angel/ Doris/ D'ouwe Draeck

969 was sold out of service in February 1992 and became a pleasure boat named Blue Angel, kept in the Menai Straits. In 1994 she was sold to an owner in Harlingen, Netherlands and renamed Doris. By 2003 she had been renamed D'ouwe Draeck and in 2012 was at Harlingen Oostpoort (pictured).

970 • Frederick Edward Crick

47'x 13' Watson motor • J. S. White • W 5532
Built 1963 • Lowestoft 1963-86 • Sold 11.1986 • Helen Christina/ Surf Rescue/ Beluga/ Frederick Edward Crick

970 was sold in 1986 and went to Canvey Island as a pleasure boat. She was renamed Surf Rescue for a TV commercial in May 1989. By mid-1993, renamed Beluga, she had moved to Medway Bridge Marina. By 1996 she was at Otterham Quay. In 2000 she went to Simon Evans' yard at Saint Denis Les Sens, France (pictured), and was moved to Migennes in 2012.

971 • Joseph Soar (Civil Service No.34)

47'x 13' Watson motor • J. S. White • W 5533
Built 1963 • St Davids 1963-85, Dunbar 1986-88, Shoreham Harb 88-90
Sold 9.1992 • City of Bristol/ Joseph Soar

971 was sold in 1992 and became a display boat named City of Bristol in Bristol. By 1996 she had moved to Penarth and in 2000, renamed Joseph Soar, she became a trip boat at Salcombe. In 2008 she went to Londonderry (pictured), then Fahan Marina. In 2011 she went to Coleraine for full survey.

972 • The Will and Fanny Kirby

37' x 11'6" Oakley • William Osborne • WO 972
Built 1963 • Seaham 1963-79, Relief 1979-83, Flamborough 1983-93
Left service 8.1993 • The Will and Fanny Kirby

After 972 left Flamborough lifeboat station she was initially taken to Grimsby Marina in August 1993 where she was stored. In April 1996 she was taken by road and placed on display as part of the RNLI Historic Lifeboat Collection at Chatham Historic Dockyard (pictured), with her hull sectioned.

973 • Fairlight

37' x 11'6" Oakley • William Osborne • WO 973
Built 1964 • Hastings 1964-88, St Ives 1989-90, New Quay 1991-92, Relief 1992-93 • Sold 10.1994 • Almalux/ Fairlight

973 was sold to a Norwich firm to be broken up, but was instead sold on to a Norfolk owner who used her as a pleasure boat based at Blakeney Pit. She remained in Blakeney but was taken to Wells (pictured) for an old lifeboat rally in 1998 and to Hastings for the station's 150th anniversary in 2008.

974 • Jane Hay

37' x 11'6" Oakley • William Osborne • WO 974
Built 1964 • St Abbs 1964-74, Relief 1974-80, Newcastle (Down) 80-93 Broken up 1995

974 left Newcastle in August 1993 and went to Arklow Marine & Leisure Ltd boatyard, in Arklow (pictured), to be broken up, with two other Oakleys. She was dismantled, but her hull ended up at Tinahealy on Wicklow Way having been completely stripped and holed in several places.

975 • Sir James Knott

37' x 11'6" Oakley • Groves & Guttridge • G&G 604
Built 1963 • Cullercoats 1963-69, Relief 1969-72 & 86-89, Redcar 72-85 Sold for display 12.1990 • Sir James Knott

975 was stored at Dickie's, Bangor until being sold for display at Kirkleatham Old Hall Museum, near Redcar (pictured), as the last offshore lifeboat to serve Redcar. In the mid-1990s she was taken to Amble Boatyard to be repainted. The area where she is displayed is not always open to the public.

976 • Lilly Wainwright

37' x 11'6" Oakley • Groves & Guttridge • G&G 605
Built 1964 • Llandudno 1964-90, Kilmore Quay 1991-92 Sold 10.1993 • Lilly Wainwright

976 was sold in October 1993 to a buyer in Co Cork and was stored at Verolme Dockyard (pictured) for display at Cobh Heritage Trust throughout the 1990s. She remained there until 2004 when she was converted into a pleasure boat and placed afloat at East Ferry Marina, Cobh.

977 • Charles Fred Grantham

37' x 11'6" Oakley • Groves & Guttridge • G&G 606
Built 1964 • Skegness 1964-90, Relief 1990-92 Scrapped 8.1993

977 served at Skegness for more than 25 years and after a couple of years as a relief lifeboat was deemed unsuitable for sale and so was scrapped in August 1993. She was taken to Branksea Marine, near Wareham (pictured), where she was broken up in accordance with RNLI instructions.

978 • The Royal Thames

37' x 11'6" Oakley • J. S. White • W 5542
Built 1964 • Caister 1964-69, Runswick 1970-78, Pwllheli 1979-91, Clogher Head 1991-93 • Sold for breaking 10.1994 • Royal Thames

After being sold from Poole (pictured), 978 was sold to a Norwich firm to be broken up, but she was sold on by them, together with 973, to an owner in Blakeney. She was moved to a farm about five miles south of Cromer, where she was stored under a tarpaulin, unaltered and unused.

979 • James and Catherine MacFarlane/Amelia

37' x 11'6" Oakley • J. S. White • W 5543
Built 1964 • Relief 1964-78, Scarborough 1978-91
Sold 3.1992 • Amelia

979 was sold in March 1992 for display purposes only at the Shipwreck & Heritage Museum, Charlestown, Cornwall, being transported there by road from Poole. Owned by Charlestown Enterprises, she has been displayed outside the Shipwreck & Heritage Museum (pictured) ever since.

980 • William Henry and Mary King

37' x 11'6" Oakley • J. S. White • W 5544
Built 1964 • Cromer No.2 1964-67, Bridlington 1967-88, North Sunderland 1988-90 • Ashore from 1991

980 was taken out of service in August 1990 and taken to the RNLI Depot at Poole for storage. It was then donated by the RNLI to a playground in Islington for use in a children's play area as part of the Children's Culture Centre, Park School, Arvon Road (pictured).

981 • Mary Pullman

37' x 11'6" Oakley • William Osborne • WO 981
Built 1964 • Kirkcudbright 1965-89
Sold 3.1989 • Mary Pullman

981 was sold after a survey at Gareloch revealed major hull deterioration. The hull was taken to the National Boatbuilding Centre at Oulton Broad, where the engines and equipment were removed. The boat ended up in the open at Baytree Garden Centre, Weston, Spalding (pictured).

982 • Ernest Tom Neathercoat

37' x 11'6" Oakley • William Osborne • WO 982
Built 1965 • Wells 1965-90, North Sunderland 1990-91
Sold 1992 • Ernest Tom Neathercoat

982 was displayed at the National Boatbuilding Centre at Oulton Broad in 1992 until about 1997, when she went to the beach car park at Wells. In 2000 she was moved to a nearby farm and in 2007 to Hewitt's yard at Stiffkey. In 2012 she was placed afloat at Wells (pictured), where she has been based.

983 • The Doctors

37' x 11'6" Oakley • William Osborne • WO 983
Built 1965 • Anstruther 1965-91, Relief 1991-93
Sold 5.1993 for display • The Doctors

983 was sold out of service and went on display at the Buckie Drifter Centre, owned by Moray District Council. She was displayed in the open at Buckie for more than ten years, until the Centre closed and the lifeboat was then sold and taken to Donaghadee (pictured) for restoration.

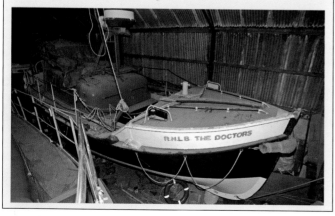

984 • Mary Joicey

37' x 11'6" Oakley • Herd & MacKenzie
Built 1966 • Newbiggin 1966-81, Relief 1981-89, Redcar 1985-86, Hastings 1988-89, St Ives 1989 • Sold 5.1989 • Mary Joicey

984 was displayed at the Child-Beale Wildlife Trust, at Church Farm, Lower Basildon, Pangbourne, near Reading, until 2005. In May 2005 she returned to the north-east and was restored at Sleekburn before being taken to Newbiggin to be displayed in the town's new Maritime Centre (pictured).

985 • Valentine Wyndham-Quin

37' x 11'6" Oakley • Herd & MacKenzie
Built 1967 • Clacton 1967-83, Clogher Head 1984-88
Display from 1989 • Valentine Wyndham-Quin

985 was placed on display after leaving service, going to Cromer Lifeboat Museum in 1989, where she stayed until 1993 being kept outside the East Gangway boathouse (pictured). She was moved to Harwich in July 1993 and moved into the Old Boathouse at The Green for display.

986 • Lloyd's II

37' x 11'6" Oakley • Morris & Lorimer
Built 1966 • Ilfracombe 1966-90, Sheringham 1990-92
Broken up 8.1993

986 was taken out of service in April 1992 after a short stint at Sheringham, where she was the station's last offshore lifeboat. She was then taken to Crescent Marine at Otterham Quay (pictured) and by August 1993 had been dismantled and broken up in accordance with RNLI instructions.

987 • Charles H. Barrett (Civil Service No.35)

71' x 18' Clyde • Yarrow • Y 2271
Built 1965 • Trials 1966-68, Clovelly 1968-75, Relief 1975-88
Sold 12.1988 • Poplar Diver/ Dolphin

987 was sold in December 1988 and has been based at a variety of ports, initially going to Hartlepool, being used as a diving boat, moving to Oban during the summer. In about 2005 she left Oban and sailed to Holland, and has been based at Enkhuizen and Stellendam (pictured) as a trip boat.

988 • Grace Paterson Ritchie

70' x 17' Clyde • Yarrow • Y 2272
Built 1966 • Ullapool 1966-67, Relief 67-68, Kirkwall 68-74, Relief 74-75, Kirkwall 1975-88 • Sold 2.1989 • Henry A. Hálfdánsson/ Grace Ritchie

988 was sold in 1989 to the Icelandic Life Saving Association (ICE-SAR), and she served at Reykjavik renamed Henry A. Hálfdánsson. In 2002 she was sold by ICE-SAR and was sailed south to Largs, being kept in the Yacht Haven as Grace Ritchie (pictured), from where she tours regularly.

989 • James and Catherine Macfarlane

48'6" x 14' Oakley • Berthon Boat Co • 944
Built 1967 • Padstow 1967-83, Lizard-Cadgwith 1984-87
Loaned for display 1987 • James and Catherine MacFarlane

989 was loaned out for display after being replaced at the Lizard-Cadgwith station in September 1987. Having been at two Cornish stations, she was placed on display out of the water at Lands End (pictured) as part of the theme park development in the area.

990 • Ruby and Arthur Reed

48'6" x 14' Oakley • William Osborne • WO 990
Built 1966 • Cromer 1967-84, St Davids 1985-88
Sold for display 9.1988 • Ruby and Arthur Reed

990 was sold out of service in September 1988 from Dickie's Yard, Bangor, North Wales, without engines. She was taken south and placed on display at Hythe Village Marina (pictured), in the middle of a small roundabout. The Marina is situated on the west side of Southampton Water.

991 • Edward and Mary Lester

37' x 11'6" Oakley • William Osborne • WO 991
Built 1967 • North Sunderland 1967-89
Broken up 12.1989

991 was taken out of service in March 1989 and moved to the RNLI Depot at Poole (pictured). In December 1989 she was broken up at a St Denys, Southampton boatyard. The yard signed a declaration that the boat would be destroyed so that she could not be put back in the water.

992 • Frank Penfold Marshall

37' x 11'6" Oakley • William Osborne • WO 992
Built 1968 • St Ives 1968-89
Broken up 12.1989

992 was taken out of service in March 1989 and moved to the RNLI Depot at Poole (pictured). In December 1989 she was scrapped and subsequently broken up at a St Denys, Southampton boatyard. The yard signed a declaration that the boat could not be put back in the water.

993 • Har-Lil

37' x 11'6" Oakley • William Osborne • WO 993
Built 1967 • Rhyl 1968-90
Sold 12.1991 • Har-Lil

993 was sold for display purposes at the Marine Life Centre St Davids in 1991. By 2001 she was in a caravan park before being moved in 2003 to Clapson's boatyard, South Ferriby (pictured), where the righting tanks were removed, the hull rebuilt and ballast installed so she could go afloat again.

994 • Vincent Nesfield

37' x 11'6" Oakley • William Osborne • WO 994
Built 1969 • Relief 1969-72, Port Erin 1972-73, Relief 1973-88, Kilmore Quay 1988-91

994 was taken from Kilmore Quay in January 1991, her last station after a varied career in the Relief Fleet, to Tyrrell's boatyard, Arklow (pictured). She remained there for a number of years but was gradually dismantled and by 1995 she had been completely broken up.

995 • James Ball Ritchie

37' x 11'6" Oakley • William Osborne • WO 995
Built 1970 • Ramsey 1970-91
Broken up 1992

995 left Ramsey in July 1991 and was taken to R. McAllister & Son boatyard, Dumbarton (pictured), where, in December 1992, she was broken up. The boatyard signed a declaration that the boat would be destroyed in such a way she was no longer capable of being put back in the water.

996 • Birds Eye

37' x 11'6" Oakley • William Osborne • WO 996
Built 1970 • New Quay 1970-90
Displayed • Birds Eye

996 was placed on display at the Seawatch Centre, Moelfre, Anglesey (pictured) in May 1991. She was displayed inside as the centrepiece of an exhibition which includes tributes to the medal-winning Moelfre coxswain Richard Evans. In 2013 the RNLI took over the running of the Centre.

997 • Lady Murphy

37' x 11'6" Oakley • William Osborne • WO 18
Built 1971 • Kilmore Quay 1972-88
Broken up 9.1995

997 left service in September 1988 and during the early 1990s was stored at Tyrrell's boatyard, Arklow, for possible display by the Arklow Enterprise Trust. However, this never came to fruition and in 1995 she was dismantled and broken up at Arklow Marine & Leisure Ltd boatyard (pictured).

998 • Osman Gabriel

37'6" x 11'6" Rother • William Osborne • WO 19
Built 1972 • Port Erin 1973-92, Relief 1992-93
Sold 3.1993 • Anita

998 was sold to the Estonian Lifeboat Service (Eesti Vetelpaasteuhingu). She left Poole on 11 March 1993 and went via Felixstowe to Estonia. Renamed Anita, she was handed over on 18 March 1993 at Tallinn, and stationed at Haapsalu. She is now a private pleasure boat at Dirhami Harbour (pictured).

999 • Diana White

37'6" x 11'6" Rother • William Osborne • WO 20
Built 1973 • Sennen Cove 1973-91
Sold 1992 • Joseph Day/ Diana White

999 was sold to the Sumner Lifeboat Institution, New Zealand, arriving there on 5 August 1992. In 2001 Sumner sold her and she became a charter boat at Tauranga, Bay of Plenty (pictured), under her original name. In 2011 she was sold and become a pleasure boat at Glenbrook, South Auckland.

1000 • Mary Gabriel

37'6" x 11'6" Rother • William Osborne • WO 21
Built 1974 • Hoylake 1974-90, Rhyl 1990-92
Sold 10.1992 • Mary Gabriel

1000 was sold in 1992 to a Northamptonshire owner and was kept on the Nene at Peterborough, and later at Wells harbour. In 2001 she became a floating exhibit at Chatham Historic Dockyard, operated by a group of volunteers. In 2012 she took part in the Diamond Jubilee Pageant (pictured).

1001 • John F. Kennedy

44'10" x 12'8" Waveney • Brooke Marine • B 348
Built 1966 • Dun Laoghaire 1967-90, Relief 1990-96
Sold 8.1996 • Sarah JFK

1001 was sold out of service in 1996 and converted into a fishing boat on the Tyne (pictured), initially based at Davey Bank and later Royal Quays Marina. Renamed Sarah JFK, she had her after cabin removed, her wheelhouse enlarged and she was certified to carry 12 passengers.

1002 • Khami

44'10" x 12'8" Waveney • Brooke Marine • B 349
Built 1967 • Gt Yarmouth & Gorleston 1967-80, Relief 1980-97
Sold 5.1999 • P&O Nedlloyd Stratheden

1002 was sold in 1999 to the Royal Volunteer Coastal Patrol, Australia. She was repainted at Souter Marine, Cowes before being shipped from Tilbury to RVCP's Botany Bay Division as a Coast Guard boat and lifeboat. In 2012 she was sold to a private buyer at Port Hacking, Western Australia (pictured).

1003 • Faithful Forester

44'10" x 12'8" Waveney • Brooke Marine • B 350
Built 1967 • Dover 1967-79, Relief 79-84, Holyhead 84-85, Relief 85-97
Sold 5.1999 • P&O Nedlloyd Strathmore/ Harbour Conquest

1003 was sold in 1999 to the Royal Volunteer Coastal Patrol. She was painted in RVCP colours at Souter Marine, Cowes, and shipped to Australia for service at Narooma. In 2011 she was sold and taken to Fremantle as a service vessel Harbour Conquest with after cabin removed (pictured).

1004 • Margaret Graham

44'10" x 12'8" Waveney • Brooke Marine • B 351
Built 1967 • Harwich 1967-80, Relief 1980-86, Amble 1986-99
Sold 8.1999 • St Hilda of Whitby

1004 was sold out of service in August 1999, having been the last Waveney in service, to Scarborough Borough Council for use as the Whitby Harbour Board's pilot boat, renamed St Hilda of Whitby (pictured). She remained unaltered and is kept at various locations round Whitby harbour.

1005 • Arthur and Blanche Harris

44'10" x 12'8" Waveney • Brooke Marine • B 352
Built 1968 • Barry Dock 1968-74, Donaghadee 1979-85, Relief 1974-79, 1985-93 and 1995-96, Courtmacsherry Harbour 1993-95
Sold 5.1999 • P&O Nedlloyd Strathallan/ Harbour Crusader

1005 was sold in May 1999 to the Royal Volunteer Coastal Patrol, Australia, and she served in the Ulladulla Division, NSW, as a lifeboat. In 2009 she was bought by Harbour Services for their fleet in Fremantle (pictured).

1006 • Connel Elizabeth Cargill

44'10" x 12'8" Waveney • Brooke Marine • B 353
Built 1968 • Troon 1968-85, Arklow 1986-90, Relief 1990-97
Sold 5.1999 • P&O Nedlloyd Rawalpindi

1006 was sold in May 1999 to the Royal Volunteer Coastal Patrol, Australia, and served in to the Sydney Division (pictured), renamed P&O Nedlloyd Rawalpindi. She was used as a Coast Guard boat and lifeboat at Mosman and in 2011 became a spare lifeboat.

1007 • George Urie Scott

48'6" x 14' Solent • Groves & Guttridge • G&G 625
Built 1969 • Lochinver 1969-79, Rosslare Harb 1979-84, Lochinver 85-89
Sold 5.1990 • Lunga/ Blue Highlander/ Highlander

1007 was sold in 1990 and was unaltered as the trip boat Lunga at Lochinver. She was sold in the mid-1990s and taken to Inverness. In 1999 she was sold again, taken to the Netherlands, painted blue and renamed Blue Highlander. In 2007 she was sold again and taken to Ballumerbocht, Ameland (pictured).

1008 • James and Mariska Joicey

48'6" x 14' Solent • Groves & Guttridge • G&G 626
Built 1969 • Peterhead 1969-86, The Lizard 1987-88, Relief 1988-89
Sold 3.1990 • Mariska/ Mirage of Dart/ Thee Hearts

1008 was sold in 1990 and, renamed Mariska, was used unaltered as a trip boat at Southampton. In the mid-1990s she was moved to Plymouth and then to the Dart, being renamed Mirage. By 2007, having been fitted with a raised wheelhouse, she was on a beach at Moross, Co Donegal (pictured).

1009 • Jack Shayler & the Lees

48'6" x 14' Solent • Groves & Guttridge • G&G 627
Built 1970 • Bembridge 1970-87, Relief 1987-93
Sold 6.1994 • Anni

1009 was sold in 1994 to the Estonia Life-saving Association. She had been used for filming BBC TV series Lifeboat, for which she was named St Teilo, and after this she was sold to Estonia. In 2012 she was ashore near the new Lennusadam/Seaplane Harbour Museum in Tallinn (pictured).

1010 • David and Elizabeth King & E. B.

48'6" x 14' Solent • Groves & Guttridge • G&G 628
Built 1970 • Longhope 1970-88, Invergordon 1988-89
Sold 3.1990 • Island Lass/ Storm

1010 was sold in 1990 and, named Island Lass, was unaltered as a pleasure boat at Castletown, IOM, and then went to St Katharine Dock, London. She was later kept at Millport and Kirkcudbright. Since about 2003 she has been based at the canal basin at Bowling, Dumbarton renamed Storm.

1011 • R. Hope Roberts

48'6" x 14' Solent • Camper & Nicholson • 930
Built 1969 • Rosslare Harb 1969-78, Fraserburgh 1979-85, Galway Bay 1985-87, Courtmacsherry Har 1987-93 • Sold 1993 • ANL Sea Guardian

1011 was sold in 1993 to Coastal Volunteer Rescue, Batemans Bay, NSW, Australia. She was used as a rescue boat at Wollongong from 1993 to 1998 and at St Helens, Tasmania (pictured) from 1998 to 2009. Since 2009 she has been for sale at Maurice Dent Boat Services Sandy Bay, Hobart.

1012 • City of Birmingham

48'6" x 14' Solent • Camper & Nicholson • 931
Built 1970 • Exmouth 1970-83, Walton & Frinton 1984-93
Sold 1995 • St Teilo/ Ades 14 ILC 95

1012 was taken out of service in 1994 and was temporarily renumbered and renamed St Teilo for use by the BBC to shoot scenes for the TV series Lifeboat at St Davids. She was then sold to the Uruguayan lifeboat service. Renamed Ades 14 ILC 95, she has been at Puerto de Colonia (pictured) since 1995.

1013 • Royal British Legion Jubilee

48'6" x 14' Solent • Camper & Nicholson • 932
Built 1971 • Relief 1971-78, Fraserburgh 1978-79, Relief 1979-89
Sold 4.1990 • Ocean Jubilee

1013 was sold in 1990 to Thousand Island Tours at Neyland. Sold in 1995, she was seized by customs at Wick after smuggling and impounded at Rosyth Naval Dockyard until sold in 2003. She went to Shirley Nursery, Nottingham, until 2011 when she was moved to the river Calder near Wakefield (pictured).

1014 • The Three Sisters

48'6" x 14' Solent • Camper & Nicholson • 933
Built 1970 • Thurso 1970-88, Wicklow 1988-89, Relief 1989-90
Sold 4.1990 • The Three Sisters

1014 was sold in 1990 and taken to Newcastle to become an expedition boat, but was laid up until being sold, ending up at Portmadoc. Another sale took her to Levington Marina, Suffolk (pictured) in 1999 until 2011, when she went to Newark Marina. In 2012 another new owner moved her to Plymouth Yacht Haven Marina.

1015 • Charles Henry

48'6" x 14' Oakley • William Osborne • WO 1015
Built 1968 • Selsey 1969-83, Baltimore 1984-87
Display at Dudley 1989 • Charles Henry

1015 was displayed for ten years at Waterfront Way, Merry Hill, Dudley.
In 1999 she was sold into private ownership and, after the water ballast
tanks were removed, she went to Brixham. She was later moved to Spain,
returning in 2004, taking up residence in the Canal Basin at Exeter (pictured).

1016 • Princess Marina

48'6" x 14' Oakley • William Osborne • WO 1016
Built 1970 • Wick 1970-88
Display at Pitsea • Princess Marina

1016 was displayed at the National Motor Boat Museum, Pitsea, Basildon,
on permanent loan from the RNLI (pictured). By 2001, her condition having
deteriorated, she faced an uncertain future and in 2003 she was broken up
at Portishead. Her cabin and engines were retained and sold to other projects.

1017 • Ernest William and Elizabeth Ellen Hinde

41' x 12' Keith Nelson • Halmatic/Keith Nelson
Built 1969 • Sheerness 1969-70, Calshot 1970-85
Sold 9.1985 • Parhelia

1017 was sold out of service in 1985 from Poole, was taken to Carrickfergus
(pictured) and renamed Parhelia. She remained in Carrickfergus Marina as a
pleasure boat in the 1990s. She was taken out of the water at various times
for maintenance, and in 2012 was converted with a new cabin.

1018 • Arun

52' x 17' Arun • William Osborne • WO 22
Built 1971 • St Peter Port 1972-3, Barry Dock 1974-97
Sold 10.1997 • Arun Adventurer

1018 was sold in October 1997 to engineering firm LADCO, of Dundee,
who renamed her Arun Adventurer and based her in Dundee Docks for
use promoting the firm around the UK until 2009. The firm relocated to
Arbroath and the boat was taken there (pictured) and painted white.

1019 • Lady MacRobert

48'6" x 14' Solent • Groves & Guttridge • G&G 653
Built 1972 • Montrose 1973-89, Relief 1989-93
Sold 3.1994 • Ades 12 Intendencia Municipal de Maldonado

1019 was sold out of service in 1994 to ADES, the Uruguayan lifeboat
service. After being stored at Titchmarsh Marine, Walton (pictured), she was
taken by road to Tilbury Docks for shipment, leaving there on 2 March 1994.
She has since been used as a lifeboat stationed at Punta Del Este, Uruguay.

1020 • Hugh William, Viscount Gough

48'6" x 14' Solent • Groves & Guttridge • G&G 654
Built 1973 • Stornoway 1973-84, Barra Island 1984-88, Dunbar 1988-93
Sold 9.1993 • Onward/ Hugh William, Viscount Gough

1020 was sold in 1993 and taken to Albert Edward Dock, North Shields.
In 1998 she was sold and taken to Fox's yard, Ipswich. She then moved to
Battlesbridge, Essex, on the river Crouch (pictured). In 2006, after another
sale, she was shipped out to Nusajaya, Malaysia from Southampton.

1021 • Douglas Currie

48'6" x 14' Solent • Groves & Guttridge • G&G 655
Built 1973 • Reserve 1973-74, Kirkwall 1974-75, Macduff 1975-84,
Fraserburgh 1985, Portpatrick 1986-89, Workington 1990-92
Sold 1992 • Sealion/ Solent Sealion/ Douglas Currie

1021 was sold in 1992 for use as a lifeboat in Tenerife. After being replaced
as the lifeboat at Los Christianos in 1997, she was sold and returned to
Portishead where she has been based ever since, attending lifeboat rallies.

1022 • Harold Salvesen

37'6" x 11'6" Rother • Groves & Guttridge • G&G 656
Built 1974 • Amble 1974-86, Relief 1986-92, Rhyl 1992
Sold 10.1992 • TS Salvesen/ Harold Salvesen/ Ex RNLB Harold Salvesen

1022 was sold in 1992 and kept in the river Tawe Marina, Swansea Marina.
During the 1990s she was based at Bristol, Bideford Quay, Instow and
lastly Mylor, Cornwall. She remained at Mylor until 2006, and then went via
Donaghadee to Aberystwyth (pictured) and to Barmouth in 2012, unaltered.

1023 • J. Reginald Corah

37'6" x 11'6" Rother • Groves & Guttridge • G&G 657
Built 1974 • Swanage 1975-92
Sold 6.1995 • Louise

1023 was sold in 1995 and was used as a pleasure boat at Birdham Quay,
Chichester, where she remained until 2002. She then moved to Chichester
Yacht Harbour. In 2007 she moved to St Osyth near Clacton, unaltered, and
in 2008 went from Brightlingsea (pictured) to Gulberg, Denmark.

1024 • The Hampshire Rose

37'6" x 11'6" Rother • William Osborne • WO 22/1024
Built 1974 • Walmer 1975-90, Relief 1990-92
Sold 10.1992 • The Hampshire Rose

1024 was sold in 1992 and taken to Monkston Marina, Swansea. In 2000 she
moved to Plymouth, and later to Truro and Ilfracombe as a trip boat. In 2006
she was taken to Gun Wharf, Portsmouth and in 2008 to Hayling Island. In
October 2012 she returned to Ilfracombe (pictured) for use as a trip boat.

1025 • Sir William Arnold

52' x 17' Arun • William Osborne • WO 93
Built 1973 • St Peter Port 1973-97
Sold 2.1998 • Our Lady/ Theocrat/ Samuel J

1025 was sold in February 1998 and, renamed Our Lady, kept at Fleetwood.
In 2001 she was sold and renamed Theocrat. She was kept around the
Solent area until September 2005, when John O'Regan bought her and took
her to Cork. He kept her at East Ferry and Kinsale (pictured) as Samuel J.

1026 • Eric Seal (Civil Service No.36)

44'10" x 12'8" Waveney • Groves & Guttridge • G&G 658
Built 1974 • Eyemouth 1974-96
Sold 7.1999 • Spirit of Standard Bank

1026 was sold out of service in 1999 to become a lifeboat at Walvis Bay,
Namibia. The vessel was shipped to Namibia (pictured) with a grey hull and
was renamed Spirit of Standard Bank in April 2000. In 2005 she was moved
from Walvis Bay to Luderitz, and continued being used as a lifeboat.

1027 • Helen Turnbull

44'10" x 12'8" Waveney • Groves & Guttridge • G&G 659
Built 1974 • Sheerness 1974-96, Achill 1996-97, Relief 1997-98
Sold 11.1998 • Badger

1027 was sold in November 1998 and was kept at Douglas, Isle of Man (pictured), renamed Badger. In 2000 she was altered with her wheelhouse enclosed by a removable cabin. She has been based on the Isle of Man, as a pleasure boat travelling to places such as Preston and Liverpool.

1028 • Thomas Forehead and Mary Rowse II

44'10" x 12'8" Waveney • Groves & Guttridge • G&G 660
Built 1974 • Plymouth 1974-87, Fowey 1988-96, Relief 1996-97
Sold 11.1999 • Westgate Rescue

1028 was sold in November 1999 to the Royal New Zealand Coastguard Federation and shipped to New Zealand. Based at New Plymouth, Taranaki, she was used as a Coast Guard boat and lifeboat renamed Westgate Rescue. She left service in September 2012 and was sold to a Picton (NZ) owner.

1029 • Augustine Courtauld

44'10" x 12'8" Waveney • Groves & Guttridge • G&G 661
Built 1974 • Poole 1974-83, Relief 1983-85, Troon 1985-87, Relief 1987-90, Arklow 1990-97, Relief 1997-98
Sold 5.1999 • P&O Nedlloyd Strathaird/ Augustine Courtauld

1029 was sold in 1999 and went to the Broken Bay Division of the Royal Volunteer Coastal Patrol, Australia, as a lifeboat. In 2011 she was sold to Melbourne Charter Services to become a work boat in the port (pictured).

1030 • City of Bristol

71' x 18' Clyde • Bideford Shipyard • Y 44
Built 1974 • Clovelly 1975-88
Sold 12.1988 • John V. Story/ Gemini Storm/ Gemini Explorer

1030 was sold in 1988 and became a fisheries protection vessel for Kent & Essex Sea Fisheries Committee, based at Ramsgate. In 2000 she was sold and was used as a diving boat out of Oban and Tobermory. In 2004 she moved to Buckie (pictured) as a trip boat and in 2012 to Montrose as a work boat.

1031 • Rotary Service

50' x 14'6" Thames • Brooke Marine • B 394
Built 1973 • Falmouth 1974-78, Dover 1979-97
Sold 6.1998 • Treffry

1031 was sold to Fowey Harbour Commissioners and used as a pilot boat, largely unaltered, renamed Treffry and based at Fowey. In 2006 she was sold and moved to Bantry Bay to become a pilot boat based at Castletownbere and Bere Island (pictured), retaining the name Treffry.

1032 • Helmut Schroder of Dunlossit

50' x 14'6" Thames • Brooke Marine • B 395
Built 1974 • Trials 1974-78, Islay 1979-97
Sold 6.1998 • P&O Nedlloyd Rescue/ LPC Rescue

1032 was sold in 1998 to the Sumner Lifeboat Institution, New Zealand, and was transported to Lyttelton on board the ship Pegasus Bay. Renamed P&O Nedlloyd Rescue, she was used as rescue boat and a pilot/work boat. In 2008 she was renamed LPC Rescue (pictured), continuing in her role.

1033 • The White Rose of Yorkshire

44'10" x 12'8" Waveney • Groves & Guttridge • G&G 663
Built 1974 • Whitby 1974-88, Invergordon 1989-96, Relief 1996-97
Sold 3.1999 • IA.001

1033 was sold in 1999 to the Canadian Lifeboat Institution and was at Poole in June 1999 for the RNLI's 175th anniversary (pictured). Shipped to Canada via Sheerness, she became a lifeboat based at Roberts Bank, south of Vancouver. In 2009 she was sold and moved to the Westham Island Bridge.

1034 • Thomas James King

44'10" x 12'8" Waveney • Groves & Guttridge • G&G 664
Built 1974 • St Helier 1975-89, Relief 90-93, Dunbar 93-95, Relief 95-97
Sold 5.1998 • North Esk

1034 was sold in 1998 to Montrose Harbour Authority for use as a pilot boat named North Esk at Montrose docks (pictured). She was initially unaltered, but her livery was later changed and the wheelhouse was enclosed. She was sold in 2012 to Bay Towage & Salvage Co Ltd, Ramsden, Barrow.

1035 • St Patrick

44'10" x 12'8" Waveney • Groves & Guttridge • G&G 665
Built 1974 • Dunmore East 1975-96 • Sold 5.1999
P&O Nedlloyd Strathnaver Community Spirit/ St Patrick Strathnaver

1035 was sold in May 1999 to the Royal Volunteer Coastal Patrol, Australia, and was repainted at Cowes. She went to Batemans Bay Division in New South Wales, as a rescue boat. In 2009 she was acquired by a private buyer and taken to Yaringa Marina, Western Port, Victoria , Australia (pictured).

1036 • Lady of Lancashire

44'10" x 12'8" Waveney • Groves & Guttridge • G&G 666
Built 1975 • Fleetwood 1976-89, Dun Laoghaire 1990-95, Relief 1995-96
Sold 11.1996 • St Boisel

1036 was sold in 1996 to the Berwick Pilot Service and taken to Northumberland to become the third ex-lifeboat they have owned. She sailed north almost straight after the sale had been completed and was renamed St Boisel, remaining largely unaltered at Berwick docks (pictured).

1037 • Edward Bridges (Civil Serv & P. O. No.37)

52' x 17' Arun • William Osborne • WO 700
Built 1974 • Torbay 1975-94
Withdrawn 1994 • Edward Bridges (Civil Service & Post Office No.37)

1037 was withdrawn from service in 1994 and in 1995 was towed to Chatham for display at the Dockyard as part of the RNLI Historic Lifeboat Collection (pictured). The only Arun lifeboat to be preserved for display, she is maintained by a team of volunteers who work on all the historic lifeboats.

1042 • Ralph and Joy Swann

44'10" x 12'8" Waveney • Bideford Shipyard • Y 59
Built 1976 • Ramsgate 1976-90, Tobermory 1990-91, Portree 1991-96, Relief 1996-98 • Sold 6.1998 • West Swann

1042 was sold in June 1998 to a Falkland Islander and was shipped there to be used as a trip boat based at Port Howard, West Falklands under the ownership of Robin Lee, renamed West Swann. She was used to take tourists to see the penguins and also as a ferry to Port San Carlos.

1043 • The Nelsons of Donaghadee/ Wavy Line

44'10" x 12'8" Waveney • Bideford Shipyard • Y 60
Built 1976 • Donaghadee 1976-77, Relief 1978-90, Sunderland 1990-97
Sold 11.1997 • Nicholsons Rescue/ Trust Porirua Rescue/ Toucan

1043 was sold in November 1997 to the Royal New Zealand Coastguard as a lifeboat and coastguard boat based at Mana near Wellington for operations in the Cook Strait. In 2010 she was sold and became a work boat based at Lyttelton for use in salvage and crew transport renamed Toucan (pictured).

1044 • The Scout

44'10" x 12'8" Waveney • Bideford Shipyard • Y 61
Built 1977 • Hartlepool 1977-97
Sold 1997 • ADES 16 14-016

1044 was sold in 1997 to the Uruguay lifeboat service, ADES, to became the lifeboat ADES 16 (pictured) stationed at Puerto del Bueco, Montevideo. She was taken by cargo ship from Tilbury to South America. In September 2012 she was damaged during a storm, and needs repairing before being usable.

1045 • Louis Marchesi of Round Table

44'10" x 12'8" Waveney • Bideford Shipyard • Y 62
Built 1977 • Newhaven 1977-85, Relief 1985-86, Alderney 1986-94, Exmouth 1994-96, Relief 1996-97 • Sold 2.1999 • P&O Nedlloyd Rescue

1045 was sold to New Zealand Coastguard and shipped via Tilbury in 1999. She went to Waiheke Island, near Auckland for use as a lifeboat named P&O Nedlloyd Rescue. In 2006 she was sold by the Coastguard to a private owner at Whangarei, New Zealand. In 2010 she went to Auckland as a pleasure boat.

1046 • Silver Jubilee (Civil Service No.38)

37'6" x 11'6" Rother • William Osborne • WO 1117
Built 1977 • Margate 1978-91, Relief 1991-93
Sold 3.1994 • Catherie/ Silver Jubilee

1046 was sold in 1994 to become a pleasure boat at East Ferry. She was at Old Cork Boatyard, Skibbereen until 2002 when she moved to Shannon Harbour. In 2006 she was surveyed at Donaghadee and in 2007 was taken to Ossining, USA (pictured), being is based at Yonkers Yacht Club, New York.

1047 • Horace Clarkson

37'6" x 11'6" Rother • William Osborne • WO 1118
Built 1977 • Moelfre 1977-86, Relief 1987-93
Sold 5.1993 • Horace Clarkson

1047 was sold in 1993 to a buyer in Hampshire and was kept on the river Itchen below Northam Bridge, Southampton. She remained there until about 2006, when she was moved to Hewitt's boatyard at Stiffkey, Norfolk and was restored. In 2012 she was sold and taken to Wells (pictured).

1048 • Alice Upjohn

37'6" x 11'6" Rother • William Osborne • WO 1119
Built 1977 • Dungeness 1977-92, Relief 1992-95
Sold 1995 • Ivan Talley Rescue/ Lindisfarne/ Alice Upjohn

1048 was sold in 1995 and became a lifeboat with West Coast Buller Marine, New Zealand, renamed Ivan Talley Rescue at Greymouth. In 2009 she was sold again and became a pleasure boat named Lindisfarne at Purau Bay, Lyttelton, Christchurch (pictured), before her lifeboat name was restored.

1049 • Tony Vandervell

54' x 17' Arun • Halmatic/William Osborne • WO 1250
Built 1975 • Weymouth 1976-99
Sold 5.1999 • PR Mac Elliott

1049 was sold out of service on 5 May 1999 to the Finnish Lifeboat Service, Suomen Meripelastusseura, and was renamed PR Mac Elliott at a ceremony in Finland on 14 August 1999. She was based at Porkkala (pictured), 20 miles west of Helsinki, and operated as a lifeboat.

1050 • B. P. Forties

54' x 17' Arun • Halmatic Ltd • WR4665
Built 1975 • Aberdeen 1976-98
Sold 10.1998 • Oddur V. Gíslason/ Hannes Þ. Hafstein

1050 was sold in 1998 to ICE-SAR, the National Lifesaving Association of Iceland, and sailed from Buckie on 11 November 1998 . She was renamed Oddur V. Gíslason and served at Grindavík from 1998 to 2007, when she was moved to Sandgerði (pictured) and renamed Hannes Þ. Hafstein.

1051 • The Gough-Ritchie

54' x 17' Arun • Halmatic/William Osborne • WO 1255
Built 1976 • Port St Mary 1976-98
Sold 7.1998 • Capitan Eduardo Simpson Roth (B.S.07)

1051 was sold in July 1998 to Cuerpo de Volantarios de los Botes Salvavidas de Valparaiso, Chile, and shipped free of charge to Chile via Liverpool, aboard the Hamburg Süd container ship Veruda. In Chile, she was renamed Capitan Eduardo Simpson Roth and based at Valparaiso (pictured).

1052 • City of Bradford IV

54' x 17' Arun • Halmatic • WR4908
Built 1977 • Humber 1977-87; Thurso 1988-89; Ballyglass 1989-90; Tobermory 91-98 • Sold 10.1998 • Lady Arun/ Theocrat/ Restless/ Solidian

1052 was sold in October 1998 to a buyer in the West Midlands and was unaltered as the pleasure boat Lady Arun at Southampton. In May 2003 she was moved to the river Severn and then went to Mountbatten Marina, Plymouth. In 2006 she was taken to Sweden as a tender renamed Solidian (pictured).

1053 • Joy and John Wade

52' x 17' Arun • Halmatic/William Osborne • WO 1565
Built 1977 • Yarmouth 1977-2001, Relief 2001
Sold 6.2002 • Björg

1053 was sold out of service in June 2002 to ICE-SAR, the National Lifesaving Association of Iceland, for continued service as a lifeboat together with a number of other Aruns. She was renamed Björg and stationed at Rif (pictured), a small harbour on Iceland's west coast

1054 • Shoreline

37'6" x 11'6" Rother • William Osborne • WO 1666
Built 1979 • Blyth 1979-82, Arbroath 1982-93
Sold 2.1994 • Porta Maggie/ Mairi Bhan

1054 was sold out of service in 1994 to a buyer in Wigtownshire and, renamed Porta Maggie, was based at Portpatrick being used for fishing charters. She was sold in 2004 and moved to Lossiemouth where she was heavily converted. She then moved Seaport Marina, Inverness (pictured).

1055 • Duke of Kent

37'6" x 11'6" Rother • William Osborne • WO 1667
Built 1979 • Eastbourne 1979-93
Sold 7.1995 • Duke of Kent

1055 was sold out of service in July 1995 and was taken to Tayport, near Dundee. She was left unaltered and was used as a survey boat on the river Tay, being based in Victoria Dock, Dundee. She was kept at Tayport and has remained out of the water (pictured) for much of the time.

1056 • Spirit of Tayside

52' x 17' Arun • Halmatic Ltd, Havant • WR5172
Built 1978 • Broughty Ferry 1978-99
Sold 5.1999 • PV Daniel Thain

1056 was sold out of service on 30 May 1999 to the Royal Volunteer Coastal Patrol, Australia. She was shipped to Australia by cargo ship and, renamed PV Daniel Thain, was stationed in Port Stephens (pictured) for deployment by the Port Stephens Division, Australia, as a rescue boat.

1057 • Soldian

52' x 17' Arun • Halmatic/William Osborne • WO 1850
Built 1978 • Lerwick 1978-97, Relief 1997-98 and 99-2002, Achill 98-99
Sold 3.2002 • Ásgrímur S. Björnsson

1057 was sold in March 2002 to ICE-SAR, the National Lifesaving Association of Iceland, and was renamed Ásgrímur S. Björnsson after a former coxswain at Reykjavík. She was placed in service at Reykjavík (pictured) in June 2002, replacing former RNLI lifeboat Grace Paterson Ritchie (ON.988).

1058 • Elizabeth Ann

52' x 17' Arun • Halmatic/William Osborne • WO 1945
Built 1979 • Falmouth 1979-97, Relief 1997-2002
Sold 6.2002 • P&O Nedlloyd Encounter/ Encounter

1058 was sold in June 2002 to Australia and was based at The Spit, Mosman, in Sydney's Middle Harbour as part of the Royal Volunteer Coastguard fleet. In 2006 she was relocated to Ulladulla, New South Wales, and served there until 2012. She was sold in January 2013 at Ulladulla (pictured).

1059 • Walter and Margaret Couper

52' x 17' Arun • Halmatic Ltd, Havant • WR5845
Built 1979 • Campbeltown 1979-99, Relief 1999-2001
Sold 5.2001 • Arvinsilma/ PR Russarö

1059 was sold in 2001 to Suomen Meripelastusseura, the Finnish Lifeboat Service, and left Poole on 19 May 2001. She was stationed at Turku renamed Arvinsilma. In 2002 she was replaced by another lifeboat which took that name in 2004. She was later stationed at Hanko as PR Russarö (pictured).

1060 • John Fison

44'10" x 12'8" Waveney • Fairey Marine • FM 687
Built 1980 • Harwich 1980-96, Relief 1996-99
Sold 8.1999 • Hamilton Rotary Rescue

1060 was sold in August 1999 to the Royal New Zealand Coastguard and was based at Raglan as a Coast Guard boat and lifeboat. In December 2005 she was replaced and was sold to a private owner at Napier. In 2009 she became the work boat Harbour Cruiser at Fremantle (pictured), Australia.

1061 • George and Olive Turner

52' x 17' Arun • Halmatic/William Osborne • WO 2020
Built 1979 • Tynemouth 1980-99, Relief 1999-2000
Sold 8.2000 • Gunnar Friðriksson/ Jon Oddgeir

1061 was sold on 18 August 2000 to ICE-SAR, the National Lifesaving Association of Iceland. Renamed Gunnar Friðriksson, from 2000 to 2007 she was stationed at Ísafjörður. She was replaced by 1160 and was then used as a relief boat, being kept at Njarðvík, renamed Jon Oddgeir (pictured).

1062 • Edith Emilie

52' x 17' Arun • Halmatic/W. A. Souter
Built 1980 • Relief 1980-99
Sold 9.1999 • Ex RNLI Edith Emilie SB 1062/ Mare Rose

1062 was sold in 1999 to Osprey Aviation and taken to Weymouth from where she was used as a safety boat in Portland Harbour. She has been based at Exeter, the Solent, Southampton and Portsmouth. In 2008 she was sold to Montrose Harbour Authority to become a pilot boat (pictured).

1063 • Princess of Wales

37'6" x 11'6" Rother • William Osborne • WO 2091
Built 1981 • Barmouth 1982-92, Relief 1992-93
Sold 5.1993 • Glow Worm

1063 was sold in 1993 to a buyer in Hampshire and, renamed Glow Worm, was kept at Port Solent Village Marina, near Portsmouth. In 2000 she was sold to an owner in Rush, Co Dublin and taken to Skibbereen (pictured). In 2006 she was moved into store in a shed at Portraine, near Swords, Dublin.

1064 • The Davys Family

37'6" x 11'6" Rother • William Osborne • WO 2092
Built 1981 • Shoreham Harbour 1981-86, Relief 1986-93
Sold 7.1995 • The Martin Family

1064 was sold in 1995 to the Sea Scouts and was taken by road from Poole to Shepperton Marina in January 1996. She then went to the West India Docks, London (pictured) for use as a Scout boat, remaining unaltered. In 2008 she was moved to Quinton Nelson's yard, Donaghadee, for survey.

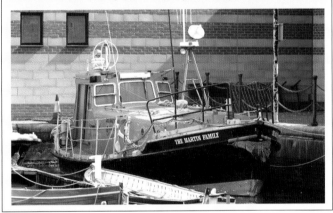

1065 • Barham

44'10" x 12'8" Waveney • Fairey Marine • FM 694
Built 1980 • Great Yarmouth and Gorleston 1980-96, Relief 1996-99
Sold 11.1999 • Waveney/ Legend

1065 was sold in 1999 to the Royal New Zealand Coastguard, for use as a lifeboat at Napier, Hawke Bay. She was sold in 2003 to an owner who converted her into a dive charter and pleasure boat with the aft cabin removed and the wheelhouse enclosed, based at Seaview Marina, Wellington (pictured).

1066 • [Not named]

33' x 12' Brede • Lochin Marine • 1066
Built 1980 • Trials 1981-82
Sold 1.1983 • Battle of Hastings/ John Alexander

1066 was sold in 1983 and the buoyancy block on her stern was removed. She was used as a work boat at Yarmouth, IOW until sold in 2007. She is sometimes moored at Venture Quays, Cowes but is usually in a cradle at Berth 24/25 Southampton East Docks (pictured), and launched as required.

1067 • Hyman Winstone

52' x 17' Arun • Halmatic/William Osborne • WO 2150
Built 1980 • Holyhead 1980-84, Relief 1984-85, Ballycotton 1985-98, Larne 1998-2000, Relief 2000-02 • Sold 4.2003

1067 was sold in 2003 to SANAS, Madeira for use as a lifeboat. In November 2003 she was taken to Madeira by sea. She has been stored out of the water with 1077 in the freeport area of Canical (pictured) at the far eastern tip of Madeira awaiting completion of the Porto Santo lifeboat station.

1068 • James Cable

37'6" x 11'6" Rother • William Osborne • WO 2222
Built 1981 • Aldeburgh 1982-93
Sold 5.1994 • Ades 13 Augustin Carlevaro/ Nauti II

1068 was sold out of service in 1994 to ADES, the Uruguayan lifeboat service. She was shipped via Tilbury to Montevideo in July 1995. Renamed ADES 13 Augustin Carlevaro, she was stationed at Puerto de Carmelo. In 2012 she became the work boat Nauti II at Montevideo (pictured).

1069 • Mountbatten of Burma

39'9" x 14'3" Medina • W. A. Souter
Built 1980 • Trials 1981-89
Sold 10.1989 • Swanage Diver

After being used only for trials by the RNLI, 1069 was sold in 1989 and became a pleasure boat at Bradwell and Littlehampton in the 1990s. She moved along the south coast and, by 2000, renamed Swanage Diver, was in use as a charter boat in Swanage Bay (pictured), taking divers to wreck sites.

1070 • Richard Evans (Civil Service No.39)

52' x 17' Arun • William Osborne • WO 2250
Built 1981 • Portrush 1981-2000, Relief 2000-03
Sold 2003

1070 was sold in July 2003 to ICE-SAR, the National Lifesaving Association of Iceland, but en route to Iceland came free from the motor vessel Skaftarfell, on board which she was being transported, and was wrecked. The remains were found three days later on a rocky beach in Iceland.

1071 • Sir Max Aitken

52' x 17' Arun • Halmatic/Fairey Marine • FM 707
Built 1981 • Relief 1981-2002
Sold 2.2003 • R. S. C. Maximus

1071 was sold in February 2003 to Tenby Marine Services and, renamed RSC Maximus, was used as safety boat at Pendine based at Tenby and Milford Haven (pictured). She was sold in 2006 and went to South Woodham Ferrers in Essex, in 2011 to Ramsgate, and in 2012 was at Hayling Yacht Club.

1072 • Countess Mountbatten of Burma

39'9" x 14'3" Medina • W. A. Souter
Built 1981 • Trials 1981-89
Sold 8.1989 • Cheetah

1072 was sold in 1989 and became a work boat at British Gypsum Jetty, Erith. She was later moved to South Wales as a diving boat, renamed Cheetah. Her wheelhouse was altered and she was based at Waterloo, Pembrokeshire, moored by the toll bridge at Pembroke Dock (pictured).

Part 5

Motor Lifeboats since 1980

The development of the lifeboat fleet since the 1980s has been characterised by the building of lifeboats able to reach speeds of more than nine knots, with boats capable of twenty-five knots becoming the norm. However, two incidents in the early 1980s brought home the dangers of life-saving with the Penlee lifeboat Solomon Browne (ON-954) being tragically lost during an horrific storm off the Cornish coast on the night of 19 December 1981. And on 10 April 1983 the Salcombe lifeboat The Baltic Exchange (ON-964) capsized and righted successfully with the aid of an air-bag, and none of her crew were lost.

During the 1970s the RNLI looked to place fast lifeboats at key stations. In implementing this plan, several new designs were introduced during the decade, using new building materials for the hulls, new and more sophisticated

layouts for the superstructures, more powerful and reliable engines. Three classes of offshore lifeboat were introduced during the 1980s: the 47ft Tyne fast slipway lifeboat, with a steel hull, and bilge keels protecting the propellers; the 33ft Brede class, developed from a commercial hull; and, towards the end of the decade, the Mersey class fast carriage lifeboat came into service, measuring 38ft in length, and designed for launching from a carriage. With the Mersey the RNLI was able to fulfil its aim of providing 'fast' lifeboats, capable of fifteen knots or above, at all of its lifeboat stations.

By 1993, when the last of the Merseys entered service, the displacement-hulled boats had all been replaced. Meanwhile, even faster lifeboats, in the shape of the twenty-five-knot Severn and Trent classes, were being developed and these

new classes began entering service in the mid-1990s at stations served by Aruns and Waveneys since the 1960s. The 17m Severns and 14m Trents, designed simultaneously, had a shared hull shape, and the hull was built from a newly-developed fibre-reinforced composite.

The newest developments have concerned the Tamar and Shannon classes, which are highly sophisticated rescue craft. The Tamar, developed primarily for slipway-launching, is fitted with a SIMS computer system through which the crew can manage every function of the boat. The Tamar build programme ended in 2013, with attention then turning to the Shannon class. This was developed as the Fast Carriage Boat 2 (FCB2) to replace Merseys, and is the first RNLI lifeboat powered by waterjets. A new launch and recovery system has also been developed for the Shannon.

The 14m Trent Barclaycard Crusader (ON-1209) from Eyemouth is one of the RNLI's modern fleet of fast all-weather lifeboats. (Nicholas Leach)

1073 • Robert Edgar

52' x 17' Arun • Halmatic/William Osborne • WO 2305
Built 1981 • St Marys 1981-97, Relief 1997-99, Weymouth 1999-2002
Sold 2003 • 52-18

1073 was sold in 2003 and taken to Tilbury, via Ramsgate on 26 April 2003, to be shipped to New Zealand. She has since been kept at Tutukaka Marina, 100 miles north of Auckland. She was placed at the disposal of the New Zealand Coast Guard for rescue work, and was named 52-18 (pictured).

1074 • City of London

47' x 15' Tyne • Fairey Allday Marine • FM 708
Built 1982 • Selsey 1983-2006
Sold 2007 • Huaying 388

1074 was sold from Poole in 2007 to the Chinese Salvage and Rescue and was shipped to China in mid-July 2007. It took exactly a month to get to Hong Kong, where she was unloaded. Renamed Huaying 388, she was stationed at the Waigaoqiao Base, Donghai Bureau (pictured).

1075 • Sam and Joan Woods

47' x 15' Tyne • Fairey Allday Marine • FM 709
Built 1982 • Relief 1984-93, Walton & Frinton 1993-6, Relief 1996-2006
Sold 2007 • Huaying 389

1075 (pictured at Buckie in 2006) was sold in 2007 to the Chinese Salvage and Rescue and taken to China via Felixstowe in July 2007, taking a month to get to Hong Kong, where she was unloaded. Renamed Huaying 389, she was stationed at Ningbo Base, Donghai Bureau, as a rescue boat.

1076 • Marie Winstone

52' x 17' Arun • Halmatic/W. A. Souter
Built 1981 • Fishguard 1981-94, Torbay 1995-2001, Relief 2001-02
Sold 10.2002 • PR Torbay

1076 was sold in October 2002 to the Finnish Lifeboat Service and since 2003 has been based at Kaskinen, a small village in west Finland (pictured), between Vaasa and Pori. She was renamed PR Torbay and operates alongside an Atlantic 21, named PV Orion, also bought from the RNLI.

1077 • Duchess of Kent

52' x 17' Arun • Halmatic/William Osborne • WO 2400
Built 1982 • Relief 1982-2002
Sold 4.2003 • Salvador-Do-Mar

1077 was sold to SANAS, Madeira, Portugal and was taken to Madeira on a P&O Nedlloyd cargo vessel in November 2003. She was stored out of the water in Canical, but by 2009 had been renamed and registered in Funchal, and was back in water again to operate from Funchal or Santa Cruz.

1078 • Davina and Charles Matthews Hunter

52' x 17' Arun • Halmatic/William Osborne • WO 2450
Built 1982 • Mallaig 1982-2001, Relief 2001-03
Sold 7.2003 • Einar Sigurjónssonm (2593)

1078 was sold on 15 July 2003 to ICE-SAR, the National Lifesaving Association of Iceland, and was stationed at Hafnarfjörður (pictured), a port just south of Reykjavik, in August 2003. She was renamed Einar Sigurjónsson after a president of National Life-Saving Association of Iceland in the 1990s.

1079 • The William and Jane

44'10" x 12'8" Waveney • Fairey Allday Marine • FM 710
Built 1982 • Blyth 1982-95, Larne 1996-98
Sold 6.1999 • John Barton Acland Rescue/ Gryphon

1079 was sold in June 1999 to the Royal New Zealand Coastguard and was stationed at Kaikoura, about 180km north of Christchurch, as a Coast Guard boat and lifeboat (pictured). In 2004 she left Kaikoura and became a privately owned coastal cruiser at Picton, moving to Australia in 2013.

1080 • Ann Ritchie

33' x 12' Brede • Lochin Marine • 1080
Built 1982 • Oban 1982-87
Scrapped 1.1988

1080 was the first 33ft Brede to enter service, and she was stationed at Oban (pictured) from October 1982 until September 1987 and then stored at McAlister's yard, Dumbarton, before a decision was made to scrap her hull. At Oban, she launched 187 times on service and saved 20 lives.

1081 • Ralph and Bonella Farrant

52' x 17' Arun • Halmatic/Souter
Built 1982 • Relief 1982-94, Fenit 1994-99, Relief 1999-2003
Sold 11.2005 • Huaying 393

1081 was sold in 2005 from the RNLI Depot, Poole, to the China Rescue and Salvage Bureau and was shipped to China via Felixstowe in April 2006. She was taken to Shanghai and then allocated to Fuzhou, serving as a lifeboat and rescue boat, renamed Huaying 393 (pictured), from 2006.

1082 • Margaret Frances Love

52' x 17' Arun • Halmatic/William Osborne • WO 2510
Built 1982 • Valentia 1983-96, Barry Dock 1997-2003
Sold 7.2005 • Huaying 398

1082 was sold in 2005 from the RNLI Depot, Poole, to the China Rescue and Salvage Bureau and was transported to China on board a COSCO container ship departing Felixstowe on 5 August 2005. Renamed Huaying 398, she was stationed at Donghai, Shanghai (pictured).

1083 • Leonore Chilcott

33' x 12' Brede • Lochin Marine • 1083
Built 1982 • Fowey 1982-88
Sold 9.1990 • Privateer/ Leonore Chilcott

1083 was sold in 1990 and was initially used as a diving and survey boat at Littlehampton Marina. In August 1999 she was bought by Alderney Pilots for approximately £35,000 and was operated out of Braye Harbour, Alderney (pictured) as a pilot boat with black hull and red superstructure.

1084 • Philip Vaux

33' x 12' Brede • Lochin Marine • 1084
Built 1983 • Girvan 1983-89
Sold 5.1990 • RTK Sea Truck 4/ Mourne Mist

1084 was sold in 1990 and used as a work boat at Hamworthy, Poole, renamed RTK Sea Truck 4 (pictured). In about 1993 she was sold and taken to Carlingford Lough, renamed Mourne Mist, and used as Carlingford pilot boat No.1, based at Greencastle, Carlingford Lough, with a grey hull.

1085 • Mabel Alice

52' x 17' Arun • Halmatic/Fairy Allday Marine • FM 715
Built 1982 • Penlee 1983-2003, Relief 2003
Sold 3.2004 • Strathclyde/ Mabel Alice

1085 was sold in March 2004 to Strathclyde Police and went to the Clyde as a police boat, renamed Strathclyde. She was kept at Greenock, and carried a yellow livery. In 2008 she was sold and taken to Portishead (pictured). Since then she has been based at East Cowes, Brighton, Wells and Lowestoft.

1086 • A. J. R. and L. G. Uridge

52' x 17' Arun • Halmatic/William Osborne • WO 2590
Built 1983 • Relief 1983-94; Torbay 1994-95; Relief 1995-97; Holyhead 1997-98; Relief 1998-2003; Penlee 2003 • Sold 8.2003 • PR Hebe

1086 was sold out of service in 2003 to the Finnish Lifeboat Service, Suomen Meripelastusseura. She was placed on station at Kemi having been renamed PR Hebe (pictured). Along with the other Aruns sold to Finland, she was adapted for the colder climate by having improved heating installed.

1087 • Merchant Navy

33' x 12' Brede • Lochin Marine • 1087
Built 1983 • Relief 1983-87, Oban 1987-89
Sold 6.1990 • Lyonesse/ Rescue 15

1087 was sold in 1990 and was used as the pleasure boat Lyonesse in The Netherlands. In 2006 she was sold, returned to England and was based on the river Hamble as Lyonesse. In 2012 she was bought by the NSRI and shipped to South Africa (pictured) and became a lifeboat at Mossel Bay.

1088 • Caroline Finch

33' x 12' Brede • Lochin Marine • 1088
Built 1983 • Exmouth 1983-94
Sold 1994 • South Star

1088 was sold in 1994 to become a lifeboat in South Africa and was stationed at Hermanus to cover the area between Gordon's Bay and Mossel Bay. Renamed South Star (pictured), she remained largely unaltered as a lifeboat in South Africa, with a red hull and yellow superstructure.

1089 • Inner Wheel

33' x 12' Brede • Lochin Marine • 1089
Built 1983 • Poole 1983-2001, Calshot 2001-02
Sold 2002 • Spirit of Nadine Gordimer/ MTU Nadine Gordimer

1089 was sold in 2002 to NSRI, the South Africa lifeboat service and was shipped out from Sheerness without engines in February 2003. She was re-engined in 2006 after fund-raising for new engines. She was based at Hout Bay and renamed Spirit of Nadine Gordimer, then MTU Nadine Gordimer.

1090 • Foresters Future

33' x 12' Brede • Lochin Marine • 1090
Built 1982 • Alderney 1984-86, Relief 1986-2002
Sold 6.2002 • Spirit of Safmarine III

1090 was sold without engines in 2002 to NSRI, the South Africa lifeboat service, and was shipped via at Sheerness in February 2003. She entered service in 2007 and was renamed Spirit of Safmarine III. In 2007 she was reallocated from Rescue 3 at Table Mountain to Rescue 10 at Simon's Town.

1091 • [Not named]

39'9" x 14'3" Medina • William Osborne • WO 2576
Built 1981 • Trials 1981-83
Sold 4.1989 • Fury III/ Venturer/ Mountbatten Venturer/ David Stogdon

1091 was sold in 1989 to Hamble Point Marina and used as the work boat Fury III. She was later used as a rescue boat at Lepe by Venturers Search and Rescue. She was at Port Dinorwic, near Bangor, before being sold to MRI at Stonehaven (pictured) for use as a rescue and training boat until 2013.

1092 • St Brendan

52' x 17' Arun • Halmatic/ William Osborne • WO 2620
Built 1983 • Rosslare Harbour 1984-2001
Written off 9.2001, sold as scrap 2.2003 • Irish Mist

1092 was written off by the RNLI after being damaged on 9 September 2001 at Rosslare Harbour, and was sold as scrap from Holyhead Boatyard in February 2003. She was bought by a Holyhead owner, who repaired her and used her as a fishing trip boat operating out of Holyhead (pictured).

1093 • Charles Brown

52' x 17' Arun • Halmatic/William Osborne • WO 2650
Built 1983 • Buckie 1984-2003, Relief 2003-05
Sold 11.2005 • Huaying 396

1093 was sold in 2005 to the China Rescue and Salvage Bureau. She was shipped via Harwich (pictured) and Felixstowe container port on 17 December 2005 on the container ship Cosco Shanghai. In China, renamed Huaying 396, she was stationed at Beihai base, Nanhai Rescue Bureau.

1094 • James Burrough

47' x 15' Tyne • Fairey Allday Marine • FM 716
Built 1984 • Padstow 1984-2006, Relief 2006
Sold 2007 • Huaying 386

1094 was sold in 2007 to the China Rescue and Salvage Bureau to continue as a lifeboat. She went to China via Felixstowe on board a container ship, leaving on 8 August 2007 and arriving exactly a month later. She was stationed at Rongcheng Base, Beihai Bureau, and was renamed Huaying 386.

1095 • St Cybi II (Civil Service No.40)

47' x 15' Tyne • Fairey Marine/William Osborne • FM 717
Built 1985 • Holyhead 1985-97, Relief 1997-2007
Sold 2007 • Huaying 387

1095 was sold in 2007 to the China Rescue and Salvage Bureau. She was taken to China on board a container ship from Felixstowe in August 2007 and took exactly a month to get to Hong Kong. She was stationed at Tianjin Base, Beihai Bureau, having been renamed Huaying 387.

1096 • Ethel Anne Measures

47' x 15' Tyne • Fairey Allday Marine • FM 718
Built 1985 • Mumbles 1985-2006, Relief 2006-07
Sold 2007 • Huaying 384

1096 was sold out of service in 2007 from Poole (pictured) to the China Rescue and Salvage Bureau. In late October 2007 she went to Felixstowe to be shipped to China, departing on 24 November 2007. In China she was allocated to Rongcheng stations, Nanhai Bureau and renamed Huaying 384.

1097 • Ruby and Arthur Reed II

47' x 15' Tyne • Fairey Allday Marine • FM 719
Built 1985 • Cromer 1985-96, Relief 1997-99, Cromer 1999-2007
Sold 7.2008 • Huaying 385

1097 was sold in 2008 to China Rescue and Salvage Bureau from the RNLI Depot at Poole (pictured). She was shipped to China by container ship in mid-August 2008 and, renamed Huaying 385, was allocated to Shenzhen stations, Nanhai Bureau, to serve as a lifeboat.

1098 • Sir Max Aitken II

52' x 17' Arun • Halmatic/W. A. Souter
Built 1984 • Stornoway 1984-99, Relief 1999 and 2004-05, Longhope 1999-2004 • Sold 11.2005 • Huaying 397

1098 was sold in 2005 to the China Rescue and Salvage Bureau. She was shipped to China on board the container ship Cosco Shanghai, which left Felixstowe on 17 December 2005. On arrival in China, she was renamed Huaying 397 and stationed at Zhangjiang, Nanhai Rescue Bureau from 2006.

1099 • The Joseph Rothwell Sykes and Hilda M.

52' x 17' Arun • Halmatic/William Osborne • WO 2700
Built 1984 • Stromness 1984-98, Relief 1998-99, Broughty Ferry 1999-2001, Relief 2001-02 • Sold 2002 • PR Janne Malén

1099 was sold out of service to the Finnish Lifeboat Service, Suomen Meripelastusseura, in autumn 2002. Renamed PR Janne Malén (pictured), she has been stationed in the west coast town of Uusikaupunki on the Gulf of Bothnia since 2003 little altered.

1100 • Snolda

52' x 17' Arun • Fairey Allday Marine • FM 722
Built 1986 • Aith 1986-98, Relief 1998, Training TL-01 1998-2007
Sold 10.2007 • Oddur V. Gislason

1100 was used as a training boat before being sold in 2007 to ICE-SAR, the National Lifesaving Association of Iceland. She left Poole on 8 October 2007 by road for shipping via Immingham. In Iceland she replaced 1050 at the Grindavík station (pictured) and was renamed Oddur V. Gíslason.

1101 • Enid of Yorkshire

33' x 12' Brede • Lochin Marine • 1101
Built 1984 • Relief 1984-2002
Sold 10.1997 • Spirit of Toft

1101 was sold in October 1997 to NSRI, the South African lifeboat service, and was painted in new colours before being shipped out of England. She was stationed at Port Elizabeth, Algoa Bay, from October 1997 and was renamed Spirit of Toft (pictured), operating as Rescue 6.

1102 • Nottinghamshire

33' x 12' Brede • Lochin Marine • 1102
Built 1984 • Invergordon 1984-88, Oban 1889-97
Sold 12.1997 • Sanlam Rescuer

1102 was sold in December 1997 to NSRI, the South African lifeboat service, and after arriving in South Africa was stationed at Gordon's Bay, south of Cape Town, renamed Sanlam Rescuer (pictured). In December 2010, while being surveyed prior to reallocation, she was destroyed by fire at the yard.

1103 • Newsbuoy

52' x 17' Arun • Halmatic/W. A. Souter
Built 1984 • Relief 1984-2002; Plymouth 2002-03; Relief 2003-04
Sold 7.2005 • Ziska

1103 was placed on the sale list in July 2004 and sold in July 2005 to the lifeboat service in the Faroe Islands. She became a lifeboat at Klaksvik from August 2005 and was renamed Ziska. She is pictured at Lowestoft on 28 July 2005 having been given her new livery ready for service in the Faroes.

1104 • Safeway

33' x 12' Brede • Lochin Marine • 1104
Built 1985 • Calshot 1985-2001
Sold 6.2002 • Eikos Rescuer II

1104 was sold without engines in 2002 to NSRI, the South Africa lifeboat service, and was shipped to South Africa from Sheerness in January 2003. She was re-engined and renamed Eikos Rescuer II for her service as a lifeboat, operating from the Durban station (pictured) as Rescue 5.

1105 • Amateur Swimming Associations

33' x 12' Brede • Lochin Marine • 1105
Built 1985 • Relief 1985-89, Girvan 1989-93
Sold 9.1993 • Sealord Rescue/ Girvan

1105 was sold in 1993 to the New Zealand Coastguard and shipped there at the end of 1993. From May 1994 to 2011 she was stationed at Port Nelson, South Island and used as a lifeboat named Sealord Rescue (pictured). She was sold in 2012 to become the pleasure boat Girvan at Picton, New Zealand.

1106 • Keith Anderson

52' x 17' Arun • Halmatic/William Osborne • WO 2790
Built 1985 • Newhaven 1985-99, Relief 1999-2000, Hartlepool 2000-03
Sold 1.2006 • Huaying 394

1106 was sold in 2006 from Poole (pictured) to the China Rescue & Salvage Bureau, and she passed through Dover in February 2006 on her way to Felixstowe for shipping on a container ship to China. In China she was stationed at Qinhuangdao base, Beihai Bureau, and renamed Huaying 394.

1107 • City of Belfast

52' x 17' Arun • Halmatic/William Osborne • WO 2830
Built 1985 • Donaghadee 1985-2003, Relief 2003
Sold 11.2005 • Huaying 395

1107 was sold in November 2005 to the China Rescue and Salvage Bureau. She was shipped to China on board a container ship from Felixstowe on 19 February 2006 (pictured). Renamed Huaying 395 upon entering service in China, she was based at .Dalian, Beihai Bureau.

1108 • Margaret Russell Fraser

52' x 17' Arun • Halmatic/W. A. Souter
Built 1986 • Relief 1986-2002, Calshot 2002-04
Sold 12.2004 • Ingibjörg

After ending her career at Calshot, 1108 was sold out of service in 2004 to ICE-SAR, the National Lifesaving Association of Iceland. In early 2005 she was placed on station at Höfn on the south-east coast of the country, having been renamed Ingibjörg (pictured) and remains unaltered.

1109 • City of Edinburgh

47' x 15' Tyne • Fairey Allday Marine • FM 1058
Built 1985 • Fraserburgh 1985-2002, Relief 2002-09
Sold 2010 • ADES 19 Centenario BSE

1109 was placed on the sale list in 2009 and, after a sale to Sri Lanka fell through, was sold to ADES, the Uruguay lifeboat service. She was shipped to Uruguay in December 2010 and, renamed ADES 19 Centenario BSE, was stationed at Colonia (pictured), partly funded by a private company.

1110 • Phil Mead

47' x 15' Tyne • Fairey Allday Marine • FM 1059
Built 1986 • Teesmouth 1986-2006, Relief 2006-08
Sold 6.2008 • Huaying 382

1110 was sold out of service in 2008, having been the last offshore lifeboat at Teesmouth (pictured), to China Rescue and Salvage Bureau. She was shipped to China in mid-July 2008, and was stationed at Guangzhou stations, Nanhai Bureau, having been renamed Huaying 382.

1111 • William Luckin

47' x 15' Tyne • Fairey Allday Marine • FM 1060
Built 1974 • Arranmore 1986-2000, Lough Swilly 2001-07
Sold 6.2008 • Huaying 383

1111 was sold out of service in June 2008 from the RNLI Depot, Poole (pictured) to the China Rescue and Salvage Bureau. She was shipped to China in mid-July 2008 where she was allocated to Haikou stations, Nanhai Bureau, and was renamed Huaying 383.

1112 • RFA Sir Galahad

47' x 15' Tyne • Wright/William Osborne • WO 2880
Built 1986 • Tenby 1986-2006, Relief 2006-08 and 2009, Angle 2008-09
Sold 1.2010 • Sir Galahad

1112 was sold in 2010 to a private owner based in North Wales and was taken to Bangor in February 2010. She has been kept moored in the small dock at Port Penrhyn, near Bangor (pictured) since then, with no major alterations having been made to her; she is used for fishing and diving.

1113 • City of Dublin

52' x 17' Arun • Halmatic/Berthon Boat Co • 1013
Built 1986 • Howth 1986-2002, Relief 2002-03
Sold 3.2004 • Hafbjörg

1113 was sold out of service in March 2004 to ICE-SAR, the National Lifesaving Association of Iceland, and was shipped to Iceland for further service as a lifeboat. She was renamed Hafbjörg and placed on station at Neskaupstaður (pictured) in May 2004.

1114 • The Lady Rank

47' x 15' Tyne • Wright/William Osborne • WO 2970
Built 1987 • Angle 1987-2008, Relief 2008-11
Sold 7.2011 • ADES 20 Bicentenary

1114 was sold out of service from Poole in 2011 to Fleet Wide Equipment, acting for ADES, the Uruguayan lifeboat service. She was shipped to Uruguay in December 2011, renamed ADES 20 Bicentenary in June 2012 and was operated as a lifeboat based at Montevideo (pictured).

1115 • Good Shepherd

47' x 15' Tyne • Wright/William Osborne • WO 2990
Built 1987 • Relief 1988-2000; Lough Swilly 2000-01; Relief 2001-10
Sold 6.2010 • Carnarc

1115 was sold out of service in June 2010 to the Inverness Harbour Trust for use as a pilot boat. She was renamed Carnarc and based at North Longman Marina, Inverness (pictured), repainted but otherwise little altered.

1116 • Robert and Violet

47' x 15' Tyne • Wright/Lochin • 1116
Built 1987 • Moelfre 1988-2013

1116 was placed on station at Moelfre on 22 January 1988 and was named on 2 July 1988 at Moelfre by Mrs Lesley Roberts, wife of the station's Coxswain William Roberts. At one time she had her operational number painted on her hull in yellow. She was replaced at Moelfre in 2013.

1117 • James Bibby

47' x 15' Tyne • Fairey Allday Marine • FM 1073
Built 1986 • Barrow 1986-2008, Relief 2008-10; Shoreham Harbour 2010, Relief 2010-11 • Sold 2011 • Pioneer

1117 was sold out of service in 2011 to Macdonald Ferries, Invergordon, for use as a ferry and workboat. She was renamed Pioneer and the aft cabin was removed to give more deck space. Moored at Invergordon (pictured), she was used for changing tanker crews off Nairn, Cromarty Firth.

1118 • Roy and Barbara Harding

52' x 17' Arun • Halmatic/William Osborne • WO 3010
Built 1986 • Galway Bay 1987-97, Castletownbere 1998-2004
Sold 6.2004 • Gunnbjörg

1118 was sold in 2004 to ICE-SAR, the Icelandic search and rescue service, and went as deck cargo to Iceland in October 2004. She was renamed Gunnbjörg and placed on station at Raufarhöfn (pictured), on Iceland's north-east coast, a few days after she arrived, remaining largely unaltered.

1119 • [Not named]

38' x 12'6" Mersey • Cunningham/William Osborne • WO 2940
Built 1986 • Trials 1987-88, used as a floating test bed
Sold 12.1989 • Keelman/ Spirit

1119 was sold as a stripped hull in 1989 and fitted out at Sedbury, Chepstow. She was sold in 1997 and taken to Friars Goose Marina, Newcastle, as a pleasure boat with new engines. In 2006 she became a trip boat at Ilfracombe, moving to Silgo, Co Mayo (pictured) and Westport in 2012.

1120 • Hetty Rampton

47' x 15' Tyne • Fairey Allday Marine • FM 1106
Built 1987 • Porthdinllaen 1987-2012, Relief 2012-

1120 was placed on station at Porthdinllaen (pictured) on 27 April 1987 and was named on 18 August 1987 at Morfa Nefyn by Miss Yolande Rampton, niece of the donor. She served at Porthdinllaen until August 2012 and was then reallocated to the Relief Fleet.

1121 • Norman Salvesen

47' x 15' Tyne • Wright/Harrison • 1121
Built 1988 • Wick 1988-97, Sennen Cove 1988-2009, Relief 2009-

1121 was stationed at Wick in September 1988, and was named on 16 September 1988 at Wick by Mrs Bright Gordon MBE. After being replaced at Wick she served at Sennen Cove (pictured), and then in the Relief Fleet.

1122 • Owen and Ann Aisher

47' x 15' Tyne • Wright/Souter • 0012
Built 1988 • Relief 1988-2012 • Sold 2013

1122 entered the Relief Fleet in August 1988 and was named on 18 August 1988 at the RNLI Depot, Poole, by Lady Anne Aisher, and she was often kept at Poole (pictured). In 2013 she was at Ridge Wharf, Wareham for sale.

1123 • Kenneth Thelwall

52' x 17' Arun • Halmatic/Berthon • 1014
Built 1987 • Humber 1987-97, Relief 1997-98 and 2003-04, Holyhead 1998-2003 • Sold 7.2005 • Huaying 399

1123 was placed on the sale list in 2004 and sold in 2005 to China Rescue and Salvage Bureau. She was transported to China on the COSCO container ship Cosco Rotterdam from Felixstowe, leaving on 5 August 2005. She was renamed Huayling 399 (pictured) and stationed at Wenzhou, Zhejiang.

1124 • Peggy and Alex Caird

38' x 12'6" Mersey • Aluminium Shipbuilders/Wm Osborne • WO 3130
Built 1988 • Bridlington 1988-95, Relief 1995-99, Lytham St Annes 1999, Relief 1999-2009, Bembridge 2009-10, Relief 2010-

1124 was the first Mersey lifeboat to go into service, and she served at Bridlington for seven years before being reallocated to the Relief Fleet. She was named on 17 June 1989 by Lady Macdonald of Sleat. From 2009 to 2010 she was on temporary duty at Bembridge (pictured).

1125 • Sealink Endeavour

38' x 12'6" Mersey • Aluminium Shipbuilders/Wm Osborne • WO 3070
Built 1987 • Trials 1987-89, Hastings 1989-

1126, the second of the two prototype Mersey, was placed on station at Hastings in March 1989 after being used for trials around the coast. She was named on 21 September 1989 at Hastings by HRH The Duke of Kent.

1126 • Max Aitken III

47' x 15' Tyne • Fairey Allday Marine • FM 1189
Built 1987 • Bembridge 1987-2009, Relief 2009-12 • Sold 2013

1126 went on station at Bembridge in August 1987 and was named on 10 September 1987 at Bembridge Harbour by Lady Beaverbrook. She was in Relief until 2012, and in 2013 she was at Ridge Wharf, Wareham for sale.

1127 • Babs and Agnes Robertson

47' x 15' Tyne • Fairey Allday Marine • FM 1190
Built 1987 • Peterhead 1988-2006, Relief 2006, Mumbles 2006-

1127 was placed on station at Peterhead in January 1988 and served there until April 2006. She was named on 21 May 1988 at Peterhead by Mrs Bruce McNeil after two sisters. In 2006 she spent a few months in the Relief Fleet and in July 2006 was placed on station at Mumbles (pictured).

1130 • The Baltic Exchange II

47' x 15' Tyne • Wright/Lochin Marine • 1130
Built 1974 • Salcombe 1988-2008, Relief 2008-09
Sold 2010 • Fortune

1130 was sold in 2010 from Poole (pictured) to Seychelles via the Foreign & Commonwealth Office for use as an anti-piracy craft, renamed Fortune and painted grey, by the Seychelles Coast Guard on the island of Mahé.

1131 • City of Sheffield

47' x 15' Tyne • Wright/Souter • 0027
Built 1988 • Whitby 1988-96, Ramsgate 1996, Hartlepool 1997-2000, Relief 2000-01, Poole 2001-

1131 was originally stationed at Whitby in December 1988, but has since served at several stations, latterly Poole (pictured) from September 2001.

1132 • Spirit of Lowestoft

47' x 15' Tyne • Fairey Allday Marine • FM 1191
Built 1987 • Lowestoft 1987-

1132 has been stationed at Lowestoft (pictured) since November 1987 having been funded mainly by the Lowestoft Lifeboat Appeal. She was named on 26 May 1988 at Lowestoft by HRH The Duke of Kent.

1133 • The Famous Grouse

47' x 15' Tyne • Fairey Allday Marine • FM 1192
Built 1987 • Relief 1987-2004, Kilmore Quay 2004-10, Relief 2010-12
Sold 2013

1133 entered the Relief Fleet in December 1987. She was named on 11 December 1987 at Cowes by Mrs C. M. Barrie, of the Old Mill Hotel, Motherwell. Between April 2004 and October 2010 she served at Kilmore Quay. In 2013 she was at Ridge Wharf, Wareham (pictured) for sale.

1134 • City of Glasgow III

52' x 17' Arun • Halmatic/W. A. Souter • 0002
Built 1987 • Troon 1987-2004, Relief 2004-05
Sold 11.2005 • Sveinbjörn Sveinsson

1134 was sold out of service in November 2005 to ICE-SAR, the National Lifesaving Association of Iceland. She was shipped from the UK to Iceland in January 2006. She was stationed at Vopnafjörður (pictured) after being renamed Sveinbjörn Sveinsson.

1135 • Mickie Salvesen

52' x 17' Arun • Halmatic • WR8722
Built 1988 • Kirkwall 1988-98, Relief 1998, Aberdeen 1998-2000, Relief 2000-03, Barry Dock 2003-06 • Sold 2006 • Vörður II

1135 was sold in 2006 to ICE-SAR, the National Lifesaving Association of Iceland, and left the RNLI Depot at Poole in September 2006. Renamed Vörður II, she was stationed at Patreksfjörður (pictured) on the west coast.

1136 • City of Plymouth

52' x 17' Arun • Halmatic/W. A. Souter • 0007
Built 1987 • Plymouth 1988-2002, Relief 2002-04
Sold 10.2004 • Hunabjörg

1022 was sold in October 2004 to ICE-SAR, the National Lifesaving Association of Iceland, and was placed at Skagaströnd (pictured) on Iceland's north coast, in early 2005 after being renamed Húnabjörg.

1137 • Hilda Jarrett

47' x 15' Tyne • Fairey Allday Marine • FM 1193
Built 1987 • Baltimore 1988-2012, Relief 2012-

1137 was stationed at Baltimore from March 1988 to 2012, and was named on 17 September 1988 by Mrs Elizabeth Love, wife of Clayton Love Jr, Chairman of the RNLI Ireland Committee. She joined the Relief Fleet in 2012.

1138 • Lord Saltoun

47' x 15' Tyne • Fairey Allday Marine • FM 1194
Built 1988 • Longhope 1988-99, Relief 1999-2012
Sold 2012 • Norma-G

1138 served Longhope from March 1988 to 1999, and then from 1999 she was in the Relief Fleet (pictured at Baltimore) until being sold in 2012 and taken to Belfast to run ship's crew, for survey work and as a relief pilot boat.

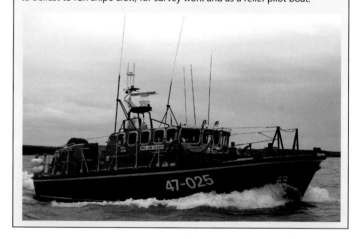

1139 • Garside

47' x 15' Tyne • Fairey Allday Marine • FM 1195
Built 1988 • St Davids 1988-2013

1139 was placed on station at St Davids (pictured) in May 1988 funded from the bequests of Thomas Harold Garside and his sister Dorothy Garside. She was officially named on 2 June 1989 by HRH The Duke of Kent.

1140 • George Gibson

47' x 15' Tyne • Fairey Allday Marine • FM 1196
Built 1988 • Appledore 1988-2010, Relief 2010-11 • Sold 1.2013

1140 went on station at Appledore (pictured) in June 1988. She was named on 25 June 1988 by Mrs Frank Homfray, and served at Appledore until 2010, then in the Relief Fleet. In 2013 she was at Ridge Wharf, Wareham for sale.

1141 • Sir John Fisher

47' x 15' Tyne • Wright/Harrison • 1141
Built 1989 • Relief 1989-92, Workington 1992-

1141 served in the Relief Fleet for a year while the launching crane was installed at Workington. She was placed on station at Workington (pictured) on 8 June 1992 and was named on 24 April 1993 by Mrs Diane Meacock.

1142 • Mariners Friend

47' x 15' Tyne • Wright/Souter • 0056
Built 1989 • Relief 1989-2007, Lough Swilly 2007-12, Relief 2012-13

1142 served in the Relief Fleet from December 1989, serving at stations including Kilmore Quay (pictured). She was named on 20 September 1989 at Cowes. She was offered for sale from Cobbs Quay, Poole in 2013.

1143 • Ann Lewis Fraser

52' x 17' Arun • Halmatic/Berthon
Built 1988 • Barra Island 1988-98, Tobermory 1998-2003, Relief 2003-04, Rosslare Harbour 2004 • Sold 2005 • Huaying 392

1143 was sold in 2005 to the China Rescue and Salvage Bureau and was shipped to China via Felixstowe (pictured at Harwich beforehand) in April 2006. She was renamed Huaying 392 and was allocated to Shantou, Nanhai Rescue Bureau, where she continued to serve as a lifeboat, largely unaltered.

1144 • Murray Lornie

52' x 17' Arun • Halmatic/Robson
Built 1988 • Lochinver 1989-2003, Relief 2003-04, Castletownbere 2004, Relief 2004-05 • Sold 2005 • Sigurvin

1144 was sold in 2005 to ICE-SAR, the National Lifesaving Association of Iceland, and was stationed at Siglufjörður (pictured) on the country's north coast. She was shipped to Iceland in January 2006 and took up her operational duties shortly afterwards, having been renamed Sigurvin.

1145 • David Robinson

47' x 15' Tyne • Fairey Allday Marine • FM 1208
Built 1988 • The Lizard 1988-2011, Relief 2011-

1145 was stationed at The Lizard (pictured) from August 1988 until July 2011 and was then reallocated to the Relief Fleet. She was named on 13 May 1989 by Mrs Jean Baker, daughter of donor Sir David Robinson.

1146 • Voluntary Worker

47' x 15' Tyne • Fairey Allday Marine • FM 1209
Built 1988 • Lytham St Annes 1988-90, Relief 1990-2005, Selsey 2006-

Built for the Relief Fleet 1146 was stationed at Lytham St Annes for just over a year before taking up duties as a Relief lifeboat. She was reallocated to Selsey (pictured) in 2005 and arrived at the station in February 2006.

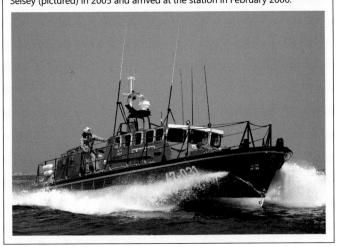

1147 • Sir William Hillary

47' x 15' Tyne • Fairey Allday Marine • FM 1210
Built 1988 • Douglas 1988-

1147 was placed on station at Douglas (pictured) in November 1988. Funded from the legacy of Alan J. Woolfenden, she was named on 21 July 1989 at Douglas by His Grace The Duke of Atholl after the RNLI's founder.

1148 • Lifetime Care

38' x 12'6" Mersey • Green Marine/Souter • 0061
Built 1988 • Relief 1989-

1148 was placed in the Relief Fleet in October 1989. She was named on 21 October 1989 at RNLI Depot, Poole, by Mrs Susan Hunter-Pease. In May 2012 she was used to open a new lifeboat station at Leverburgh (pictured).

1149 • The Queen Mother

52' x 17' Arun • Halmatic/William Osborne • WO3170
Built 1989 • Thurso 1989-2004, Longhope 2004-06, Relief 2009-09
Sold 2009 • Ederra 4

1149 was sold in 2009 to the Sociedad de Practicos del Puerto de Montevideo (Society of Pilots for Montevideo), Uruguay, and in June 2009 passed through Dover en route to Gravesend and Felixstowe for shipping. She was used as a pilot boat from July 2009, renamed Ederra 4 (pictured).

1150 • Hibernia

52' x 17' Arun • Halmatic/William Osborne • WO 3200
Built 1988 • Relief 1989-2007
Sold 2007 • Huaying 390

1150 was sold in 2007 to the China Rescue and Salvage Bureau, and in July 2007 was transported from Felixstowe (pictured) to China. She left on 18 July 2007 and took a month to reached Hong Kong. She was stationed at Waigaoqiao Base, Donghai Bureau, and renamed Huaying 390.

1151 • Mary Irene Millar

47' x 15' Tyne • FBM Ltd • 1237
Built 1989 • Portpatrick 1989-2011, Relief 2011-

1151 was placed on station at Portpatrick (pictured) in March 1989 and was named on 19 May 1989 at her station by Princess Alexandra. She was replaced in November 2011 and reallocated to the Relief Fleet.

1152 • Moonbeam

47' x 15' Tyne • FBM Ltd • 1238
Built 1989 • Montrose 1989-

1152 was placed on station at Montrose (pictured) in May 1989. Funded by Mr and Mrs Roland Sutton, of Grampian, she was named at her station on 1 July 1989 by Mrs Sutton, one of the donors.

1153 • Annie Blaker

47' x 15' Tyne • FBM Ltd • 1239
Built 1989 • Wicklow 1989-

1153 was placed on station at Wicklow in October 1989. She was named on 19 May 1990 by Dr Patrick Hillery, President of Ireland. She was usually slipway launched at Wicklow (pictured), but has also been kept afloat.

1154 • Kenneth Thelwall II

47' x 15' Tyne • Wright/Souter • 0068
Built 1989 • Ramsgate 1990-95, Walton and Frinton 1996-2011
Sold 9.2011 • Ocean Lad

1154 was sold in September 2011 to Bere Island Ferries, Ireland, and was used as a pilot boat, work boat and ferry at Bere Island (pictured).

1155 • Sarah Emily Harrop

47' x 15' Tyne • FBM Ltd • 1257
Built 1990 • Lytham St Annes 1990-98, Relief 1998-2007, Calshot 2007-10, Relief 2010, Shoreham Harb 2010 • Sold 2010 • Ocean Lass

1155 was sold in 2010 to Bere Island Ferries, Ireland. She was renamed Ocean Lass and was operated as a ferry and pilot boat perating out of Castletownbere and Bere Island (pictured) in West Cork.

1156 • William Street

47' x 15' Tyne • FBM Ltd • 1258
Built 1989 • Fleetwood 1989-

1156 was placed on station at Fleetwood (pictured) in October 1989 and she was named on 12 May 1990 at Wyre Dock Marina, Fleetwood by Mrs Elizabeth Acland. She was one of a number of Tynes to be re-engined in the 1990s with twin 565hp General Motors 6V-92TA diesels.

1157 • Alexander Coutanche

47' x 15' Tyne • FBM Ltd • FM 1259
Built 1989 • St Helier 1989-2009, Relief 2009-10, Calshot 2010-12, Lough Swilly 2012-

1157 was stationed at St Helier in December 1989 and was named on 9 May 1990 at St Helier Marina by Jurat the Hon John Coutanche. After being replaced at St Helier, she went to Calshot (pictured) and then Lough Swilly.

1158 • Hermione Lady Colwyn

47' x 15' Tyne • Wright/Marshall Branson • 1158
Built 1990 • Shoreham Harbour 1990-2010
Sold 7.2010 • Odin

1158 was sold in 1999 to a private buyer in Douglas, Isle of Man, and was used as the work boat Odin in Douglas Harbour until being sold on in June 2012. She went to Lymington, and visited Calshot (pictured) in July 2012.

1159 • Mabel Williams

52' x 17' Arun • Halmatic/Robson
Built 1990 • Ballyglass 1990-98, Relief 1998-2001, Rosslare Harbour 2001-04, Calshot 2004-07 • Sold 2007 • Huaying 391

1159 was sold from Poole in 2007 to the China Rescue and Salvage Bureau and was shipped to China in July 2007 from Felixstowe on board a container ship. She arrived a month later in Hong Kong and was stationed at Xiamen (Amoy), serving as a lifeboat renamed Huaying 391 (pictured).

1160 • Duke of Atholl

52' x 17' Arun • Halmatic/Osborne • WO 3269
Built 1990 • Relief 1990-99, Weymouth 1999, Relief 1999-2003, Hartlepool 2003-04, Relief 2004-07 • Sold 10.2007 • Gunnar Friðriksson

1160 was sold in December 2007 to ICE-SAR, the National Lifesaving Association of Iceland, and shipped north in the same month. She replaced the Arun 1061 at Ísafjörður (pictured), on Iceland's north-west coast, was renamed Gunnar Friðriksson, and took up her duties there in March 2008.

1161 • Doris M. Mann of Ampthill

38' x 12'6" Mersey • FBM Ltd • 1266
Built 1990 • Wells 1990-

1161 was funded from the legacy of Doris M. Mann, Ampthill, Bedfordshire and she was placed on station at Wells in July 1990. She was named on 17 July 1990 at The Quay, Wells, by HRH the Duchess of Kent.

1162 • Royal Shipwright

38' x 12'6" Mersey • FBM Ltd • 1267
Built 1990 • Relief 1990-2007, Cromer 2007-08, Relief 2008-

1162 was placed in the Relief Fleet in June 1990 and was named on 19 June 1990 at the Royal Naval College, Greenwich, by HRH The Duke of Kent. She served at Cromer (pictured) while the slipway there was being modified.

1163 • Lady of Hilbre

38' x 12'6" Mersey • FBM Ltd • 1268
Built 1990 • Hoylake 1990-

1163 was placed on station at Hoylake in October 1990, funded by the Port of Liverpool Branch Appeal. She was named on 12 November 1991 by HRH The Duke of Kent at the Coburg Dock, Liverpool.

1164 • Andy Pearce

38' x 12'6" Mersey • FBM Ltd • 1269
Built 1990 • Llandudno 1990-

1164 was placed on station at Llandudno (pictured) in November 1990. She was named and dedicated on 18 June 1991 by HRH The Duchess of Kent, on the Promenade, Llandudno.

1165 • Spirit of Derbyshire

38' x 12'6" Mersey • Aluminium Shipbuilders/Osborne • WO 3317
Built 1990 • Ilfracombe 1990-

1165 was placed on station at Ilfracombe (pictured) in July 1990. She was named on 29 September 1990 by Mrs Winifred Hilton, Chairman of the Derbyshire Appeal, at Ilfracombe.

1166 • Lincolnshire Poacher

38' x 12'6" Mersey • Aluminium Shipbuilders/W. A. Souter • 0084
Built 1990 • Skegness 1990-

1166 was placed on station at Skegness (pictured) in August 1990. She was named on 30 September 1990 at Skegness by Mrs Lucille Van Geest, with the new lifeboat house also being opened at the same ceremony.

1167 • Princess Royal (Civil Service No.41)

38' x 12'6" Mersey • Aluminium Shipbuilders/Osborne • WO 3359
Built 1990 • St Ives 1990-

1167 was placed on station at St Ives in October 1990. She was named on 17 July 1991 at St Ives by The Princess Royal, having been funded by the Civil Service, Post Office and British Telecom Lifeboat Fund.

1168 • Lilly and Vincent Anthony

38' x 12'6" Mersey • Aluminium Shipbuilders/W. A. Souter • 0085
Built 1990 • Pwllheli 1991-

1168 was placed on station at Pwllheli (pictured) in January 1991. She was named on 18 May 1991 at Pwllheli by Mrs Eileen Lord having been funded from the bequest of Miss Amy Anthony.

1169 • Marine Engineer

38' x 12'6" Mersey • Green Marine/FBM Ltd • 1277
Built 1990 • Relief 1990-95, Bridlington 1995-

1169 entered the Relief Fleet in 1990 and was named at the Docklands Sailing Centre, Isle of Dogs on 25 April 1991 by HRH The Duchess of Kent. In August 1995 she became the station lifeboat at Bridlington (pictured).

1170 • Keep Fit Association

38' x 12'6" Mersey • Green Marine/FBM Ltd • 1278
Built 1990 • Filey 1991-

1170 was placed on station at Filey (pictured) in June 1991 and was named on 31 August 1991 at The Coble Landing, Filey, by Mrs Bond, Vice-President of the Keep Fit Association who funded the boat.

1171 • Ann and James Ritchie

38' x 12'6" Mersey • Green Marine/FBM Ltd • 1279
Built 1990 • Ramsey 1991-

1171 was placed on station at Ramsey (pictured) in July 1991 and was named on 14 October 1991 at the station by HRH The Duke of Kent. She was one of several lifeboats funded from the bequest of Mrs Ann Ritchie.

1172 • Frank and Lena Clifford of Stourbridge

38' x 12'6" Mersey • Green Marine/FBM Ltd • 1280
Built 1991 • New Quay 1992-

1172 was placed on station at New Quay (pictured) in April 1992 and was named on 25 June 1992 at the station by Mrs Pam Grice, social secretary of RNLI Stourbridge Branch, after the donors.

1173 • Grace Darling

38' x 12'6" Mersey • Green Marine/FBM Ltd • 1281
Built 1991 • Seahouses 1991-

1173 was placed on station at Seahouses (pictured) in August 1991 at which time the station was known as North Sunderland. She was named on 24 September 1991 at Seahouses by HRH The Duchess of Kent.

1174 • Kingdom of Fife

38' x 12'6" Mersey • Green Marine/FBM Ltd • 1282
Built 1991 • Anstruther 1991-

1174 was placed on station at Anstruther (pictured) in October 1991 having been funded by the Anstruther Appeal, Cotton Trust and The Doctors Appeal. She was named on 29 May 1992 by HRH The Duchess of Kent.

1175 • Fanny Victoria Wilkinson & Frank Stubbs

38' x 12'6" Mersey • Green Marine/FBM Ltd • 1283
Built 1991 • Scarborough 1991-

1175 was placed on station at Scarborough (pictured) in September 1991 and was named on 9 September 1992 by HRH the Duchess of Kent having been funded from the Legacy of the late Frank Stubbs.

1176 • The Four Boys

38' x 12'6" Mersey • Green Marine/FBM Ltd • 1284
Built 1991 • Sennen Cove 1991-98, Relief 1998-99, Amble 1999-

1176 was placed on station at Sennen Cove in December 1991 and was named on 22 April 1992 by HRH The Duke of Kent. She was replaced in 1998 and reallocated to Amble (pictured) in July 1999.

1177 • Leonard Kent

38' x 12'6" Mersey • Green Marine/FBM Ltd • 1285
Built 1991 • Margate 1991-

1177 was placed on station at Margate (pictured) in December 1991 and was named on 21 May 1992 by HRH Princess Alexandra. She was mainly funded from the bequest of the late Leonard Francis Kent, of St Helier.

1178 • Margaret Jean

38' x 12'6" Mersey • Green Marine/FBM Ltd • 1286
Built 1991 • Relief 1992-98 & 99-2005, Lytham 98-99, Exmouth 2008-

1178 was placed in the Relief Fleet in February 1992 and was named on 12 November 1991 at FBM Ltd, Cowes, by Elizabeth Grant, sister of the donor. In May 2008 she was reallocated as station boat at Exmouth (pictured).

1179 • Maurice and Joyce Hardy

17.28m x 5.5m Severn • Halmatic/William Osborne • WO 3444
Built 1990 • Trials 1992-98, Training 1998-2004
Sold 12.2004 • Gemini Storm/ Gemini Endeavour/ Eileen May

1179 was sold in 2004 and was used as a diving boat at Oban and Fort William before moving to Buckie (pictured) and in 2011 to Montrose.

1180 • Earl and Countess Mountbatten of Burma

14.26m x 4.9m Trent • Green Marine/Osborne • WO 3522
Built 1991 • Trials 1992-94, Alderney 1994-95, Relief 1995-

1180 was named on 17 June 1992 and was used for trials before serving at Alderney from March 1994 to July 1995. She was then reallocated to the Relief Fleet, and also being used for crew training (pictured).

1181 • Ruby Clery

38' x 12'6" Mersey • Green Marine/Souter • SSL 0101
Built 1992 • Peel 1992-

1181 was placed on station at Peel (pictured) in June 1992 and was named on 12 September 1992 by Mrs Karen Bache Nordli. The donor, Miss Ruby Clery of London, was great-great-granddaughter of Sir William Hillary.

1182 • Robert Charles Brown

38' x 12'6" Mersey • Green Marine/FBM • 1322
Built 1992 • Swanage 1992-

1182 was placed on station at Swanage (pictured) in June 1992 and was named on 3 September 1992 by Robert Brown having been funded largely by the J. Reginald Corah Foundation Fund.

1183 • Lil Cunningham

38' x 12'6" Mersey • Green Marine/Souter • SSL 0102
Built 1992 • Rhyl 1992-

1183 was placed on station at Rhyl (pictured) in June 1992. She was named 30 September 1992 at Rhyl by Betty Cunningham, who had funded the lifeboat in memory of her sister.

1184 • Bingo Lifeline

38' x 12'6" Mersey • Green Marine/FBM • 1323
Built 1992 • Relief 1992-

1184 entered the Relief Fleet in July 1992 having been funded primarily by the Bingo Association of Great Britain. She was named on 31 July 1992 at East Cowes Marina, Isle of Wight, by Lynn Foulds Wood.

1185 • Moira Barrie

38' x 12'6" Mersey • Green Marine/William Osborne • WO 3546
Built 1992 • Barmouth 1992-

1185 was placed on station at Barmouth (pictured) in October 1992. She was named on 14 May 1993 at Barmouth by Miss Sheila Barrie, sister of the donor, Miss Moira Barrie, of Broadway, Worcestershire

1186 • Pride and Spirit

38' x 12'6" Mersey • Green Marine/Souter • SSL 0103
Built 1992 • Dungeness 1992-

1186 was placed on station at Dungeness (pictured) in September 1992 after taking part in HM The Queen's Golden Jubilee Parade in June 2002 in London. She was named on 30 October 1992 by Mrs Jean Cass.

1187 • Mary Margaret

38' x 12'6" Mersey • Green Marine/William Osborne • WO 3555
Built 1992 • Kilmore Quay 1992-2004, Relief 2004-

1187 was placed on station at Kilmore Quay in December 1992 and was named on 17 April 1993 by Mrs Ann Miles, wife of the RNLI's Director. She was replaced at Kilmore in April 2004 and reallocated to the Relief Fleet.

1188 • Eleanor and Bryant Girling

38' x 12'6" Mersey • Green Marine/FBM • 1324
Built 1992 • Newcastle 1993-

1188 was placed on station at Newcastle (pictured) in September 1993 and was named on 30 April 1994 at Newcastle by Mrs Sally Parry, great niece of the donor, the late Mrs Eleanor Bertha Girling.

1189 • Her Majesty the Queen

38' x 12'6" Mersey • Green Marine/Souter • SSL 0104
Built 1992 • Relief 1993-96, Cromer 1996-99, Relief 1999, Lytham 1999-

1189 was placed in the Relief Fleet in January 1993 and was named on 16 July 1993 at Ramsgate by HM The Queen. She served temporarily at Cromer before being reallocated as station lifeboat at Lytham St Annes (pictured).

1190 • Doris Bleasdale

38' x 12'6" Mersey • Green Marine/William Osborne • WO 3560
Built 1992 • Clogher Head 1993-

1190 was placed on station at Clogher Head (pictured) in March 1993. She was named at Clogher Head on 4 September 1993 by Mrs Jane Vernon, wife of the Chairman of the RNLI.

1191 • Joy and Charles Beeby

38' x 12'6" Mersey • Green Marine/FBM • 1325
Built 1992 • Berwick-upon-Tweed 1993-

1191 was placed on station at Berwick-upon-Tweed (pictured) in February 1993. She was named on 23 March 1993 at Carr Rock Pier, Spittal, Berwick-upon-Tweed by HRH Duchess of Kent.

1192 • Fisherman's Friend

38' x 12'6" Mersey • Green Marine/Souter • SSL 0105
Built 1993 • Relief 1993-99; Lytham St Annes 1999; Relief 1999-

1192 was placed in the Relief Fleet in April 1993 and was named on 15 June 1993 at Fleetwood Yacht Marina by Mrs Lofthouse, having been funded by Lofthouse of Fleetwood, manufacturers of Fisherman's Friend lozenges.

1193 • Freddie Cooper

38' x 12'6" Mersey • Green Marine/FBM • 1326
Built 1993 • Aldeburgh 1993-

1193 was placed on station at Aldeburgh (pictured) in December 1993, arriving after a passage from Harwich. She was named on 31 May 1994 at Aldeburgh by HRH The Duke of Kent.

1194 • Inchcape

38' x 12'6" Mersey • Green Marine/FBM • 1327
Built 1993 • Arbroath 1993-

1194 was placed on station at Arbroath (pictured) in August 1993. She was named after the Inchcape Rock which lies off Arbroath on 22 April 1994 by The Countess of Airlie CVO, wife of the Lord Lieutenant of Angus.

1195 • Royal Thames

38' x 12'6" Mersey • Green Marine/Osborne • WO 3582
Built 1993 • Eastbourne 1993-2012, Leverburgh 2012-

1195 was placed on station at Eastbourne (pictured off Beachy Head) in 1993 and named on 6 September 1993 by HRH Princess Michael of Kent at Sovereign Harbour Marina. She was reallocated to Leverburgh in 2012.

1196 • Silvia Burrell

38' x 12'6" Mersey • Green Marine/Souter • SSL 0106
Built 1993 • Girvan 1993-

1196 was placed on station at Girvan (pictured) in August 1993. She was named on 16 October 1993 at Girvan in memory of a god-daughter of the donor, the late Miss Silvia Burrell, of Edinburgh.

1197 • Esme Anderson

14.26m x 4.53m Trent • Green Marine/Osborne • WO 3612
Built 1995 • Ramsgate 1995-

1197 was placed on station at Ramsgate (pictured) in August 1995 and was named on 25 September 1995 at Ramsgate by HRH Duke of Kent. She was funded from the bequest of Mrs Esme Grace Anderson.

1198 • Blue Peter VII

14.26m x 4.53m Trent • Green Marine/Souter • SSL 0107
Built 1994 • Fishguard 1994-

1198 was placed on station at Fishguard (pictured) in September 1994. She was named on 17 June 1995 at Promenade, Goodwick, near Fishguard, by Blue Peter presenters Diane-Louise Jordan, Tim Vincent and Stuart Miles.

1199 • Roy Barker I

14.26m x 4.53m Trent • Green Marine/William Osborne • WO 3617
Built 1995 • Alderney 1995-

1199 was placed on station at Alderney (pictured) in July 1995 and was the first lifeboat funded from the legacy of Frederick Roy Barker of Jersey. She was named on 18 September 1995 by HRH The Duchess of Kent.

1200 • Anna Livia

14.26m x 4.53m Trent • Green Marine/Souter • SSL 0108
Built 1995 • Dun Laoghaire 1995-

1200 was placed on station at Dun Laoghaire (pictured) in June 1995 and was named on 15 October 1995 at the East Pier, Dun Laoghaire, by Mrs Clare Hamilton, having been funded by the Dublin Bay Lifeboat Fund.

1201 • The Will

17.28m x 5.5m Severn • Green Marine/Berthon • 1023
Built 1994 • Relief 1996-97, Falmouth 1997-2001, Relief 2001-

1201 was originally destined for Stornoway, but was reallocated to the Relief Fleet in 1996. She served at Falmouth, being named on 16 July 1997 at Port Pendennis, Falmouth by Mrs Julia Redding, then returned to the Relief Fleet.

1202 • Albert Brown

17.28m x 5.5m Severn • Green Marine/Berthon • 1024
Built 1995 • Harwich 1996-

1202 was stationed at Harwich (pictured) in October 1996 and was the first Severn to go on station. She was named on 25 May 1997 at Navyard Wharf, Harwich, by Terry Waite CBE.

1203 • Spirit of Guernsey

17.28m x 5.5m Severn • Green Marine/Halmatic • MR 3845
Built 1994 • St Peter Port 1997-

1203 was placed on station at St Peter Port (Guernsey) in June 1997. She was named on 5 June 1997 at Queen Elizabeth II Marina, St Peter Port Harbour, by HRH The Princess Margaret, Countess of Snowdon.

1204 • Windsor Runner (Civil Service No.42)

14.26m x 4.53m Trent • Green Marine/Halmatic • MR 3778
Built 1994 • Blyth 1995-2004, Relief 2004-08; Dunbar 2008; Relief 2008-

1204 served at Blyth from December 1995 until July 2004. She was named on 13 July 1996 at Dun Cow Quay, Blyth, by Lady Butler. After being withdrawn from Blyth she was reallocated to the Relief Fleet.

1205 • Frederick Storey Cockburn

14.26m x 4.53m Trent • Green Marine/William Osborne • WO 3618
Built 1994 • Courtmacsherry Harbour 1995-

1205 was placed on station at Courtmacsherry Harbour (pictured) in September 1995. She was named on 23 September 1995 at Courtmacsherry by Mrs Mary Dwyer.

1206 • Douglas Aikman Smith

14.26m x 4.53m Trent • Green Marine/Souter • SSL 0109
Built 1995 • Invergordon 1996-

1206 was placed on station at Invergordon (pictured) in May 1996. She was named on 17 August 1996 at the West Harbour, Invergordon, by Mrs W. G. Stephenson having been funded from the bequest of Mr Aikman Smith.

1207 • Sir Ronald Pechell Bt

14.26m x 4.53m Trent • Green Marine/William Osborne • WO 3614
Built 1995 • Dunbar 1995-2008

1207 was stationed at Dunbar in December 1995 and was named on 7 September 1996 by Mrs Pauline Poland. On 23 March 2008 she broke from moorings at Torness and was damaged beyond economic repair (pictured).

1208 • Samarbeta

14.26m x 4.53m Trent • Green Marine/Souter • SSL 0110
Built 1995 • Great Yarmouth & Gorleston 1996-

1208 was placed on station at Great Yarmouth and Gorleston (pictured) in February 1996 and was named on 24 July 1996 by HRH Princess Alexandra of Kent. Her name means 'working together' in Swedish.

1209 • Barclaycard Crusader

14.26m x 4.53m Trent • Green Marine/William Osborne • WO 3656
Built 1995 • Eyemouth 1996-

1209 was placed on station at Eyemouth (pictured) in March 1996 and was named on 29 June 1996 by Mrs Ann Hirons, at Eyemouth. She was funded principally by Barclaycard and their Profiles points holders.

1210 • Forward Birmingham

14.26m x 4.53m Trent • Green Marine/Souter • SSL 0111
Built 1996 • Exmouth 1996-2008, Relief 2008-

1210 served at Exmouth from July 1996 to May 2008. She was named on 20 September 1996 by HRH The Duke of Kent. In 2008 she was reallocated to the Relief Fleet, serving at stations including Donaghadee (pictured).

1211 • George and Ivy Swanson

14.26m x 4.53m Trent • Green Marine/William Osborne • WO 3657
Built 1995 • Sheerness 1996-

1211 was placed on station at Sheerness (pictured) in March 1996 and was named on 11 September 1996 at Sheerness Docks by HRH The Duke of Kent having been funded mainly from the bequest of Ivy Ethel Swanson.

1212 • George and Mary Webb

14.26m x 4.53m Trent • Green Marine/Souter • SSL 0112
Built 1996 • Whitby 1996-

1212 was placed on station at Whitby (pictured) in April 1996 and was named on 12 June 1996 by HRH The Duchess of Kent at Scotch Head, Whitby. She was funded by the Mary Webb Trust.

1213 • Henry Heys Duckworth

14.26m x 4.53m Trent • Green Marine/William Osborne • WO 3658
Built 1996 • Relief 1996-2006; Barry Dock 2006; Relief 2006-

1213 was placed in the Relief Fleet in February 1996 and was named on 28 April 1996 at St Helier, Jersey, by Mrs Lilian Duckworth in memory of her husband. She has served at many stations, including Barry Dock (pictured).

1214 • Stanley Watson Barker

14.26m x 4.53m Trent • Green Marine/Souter • SSL 0113
Built 1996 • Portree 1996-

1214 was placed on station at Portree (pictured) in June 1996 and was named on 11 June 1997 at The Pier, Portree, by Mrs Henry Felicity Douglas-Home, a member of the RNLI's Committee of Management.

1215 • Elizabeth and Ronald

14.26m x 4.53m Trent • Green Marine/William Osborne • WO 3659
Built 1996 • Dunmore East 1996-

1215 was placed on station at Dunmore East (pictured) in October 1996 and was named on 17 May 1997 by Mrs Sherril Burrows. She was funded from the gift of Mrs Elizabeth Mary Manners-Clarke.

1216 • Pride of the Humber

17.28m x 5.5m Severn • Green Marine/Halmatic • MR 3861
Built 1996 • Humber 1997-

1216 was placed on station at the Humber (pictured) in March 1997, operating from Spurn Point at the mouth of the river. She was named on 24 September 1997 at The Promenade, Hull Marina, by HRH The Duke of Kent.

1217 • David Kirkaldy

17.28m x 5.5m Severn • Green Marine/Berthon • 1025
Built 1996 • Aran Islands 1997-

1217 was placed on station at Aran Islands, operating from Inishmore, in June 1997. She was named on 29 June 1997 at Kilronan Harbour, Aran Islands, by Mrs Elizabeth Acland.

1218 • John and Margaret Doig

17.28m x 5.5m Severn • Green Marine/FBM Ltd • 1426
Built 1996 • Valentia 1996-

1218 was placed on station at Valentia (pictured) in November 1996. She was named on 14 June 1997 at Valentia by Charles Haughey, Taoiseach of Ireland, and the station's new crew facility was also opened.

1219 • Helmut Schroder of Dunlossit II

17.28m x 5.5m Severn • Green Marine/FBM • 1427
Built 1996 • Islay 1997-

1219 was placed on station at Islay (pictured) in March 1997, operating from Port Askaig. She was funded by Mr Bruno Schroder and Mrs George Mallinckrodt, and was named on 30 August 1997 by Miss Leonie Schroder.

1220 • City of London II

17.28m x 5.5m Severn • Green Marine/Berthon • 1026
Built 1996 • Dover 1997-

1220 was placed on station at Dover (pictured) in March 1997 and was named on 28 May 1998 at Dover's Western Docks by HRH The Duke of Kent, having been funded by the City of London Centenary Appeal.

1221 • Michael and Jane Vernon

17.28m x 5.5m Severn • Green Marine/FBM • 1433
Built 1997 • Lerwick 1997-

1221 was placed on station at Lerwick (pictured) in June 1997 having been funded by the Lerwick Lifeboat Appeal. She was named on 18 July 1997 at Albert Quay by Lady Vernon after the RNLI's former Chairman and his wife.

1222 • Maurice and Joyce Hardy

14.26m x 4.53m Trent • Green Marine/Souter • SSL 0114
Built 1996 • Fowey 1996-

1222 was placed on station at Fowey (pictured) in October 1996 and was named on 4 October 1997 at Fowey by Mrs Joyce Hardy having been funded from the gift and bequest of Maurice G. Hardy.

1223 • Ger Tigchelaar

14.26m x 4.53m Trent • Green Marine/William Osborne • WO 3690
Built 1996 • Arklow 1997-

1223 was formally handed over to the RNLI at Poole Depot on 16 September 1996. She was placed on station at Arklow (pictured) in February 1997 and was named on 10 May 1997 by Mr J. Frits Oppenheim.

1224 • Roy Barker II

14.26m x 4.53m Trent • Green Marine/Souter • SSL 0115
Built 1997 • Wick 1997-

1224 was placed on station at Wick (pictured) in February 1997. She was named on 20 September 1997 at Fishmarket Pier, Wick, by Miss Jane Spears as the second lifeboat funded from the bequest of Frederick Roy Barker.

1225 • MacQuarie

14.26m x 4.53m Trent • Green Marine/William Osborne • WO 3691
Built 1997 • Sunderland 1997-2004, Relief 2004-

1225 was placed on station at Sunderland (pictured) in March 1997 and was named on 30 August 1997 at the North Dock Marina by Mrs C. Gaudini. She was withdrawn in October 2004 and reallocated to the Relief Fleet.

1226 • Edward Duke of Windsor

14.26m x 4.53m Trent • Green Marine/Souter • SSL 0116
Built 1997 • Relief 1997-

1226 entered the Relief Fleet in April 1997 and was named on 25 June 1997 at the RNLI Depot, West Quay Road, Poole, by HRH The Duke of Kent. She has served at many stations, including Fishguard (pictured).

1227 • Mora Edith Macdonald

14.26m x 4.53m Trent • Green Marine/William Osborne • WO 3692
Built 1997 • Oban 1997-

1227 was placed on station at Oban (pictured) in July 1997 and was named on 23 May 1998 at South Pier, Oban, by Mrs Lizanne McKerrell. She was funded from the bequest of Miss Mora Edith Macdonald, of Glasgow.

1228 • Dora Foster McDougall

14.26m x 4.53m Trent • Green Marine/Souter • SSL 0117
Built 1997 • Relief 1997-2006, Barry Dock 2006, Relief 2006-

1228 entered the Relief Fleet in October 1997 and was named on 25 September 1998 at RNLI Depot Quay, Poole, by Jonathan Foster. She has served at many stations, including Exmouth (pictured).

1229 • The Whiteheads

17.28m x 5.5m Severn • Green Marine/Berthon • 1027
Built 1997 • St Mary's 1997-

1229 was placed on station at St Mary's (pictured) in December 1997. She was named on 9 July 1998 at St Mary's Quay by Lady Wilson, past president of St Mary's Lifeboat Guild, in memory of the parents of the donor.

1230 • Edna Windsor

17.28m x 5.5m Severn • Green Marine/FBM • 1435
Built 1998 • Barra Island 1998-

1230 was placed on station at Barra Island (pictured) in June 1998 and was named on 24 April 1999 at The Pier, Castlebay, by Mrs Brenda MacInnes having been funded from the bequest from Mrs Edna Windsor.

1231 • Margaret Foster

17.28m x 5.5m Severn • Green Marine/FBM • 1436
Built 1997 • Kirkwall 1998-

1231 was placed on station at Kirkwall (pictured) in March 1998 after visiting the donor's home town of Emsworth in Hampshire. She was named on 26 September 1998 at the West Pier, Kirkwall, by Brigadier S. P. Robertson.

1232 • Charles Lidbury

17.28m x 5.5m Severn • Green Marine/Berthon • 1028
Built 1998 • Aith 1998-

1232 was placed on station at Aith (pictured) in May 1998. She was named on 22 August 1998 at Aith by Dr Margaret Shimmin, and was one of two lifeboats funded from the bequest of Miss Mary Lidbury of Dulverton.

1233 • Austin Lidbury

14.26m x 4.53m Trent • Green Marine/ William Osborne • WO 3735
Built 1998 • Ballycotton 1998-

1233 was placed on station at Ballycotton (pictured) in March 1998 and was named on 6 June 1998 at Ballycotton by Lieut Cdr Brian Miles, Director of the RNLI and previously Divisional Inspector for Ireland.

1234 • Gough-Ritchie II

14.26m x 4.53m Trent • Green Marine/William Osborne • WO 3736
Built 1998 • Port St Mary 1998-

1234 was placed on station at Port St Mary (pictured), on the Isle of Man, in May 1998. She was named on 18 July 1999 at the Inner Harbour, Port St Mary, by Lady Daunt, having been funded by the Gough Ritchie Trust.

1235 • Bryan and Gordon

17.28m x 5.5m Severn • Green Marine/FBM • 1442
Built 1998 • Ballyglass 1998-

1235 was placed on station at Ballyglass (pictured) in August 1998 and was named on 5 September 1998 at Ballyglass by Dame Veronica Sutherland, CMG, British Ambassador. She was re-engined in 2011.

1236 • Violet, Dorothy and Kathleen

17.28m x 5.5m Severn • Green Marine/Berthon • 1030
Built 1998 • Stromness 1998-

1236 was placed on station at Stromness (pictured) in October 1998. She was named on 19 June 1999 by Mrs Margaret Kirkpatrick, widow of the late Coxswain Dan Kirkpatrick, drowned in the Longhope lifeboat in March 1969.

1237 • Fraser Flyer (Civil Service No.43)

17.28m x 5.5m Severn • Green Marine/FBM • 1443
Built 1998 • Relief 1999-

1237 was placed in the Relief Fleet in February 1999 and was named on 16 June 1999 at the RNLI Depot, Poole, by Lady Wilson, having been funded by the Civil Service, Post Office and British Telecommunications Lifeboat Fund.

1238 • Tom Sanderson

17.28m x 5.5m Severn • Green Marine/Berthon • 1031
Built 1998 • Stornoway 1999-

1238 was placed on station at Stornoway in February 1999 and named on 6 August 1999 at the Ferry Terminal, Stornoway, by Mrs Anne Barns-Graham having been funded from the bequest of Mr Tom Sanderson, of Cumbria.

1239 • Robert Hywel Jones Williams

14.26m x 4.53m Trent • Green Marine/William Osborne • WO 3764
Built 1999 • Fenit 1999-

1239 was placed on station at Fenit (pictured) in February 1999 and was named on 8 September 1999 at Fenit Harbour by President of Ireland, Mary McAleese. She was funded from the legacy of Robert Hywel Jones Williams.

1240 • Sam and Ada Moody

14.26m x 4.53m Trent • Green Marine/William Osborne • WO 3765
Built 1999 • Achill 1999-

1240 was placed on station at Achill (pictured) in April 1999 and was named on 18 September 1999 at Kildavnet Pier, Achill, by Mrs Phyllis Curry. She was partly funded from the bequest of Ada Moody.

1241 • Ernest and Mary Shaw

17.28m x 5.5m Severn • Green Marine/FBM • 1448
Built 1999 • Campbeltown 1999-

1241 was placed on station at Campbeltown (pictured) in May 1999 and was named on 28 August 1999 at the Old Quay, Campbeltown by Mrs Mary Shaw, widow of the donor, the late Ernest Shaw.

1242 • Spirit of Northumberland

17.28m x 5.5m Severn • Green Marine/Berthon • 1032
Built 1999 • Tynemouth 1999-

1242 was placed on station at Tynemouth (pictured) in October 1999 and was named on 4 May 2000 at The Royal Quays Marina, North Shields, by RNLI President, HRH The Duke of Kent. She was re-engined in 2011.

1243 • David and Elizabeth Acland

17.28m x 5.5m Severn • Green Marine/FBM • 1449
Built 1999 • Newhaven 1999-

1243 was placed on station at Newhaven (pictured) in November 1999. She was named on 6 May 2000 at Newhaven by Mrs Lucy Morris, daughter of David Acland DL, Chairman of the RNLI.

1244 • Myrtle Maud

17.28m x 5.5m Severn • Green Marine/Berthon • 1033
Built 1999 • Arranmore 2000-

1244 was placed on station at Arranmore (pictured) in January 2000 having been funded from the legacy of Myrtle Maud Campbell Orde. She was named on 13 May 2000 at Arranmore, by Mrs Murray Campbell.

1245 • Inner Wheel II

14.26m x 4.53m Trent • Green Marine/Souter • SSL 0138
Built 2000 • Relief 2000-06, Barry Dock 2006-

1245 was placed in the Relief Fleet in April 2000. She was named on 1 September 2000 at RNLI Depot, Poole, by Margaret Roberts and Alma N. Smith. In September 2006 she was reallocated to Barry Dock (pictured).

1246 • Dr John McSparran

14.26m x 4.53m Trent • Green Marine/Souter • SSL 0139
Built 2000 • Larne 2000-

1246 was placed on station at Larne (pictured) in August 2000. She was named on 30 September 2000 at Larne by Miss Marguerite McCormick having been funded from the bequest of Miss Margaret McSparran.

1247 • Katie Hannan

17.28m x 5.5m Severn • Green Marine/FBM • 1455
Built 2000 • Portrush 2000-08

1247 was placed on station at Portrush (pictured) in June 2000 and was named on 22 September 2000 by HRH The Duke of Kent. In January 2008 she went on rocks at Rathlin Island and was damaged beyond repair.

1248 • Bon Accord

17.28m x 5.5m Severn • Green Marine/Berthon • 1035
Built 2000 • Aberdeen 2000-

1248 was placed on station at Aberdeen (pictured) in July 2000 and was named on 14 October 2000 at Duthie's Quay, Aberdeen Harbour, by Margaret Farquer, having been funded by a local appeal and other donations.

1249 • Eric and Susan Hiscock (Wanderer)

17.28m x 5.5m Severn • Green Marine/FBM • 1456
Built 2000 • Yarmouth 2001-

1249 was placed on station at Yarmouth in January 2001, arriving after a passage via Cherbourg. She was named on 29 May 2001 at South Quay, Yarmouth, Isle of Wight by HRH the Duke of Kent.

1250 • Henry Alston Hewat

17.28m x 5.5m Severn • Green Marine/Berthon • 1036
Built 2000 • Mallaig 2001-

1250 was placed on station at Mallaig (pictured) in January 2001 having been funded from the legacy of Miss Catherine Margaret Hewat, Glasgow. She was named on 16 June 2001 at Mallaig Pier, by Miss H. E. Stirling.

1251 • [Un-named]

14.26m x 4.53m Tamar • Devonport Royal Dockyard • 050
Built 2000 • Trials 2000-05
Sold 2006 • Princess Alexandra III

1251 was used for trials for five years until being sold in 2006 to the Kent Police and, renamed Princess Alexandra III (pictured), was based at Sheerness.

1252 • Elizabeth of Glamis

14.26m x 4.53m Trent • Green Marine/Souter • SSL 0142
Built 2001 • Broughty Ferry 2001-

1252 was placed on station at Broughty Ferry (pictured) in April 2001 and was named on 15 September 2001 at the Old Harbour by Paralympic gold medallist, Caroline Innes MBE, after HM Queen Elizabeth The Queen Mother.

1253 • Corinne Whiteley

14.26m x 4.53m Trent • Green Marine/Souter • 0143
Built 2001 • Relief 2001-

1253 was placed in the Relief Fleet in May 2001 and was named on 9 May 2001 at RNLI Depot Quay, Poole, by Mrs Diane Bacon, grand-daughter of Alfred Whiteley. She has often been stored at the RNLI Depot (pictured).

1254 • Volunteer Spirit

17.28m x 5.5m Severn • Green Marine/Souter • SSL 0144
Built 2001 • Relief 2001-

1254 was placed in the Relief Fleet in May 2001. She was named on 8 May 2001 at RNLI Depot Quay, Poole, by Mr Graham Cosslette, Chairman of RNLI Helston Branch, with RNLI fund-raisers from Helston in attendance.

1255 • Alec and Christina Dykes

17.28m x 5.5m Severn • Green Marine/Berthon • 1037
Built 2001 • Torbay 2001-

1255 was placed on station at Torbay (pictured) in October 2001. She was named on 18 August 2002 at Brixham by Mrs Heather Buckpitt, Mayor of Torbay, having been funded by the late Mrs Helen Christina Dykes.

1256 • Richard Cox Scott

17.28m x 5.5m Severn • Green Marine/Souter • SSL 0145
Built 2001 • Falmouth 2001-

1256 was placed on station at Falmouth in December 2001. She was named on 1 May 2002 by HM The Queen at the National Maritime Museum, Falmouth and was dedicated at Tinners Walk later the same day.

1257 • William Gordon Burr

17.28m x 5.5m Severn • Green Marine/Berthon • 1038
Built 2001 • Relief 2002-08, Portrush 2008-

1257 entered the Relief Fleet in February 2002 and was named on 10 April 2002 at RNLI Depot, Poole, by Mrs Margaret Kerrod. In April 2008 she was reallocated to Portrush (pictured) after 1247 was damaged on service.

1258 • Roy Barker III

14.26m x 4.53m Trent • Green Marine/Souter • SSL 0148
Built 2001 • Howth 2002-

1258 was placed on station at Howth (pictured) in March 2002 as the third lifeboat funded from the bequest of Frederick Roy Barker. She was named on 24 August 2002 at Howth by singer Geraldine Coulter.

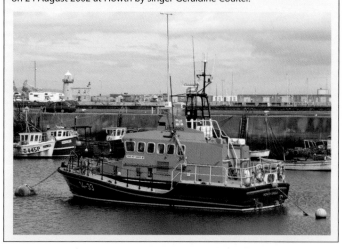

1259 • Willie and May Gall

17.28m x 5.5m Severn • Green Marine/Souter • SSL 0149
Built 2002 • Fraserburgh 2002-

1259 was placed on station at Fraserburgh (pictured) in May 2002. She was named on 7 September 2002 at Provost Anderson Jetty, Fraserburgh, by Mrs Patricia Argo

1260 • Roger and Joy Freeman

17.28m x 5.5m Severn • Green Marine/DML • 051
Built 2002 • Relief 2002-

1260 was placed in the Relief Fleet in September 2002. Named on 1 October 2002 at RNLI Depot, Poole, having been funded by the legacy of Hilda Freeman, she has served at many stations including Harwich (pictured).

1261 • Ernest and Mabel

17.28m x 5.5m Severn • Green Marine/Souter • SSL 0150
Built 2002 • Weymouth 2002-

1261 was placed on station at Weymouth (pictured) in July 2002 and was named on 14 September 2002 at The Ferry Steps, near Weymouth Pavilion, by Miss Beryl Taylor, who was representing the donor, Miss Beryl Taylor.

1262 • Beth Sell

17.28m x 5.5m Severn • Green Marine/Berthon • 1039
Built 2002 • Relief 2002-

1262 entered the Relief Fleet in August 2002 and was named on 24 March 2003 at RNLI Depot, Poole (pictured), by Mrs Dorothy Lowy, a long-time friend of the donor, Mrs Mima Elizabeth Sell.

1263 • Osier

17.28m x 5.5m Severn • Green Marine/DML • DML 052
Built 2002 • Relief 2002-

1263 entered the Relief Fleet in October 2002. She was named on 19 September 2003 at Holyhead in a private low-key ceremony. She has served at many stations in Britain and Ireland, including Holyhead (pictured).

1264 • Sybil Mullen Glover

17.28m x 5.5m Severn • Green Marine/Souter • SSL 0151
Built 2002 • Plymouth 2003-

1264 was placed on station at Plymouth (pictured) in February 2003. She was named on 23 July 2003 at Queen Anne's Battery Marina by HM The Queen, having been funded from the legacy of Daphne Sybil Glover.

1265 • Ivan Ellen

17.28m x 5.5m Severn • Green Marine/Berthon • 1040
Built 2003 • Penlee 2003

1265 was placed on station at Penlee (pictured) in March 2003. She was named on 30 September 2003 at Newlyn Fish Quay by Miss Lorna Leech having been funded from the legacy of Harold Ivan Leech.

1266 • John Neville Taylor

14.26m x 4.53m Trent • Green Marine/Souter • SSL 0154
Built 2002 • Relief 2002-08, Dunbar 2008-

1266 entered the Relief Fleet in November 2002 and was named on 2 June 2003 at RNLI Depot, Poole, by Mrs Frances Bundock. In May 2008 she was reallocated to Dunbar (pictured) after 1207 was damaged beyond repair.

1267 • Saxon

14.26m x 4.53m Trent • Green Marine/Souter • SSL 0155
Built 2003 • Donaghadee 2003-

1267 was placed on station at Donaghadee (pictured) in April 2003. She was named on 13 September 2003 at Donaghadee by Mrs Rhona McAuley, wife of the Chairman of the Donaghadee RNLI branch.

1268 • William Blannin

17.28m x 5.5m Severn • Green Marine/DML • 054
Built 2003 • Buckie 2003-

1268 was placed on station at Buckie (pictured) in May 2003. She was named on 2 August 2003 at Buckie by Mrs Lizzie Campbell having been funded from the bequest of Kenneth Maurice Williams and others.

1269 • Daniel L. Gibson

17.28m x 5.5m Severn • Green Marine/Berthon • 1041
Built 2003 • Relief 2003-

1269 took up her duties in the Relief Fleet in June 2003 and was named on 24 July 2003 at Hull Marina, Kingston-upon-Hull, by Gillian Wood. She has since served at many stations including Weymouth (pictured).

1270 • Elizabeth Fairlie Ramsey

17.28m x 5.5m Severn • Green Marine/DML • 055
Built 2003 • Tobermory 2003-

1270 was placed on station at Tobermory in August 2003, after a passage via Newlyn, Howth, Troon, Campbeltown, Islay and Barra. She was named on 18 October 2003 at Cal Mac Pier, Tobermory, by Miss Lesley Scoular.

1271 • Julian and Margaret Leonard

17.28m x 5.5m Severn • Green Marine/DML • 056
Built 2003 • Lochinver 2003-

1271 was placed on station at Lochinver (pictured) in November 2003 and was named on 17 April 2004 at the Old Lifeboat Berth in Lochinver by Mrs Rosamond Nelson, daughter of the late donor.

1272 • Christopher Pearce

17.28m x 5.5m Severn • Green Marine/Berthon • 1042
Built 2003 • Holyhead 2003-

1272 was placed on station at Holyhead (pictured) in December 2003 and was named on 6 May 2004 at Holyhead by HRH Duke of Kent. She was the second boat funded from the bequest of Christopher Michael Pearce.

1273 • The Taylors

17.28m x 5.5m Severn • Green Marine/ DML • 057
Built 2004 • Thurso 2004-

1273 was placed on station at Thurso (pictured) in April 2004. She was named on 18 September 2004 by Margaret, Viscountess Thurso, at Scrabster in memory of the family of Mrs Vera Rita Elizabeth Taylor.

1274 • Betty Huntbatch

14.26m x 4.53m Trent • Green Marine/Souter • SSL 0158
Built 2003 • Relief 2003-04, Hartlepool 2004-

1274 entered the Relief Fleet in September 2003, but was reallocated to Hartlepool (pictured), where she took up duties in September 2004. She was named and dedicated on 7 May 2005 at Hartlepool Marina.

1275 • Jim Moffat

14.26m x 4.53m Trent • Green Marine/Souter • 0159
Built 2004 • Troon 2004-

1275 was placed on station a Troon (pictured) in February 2004. She was named on 19 June 2004 at Troon by Mrs Maggie Moffat having been funded by the Moffat Charitable Trust and Lifeboats of the Clyde Appeal.

1276 • Donald and Barbara Broadhead

17.28m x 5.5m Severn • Green Marine/Souter • SSL 0160
Built 2004 • Rosslare Harbour 2004-

1276 was placed on station at Rosslare Harbour (pictured) in July 2004 and was named on 11 September 2004 by Mrs Judith Ann Ball, niece of the donor Florence Barbara Ann Broadhead, of Newark, Nottinghamshire.

1277 • Annette Hutton

17.28m x 5.5m Severn • Green Marine/Berthon • 1043
Built 2004 • Castletownbere 2004-

1277 was placed on station at Castletownbere (pictured) in August 2004. She was named on 9 October 2004 at Castletownbere by Mrs Kirstin Thomas, a close friend of the donor.

1278 • The Duke of Kent

17.28m x 5.5m Severn • Green Marine/Souter (comp. Berthon) • SSL 0161 • Built 2005 • Relief 2005-

1278 was placed in the Relief Fleet in February 2005 and was named on 12 April 2005 at The Lifeboat College, Poole (pictured), by HRH The Duke of Kent, the first all-weather lifeboat naming ceremony held at the new facility.

1279 • Margaret Joan and Fred Nye

17.28m x 5.5m Severn • Green Marine/Souter • SSL 1044
Built 2004 • Relief 2004-08, Portrush 2008, Relief 2008-

1279 was the last 17m Severn and entered the Relief Fleet in November 2004. She was named on 5 May 2005 at The Lifeboat College by Bob Cripps. She went to Portrush (pictured) in 2008 after 1247 had been damaged.

1280 • Peter and Lesley-Jane Nicholson

16m x 5m Tamar • Green Marine/DML • 062
Built 2005 • Relief 2005-

1280 was the first 16m Tamar and she entered the Relief Fleet in December 2005. She was named on 6 July 2005 at The Lifeboat College, Poole, by Lesley-Jane Nicholson, having been funded out of RNLI general funds.

1281 • Haydn Miller

16m x 5m Tamar • Green Marine/DML • 063
Built 2005 • Tenby 2006-

1281 was placed on station at Tenby in April 2006 and was named on 25 June 2006 at Tenby harbour by Mr Tony Middleton, an executor of the donor Haydn Gustav Miller's estate.

1282 • The Misses Robertson of Kintail

16m x 5m Tamar • Green Marine/DML • 064
Built 2006 • Peterhead 2006-

1282 was placed on station at Peterhead (pictured) in April 2006 and she was named on 11 May 2006 at Peterhead harbour by Shonaig Macpherson CBE, Trustee of The Robertson Trust

1283 • Spirit of Padstow

16m x 5m Tamar • Green Marine/DML • 065
Built 2006 • Padstow 2006-

1283 was placed on station at Padstow (pictured) in July 2006 and was named on 17 September 2006 at North Quay, Padstow Harbour, by Peter Shone, a friend of the donor, the late Miss Mickie Allen.

1284 • Helen Comrie

16m x 5m Tamar • Green Marine/DML • 066
Built 2006 • Longhope 2006-

1284 was placed on station at Longhope (pictured) in October 2006, escorted home by the Thurso and Stromness lifeboats. She was named on 14 June 2007 at Longhope pier by HRH The Duke of Kent.

1285 • Effseabee Too

13.7m FCB2 • Green Marine/Vosper Thornycroft
Built 2005 • Trials 2005-12 • Offered for disposal 2013

1285 was the prototype fast carriage boat 2 and used as a trial boat to prove a waterjet propulsion system. Extensive proving, launch and recovery trials took her to many other places, including Wells (pictured). She spent much time stored at the RNLI Depot at Poole, until disposal in 2013.

1286 • Frank and Anne Wilkinson

16m x 5m Tamar • Green Marine/DML • 062
Built 2007 • Relief 2007-08, Barrow 2008, Relief 2008-

1286 was placed in the Relief Fleet in April 2007 and was named on 10 July 2007 at Scarborough by Peter Gudgin. She served on temporary station duty at Barrow (pictured) from January to December 2008.

1287 • Lester

16m x 5m Tamar • Green Marine/Babcock • 068
Built 2007 • Cromer 2008-

1287 was placed on station at Cromer (pictured) in January 2008 and was named on 8 September 2008 at Cromer by HRH Duke of Kent. She was funded from the bequest of Derek Clifton Lethern, of Southfields, London.

1288 • Grace Dixon

16m x 5m Tamar • Green Marine/Babcock • 069
Built 2007 • Barrow 2008-

1288 was placed on station at Barrow in December 2008 and was named on 16 May 2009 at Ramsden Dock Basin, Barrow-in-Furness (pictured), by Colin Bourne. She was funded by the bequest of Grace Dixon.

1289 • Baltic Exchange III

16m x 5m Tamar • Green Marine/Babcock • 070
Built 2008 • Salcombe 2008-

1289 was placed on station at Salcombe (pictured) in March 2008 and was named on 17 May 2008 at Salcombe by Mrs Gail Dayton, wife of the Chairman of The Baltic Exchange.

1290 • Edward and Barbara Prigmore

16m x 5m Tamar • Green Marine/Babcock • 071
Built 2008 • Relief 2008-09; Sennen Cove 2009-10; Relief 2010-

1290 was placed in the Relief Fleet in August 2008 and was named on 19 August 2008 at the RNLI Lifeboat College, Poole, by Megan Seckington. She was used at Bembridge (pictured) for slipway launching trials in 2010.

1291 • Mark Mason

17.28m x 5.5m Severn • Green Marine/Babcock • 072
Built 2009 • Angle 2009-

1291 was placed on station at Angle (pictured) in March 2009 after a passage from Poole. She was named on 5 June 2009 by HRH Prince Michael of Kent GVCO, Grand Master of the Grand Lodge of Mark Master Masons.

1292 • George Sullivan

16m x 5m Tamar • Green Marine/Babcock • 073
Built 2009 • St Helier 2009-

1292 was placed on station at St Helier (pictured) in June 2009. She was named on 12 September 2009 by Tim Cartwright a trustee of the estate of the donor, the late Major George Langford Sullivan MBE

1293 • Victor Freeman

16m x 5m Tamar • Green Marine/Babcock • 074
Built 2009 • Relief 2009-10, Shoreham Harbour 2010, Relief 2010-

1293 was placed in the Relief Fleet in July 2009 and she was named on 9 July 2010 at Tenby lifeboat station (pictured) by HRH The Duke of Kent. She was on temporary duty at Shoreham Harbour in November 2010.

1294 • City of London III

16m x 5m Tamar • Green Marine/Babcock • 075
Built 2009 • Sennen Cove 2010-

1294 was placed on station at Sennen Cove in January 2010 and she was named on 24 April 2010 at the Harbour Beach, Sennen Cove (pictured), by Mrs Catherine Vlasto, having been funded by the City of London Branch.

1295 • Enid Collett

16m x 5m Tamar • Green Marine/Babcock • 076
Built 2010 • Shoreham Harbour 2010-

1295 was placed on station at Shoreham Harbour (pictured) in December 2010 and was named on 16 June 2011 by HRH The Duke of Kent. She was funded from the legacy of Enid Collett, of Great Shelford, Cambridgeshire.

1296 • Mollie Hunt

16m x 5m Tamar • Green Marine/Babcock • 077
Built 2010 • Appledore 2010-

1296 was placed on station at Appledore (pictured) in March 2010. She was named on 19 September 2010 at Appledore Quay by Sheila Russell and the dedication was conducted by Rev John Ewington.

1297 • Alfred Albert Williams

17.28m x 5.5m FCB2 • SAR Composites/Babcock • 078
Built 2010 • Bembridge 2010-

1297 was placed on station at Bembridge (pictured) in October 2010. She was named on 10 August 2011 by HRH Princess Anne in the newly-built lifeboat house after Alfred Albert Williams who worked on the donor's boat.

1298 • Killarney

16m x 5m Tamar • SAR Composites/Babcock • 079
Built 2010 • Kilmore Quay 2010-

After a capsize trial on 15 June 2010, 1298 was placed on station at Kilmore Quay in October 2010. She was named on 15 June 2011 at Kilmore Quay (pictured) by Mary McAleese, President of Ireland.

1299 • Irene Muriel Rees

16m x 5m Tamar • SAR Composites/Babcock • 080
Built 2011 • Walton and Frinton 2011-

1299 was placed on station at Walton and Frinton (pictured) in May 2011. She was named 26 May 2011 at Walton Pier by HRH The Duke of Kent having been funded from the bequest of Irene Muriel Rees, of Frinton.

1300 • Rose

16m x 5m Tamar • SAR Composites/Babcock • 081
Built 2011 • Lizard 2011-

1300 was placed on station at The Lizard (pictured) in July 2011. She was kept on a mooring initially until the new lifeboat house was completed, and was named on 5 May 2012 by Lady Mary Holborow.

1301 • John Buchanan Barr

16m x 5m Tamar • SAR Composites/Babcock • 082
Built 2011 • Portpatrick 2011-

1301 was placed on station at Portpatrick (pictured) on 13 November 2011, crossing from Northern Ireland escorted by the Donaghadee lifeboat Saxon. She was named on 26 May 2012 by Mrs Brenda Winterbottom.

1302 • Alan Massey

16m x 5m Tamar • SAR Composites/Babcock • 083
Built 2011 • Baltimore 2012-

1302 was placed on station at Baltimore (pictured) on 9 March 2012, arriving a few weeks earlier after a crew training passage from Poole. She was named on 22 September 2012 at Baltimore Harbour by Mrs Sue Windsor.

1303 • Diamond Jubilee

16m x 5m Tamar • SAR Composites/Babcock • 084
Built 2012 • Eastbourne 2012-

After taking part in the Diamond Jubilee Pageant on the Thames in June 2012, 1303 was placed on station at Eastbourne (pictured) on 27 June 2012 and was named on 5 July 2012 by the Earl and Countess of Wessex.

1304 • John D. Spicer

16m x 5m Tamar • SAR Composites/Babcock • 085
Built 2012 • Porthdinllaen 9.2012-

1304 was placed on station at Porthdinllaen (pictured) on 24 August 2012 having been funded from the bequest of the late Mr John Dominic Spicer, from Oxfordshire.

1305 • Kiwi

16m x 5m Tamar • SAR Composites/Babcock • 086
Built 2012 • Moelfre 2013-

1305 was placed on station at Moelfre (pictured) in March 2013 having been funded by the family of the late Reginald James Clark, a New Zealander who was rescued by the RNLI in World War II.

1306 • Norah Wortley

16m x 5m Tamar • SAR Composites/Babcock • 087
Built 2013 • St Davids 2013-

1306 was placed on station at St Davids in 2013 having been funded from the bequest of Diane Mary Symon, who died in February 2010.

1307 • Roy Barker IV

16m x 5m Tamar • SAR Composites/Babcock • 088
Built 2013 • Mumbles

1307 was allocated to Mumbles and was funded by the Roy Barker Memorial Fund. A new lifeboat house was built for her at Mumbles.

1308 • Sir Jock and Lady Slater

13m x 4.4m Shannon • SAR Composites/Berthon • 1046
Built 2012 • Trials 2012-13, Allocated to Relief Fleet

1308 was the first Shannon class all-weather lifeboat to be built, and was used for trials (pictured off Poole) around the coast of the UK and Ireland.

Part 6
Other Lifeboats, Inshore Lifeboats, and Hovercraft and Boarding Boats

As well as a fleet of capable and powerful offshore, or all-weather, lifeboats, the RNLI operates a large fleet of purpose-built and -designed inshore lifeboats (ILB) made up of various types. The most numerous of the ILBs in the fleet is the D class inflatable, which number over 100. They are described by the RNLI as the workhorse of the fleet, and carry out large numbers of rescues every year, quickly and efficiently.

The RNLI's inflatable ILB was developed during the early 1960s as a highly manoeuvrable craft ideally suited to operate closer to shore than all-weather lifeboats and well suited to surf, shallow water and confined locations. The boat has been refined and developed so that the current type is highly capable and carries a wide range of equipment.

As the D class inflatable has gone from strength to strength, so the RNLI has added larger and more capable ILBs to the fleet, the most significant of which is the Atlantic rigid-inflatable, the latest version of which is 8.3m in length, has a crew of four and a speed of 35 knots.

A variety of other small inflatable craft are also operated. The Y class inflatable is carried aboard Severn and Tamar all-weather lifeboats, while XP boats are carried on Trent lifeboats. With the RNLI taking over life guarding responsibilities at many beaches around the UK, the Arancia inshore rescue boat, from New Zealand, was introduced into the fleet. The RNLI also uses a range of boarding boats, and details of some are included.

During the 21st century two other significant developments have taken

place in the inshore rescue arena which have seen new craft developed and deployed. The E class lifeboats used on the Thames are large water-jet craft with a top speed of over 40 knots for use exclusively on the river. And hovercraft, of which seven were built, have been developed for use on mud and sand.

The other lifeboats in this section are oddities that were either never allocated an official number, or have not been operated as lifeboats but used in some capacity by the RNLI, such as the training boats which the RNLI operate from their Poole HQ. The two lifeboats operated by the Caister Volunteer Rescue Service are included, as are other private lifeboats, although details of all the independent lifeboats around the UK are not included due to lack of space.

Atlantic 75 and D class inshore lifeboats from Littlehampton. At many stations this combination of lifeboats is operated, with the ILBs now the workhorse of the RNLI's fleet. (Nicholas Leach)

Other Lifeboats and private lifeboats

44-001

44' x 12'8" Waveney • USCG Yard, Curtis Bay
Built 1923 • Trials round Britain 1964-67, Relief 1967-97
Displayed from 1997 • 44-001

44-001 was taken out of service in 1997 and used at Chatham Historic Dockyard as a floating exhibit for a year. She was then taken out of the water to become a static exhibit as part of the Lifeboat Collection (pictured).

Developmental boat Odyn

13m x 3.2m Ribworker 43 • Aluminium-hulled RIB • Ocean Dynamics, Pembrokeshire • Built 2001 • Trials 2001-

The Ribworker 43 rigid-inflatable Odyn was completed in June 2001 by Ocean Dynamics of Pembrokeshire. She is powered by two CAT 3126B engines producing 450hp each, driving two Hamilton HJ362 waterjets. She was used by the RNLI to test the viability of using waterjets in lifeboats.

Bernard Matthews/ Spirit of Blyth and Wansbeck

38'6" x 10'8" Lochin • Lochin Marine/Goodchild Marine
Built 1990 • Caister 1991-2004, Blyth 2005-

Bernard Matthews was built for service with Caister Volunteer Rescue Service, and was replaced there in 2004. She was then sold to Blyth Volunteer Lifeboat Service in December 2004 for £120,000 and entered service operating from a mooring in the harbour (pictured).

Bernard Matthews II

11m x 4.1m Valentijn • Habbeké Shipyard
Built 2004 • Caister 2004-

Bernard Matthews II is a Dutch-designed and built rigid-inflatable lifeboat that was funded by a local appeal and generous donation by Bernard Matthews for the Caister Volunteer Lifeboat Service. She is powered by twin 450hp Volvo Penta diesels which give a top speed of 37 knots.

Spirit of the West Wight

8.7m Barbarian class RIB • Twin 225hp Yamaha engines
Built 2006 • Freshwater 2006-13

The lifeboat Spirit of West Wight is operated by the independent rescue organisation Freshwater Lifeboat, which was founded in 1972 to provide better rescue provision around the local beaches. In 2013 a new and larger rigid-inflatable lifeboat was completed to replace this boat.

Pride of Sidmouth

7.66m x 2.54m Arctic 24 self-righting rigid inflatable • VT Halmatic Ltd
Built 2004 • Sidmouth 2004-

Spirit of Sidmouth is another of the numerous privately-operated inshore lifeboats, and is one of the larger ones. She is powered by twin 150hp outboard motors, has a top speed of 45 knots, carries a crew of four and can rescue up to eight survivors. She is launched by tractor and carriage.

1100 • Snolda

52' x 17' Arun • Fairey Allday Marine • FM 722
Built 1986 • Aith 1986-98, Relief 1998, Training TL-01 1998-2007
Sold 10.2007 • Oddur V. Gislason

For nine years, 1100 was used as a training boat by the RNLI out of the Poole (pictured) training centre for which she was given the operational number TL-02, before being sold out of service in 2007.

1179 • Peter and Marion Fulton

17.28m x 5.5m Severn • Halmatic/William Osborne • WO 3444
Built 1990 • Trials 1992-98, Training 1998-2004
Sold 12.2004 • Gemini Storm/ Gemini Endeavour/ Eileen May

For six years, 1179 was used as a training boat by the RNLI out of the Poole training centre for which she was named Peter and Marion Fulton and given the operational number TL-02.

Watchful

13.36m x 4.12m Nelson 44 • Halmatic Ltd, Southampton
Built 1988 • Training 2004-

In 2004 the RNLI acquired the GRP-hulled Nelson 44 boat Watchful for crew training. She is a twin-engined diesel service launch, and was built, fitted out and first commissioned by Halmatic of Southampton to designs by TT Boat Designs. She has a top speed of 18 knots and an endurance of 17 hours.

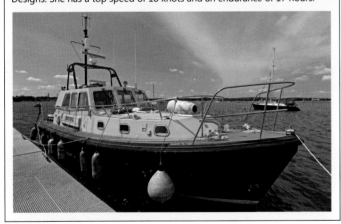

Mentor

13.7m x 4m Nelson 45 • TT Boat Designs, Seaview, IOW
Built 1974 • Training boat 2004-c2010

In 2004 the RNLI bought the GRP-hulled Nelson type service launch Mentor of Poole (pictured) and refitted her for use as a crew training vessel, but she was later sold. She was used alongside Watchful and was operated from the Lifeboat College at Poole (pictured).

Ian and Anne Butler

13m x 4.45m Hardy Commodore 42 • Hardy Marine Ltd, Norfolk
Built 2006 • Training 2006-

The training boat Ian and Anne Butler was named on 20 October 2006 after the late Mrs Anne Butler, and her first husband Ian. She was based on a Commodore 42 craft which was modified for RNLI requirements as a bespoke training craft, and operated at The Lifeboat College, Poole (pictured).

Robert S. Ellsmoor

13m x 4.45m Hardy Commodore 42 • Hardy Marine Ltd, Norfolk
Built 2007 • Training 2007-

The training boat Robert S. Ellsmoor was named on 13 June 2007 after her donor, Robert Ellsmoor, who was originally from Hoylake. She was based on a Commodore 42 craft which was modified for RNLI requirements as a bespoke training craft, and is based at The Lifeboat College, Poole (pictured).

A class Inshore Lifeboats

A class Dell Quay Dory rigid-hulled ILBs

17'1" x 7' Dell Quay Dory • Dell Quay
Built 1968-69 • Three built • Last left service in 1985

The Dell Quay Dory design was a commercially designed 17ft rigid-hulled boat manufactured by Dell Quay, a Chichester-based company. They were built of glass reinforced plastic (GRP) , and powered by two 36hp Penta outboard engines to give a top speed of 25 knots.

A class Hatch rigid-hulled ILBs

20'6" x 7'3" Hatch • William Osborne
Built 1966 • Two built • Numbered 18-01 and 18-03 (later A-1 to A-2)

The wooden-hulled Hatch boat was designed by George Hatch, an RNLI senior draughtsman and was intended to serve as both a boarding boat, to take lifeboat crews to lifeboats at moorings, and as a rescue boat. A Volvo Penta AQ110/100 petrol engine of 110bhp gave a speed of 26 knots.

A-503 • A class McLachlan rigid-hulled ILB

20'6" x 8' McLachlan • William Osborne
Built 1967 • one built • Numbered A-503

The McLachlan rigid-hulled ILB was developed during the 1960s, and incorporated a ragged chine hull and twin 60hp inboard petrol engines with outboard drives mounted in watertight compartments. A-503 was the only 20'6" version of the design and was in RNLI service for only five years.

A-504 • A class McLachlan rigid-hulled ILB

18'6" x 8' McLachlan • William Osborne
Built 1970 to 1974 • Nine built • Numbered A-504 to A-512

The McLachlan A-504, built as 18-004 but renumbered in the early 1970s, was the first of nine 18'6" McLachlan inshore lifeboats. She was stationed at Weston-super-Mare where she was launched from a special cradle down the slipway. She was later displayed at Bristol, Cromer and Chatham (pictured).

A-512 • A class McLachlan rigid-hulled ILB

18'6" x 8' McLachlan • William Osborne
Built 1970 to 1974 • Nine built • Numbered A-504 to A-512

A-512 was the last of the 18'6" McLachlans to be built. Most served at stations where they were kept afloat, such as Plymouth, Falmouth, Ramsgate, Oban and Invergordon, and used as both lifeboats and boarding boats. A-512 served Torbay 1975 to 1988, and was scrapped in May 1988.

A-513 Sam and Iris Coles

20' x 7'2" Boston Whaler Outrage • Boston Whaler
Built 1984 • Poole 1985-94, Cowes (workboat) 1994-

The Boston Whaler A-513 was a one-off lifeboat built specially for Poole (pictured) and rescues in Poole harbour. Fitted out by the RNLI at Cowes, she was powered by twin 60hp Evinrude outboards giving a top speed of 30 knots. Since leaving Poole, she has been used at the RNLI ILC at Cowes.

B class Inshore Lifeboats

B class rigid-inflatable ILBs

Atlantic rigid-inflatable hulled • Atlantic 17 and Galt 20 types
Numbered B-1 to B-8 • On trials 1970 to 1975

The rigid-inflatable inshore lifeboat was developed in the 1960s and 1970s at Atlantic College, South Wales. The early designs, pictured here on trials with a McLachlan rigid-hulled ILB, numbered B-1 to B-8, with B-1, B-2 and B-3 being adapted by the RNLI, with some types 17ft or 20ft in length.

B-500 • prototype B class rigid-inflatable

22'9" x 7'6" Atlantic 21
Numbered B-1 to B-3 • Later renumbered B-500 onwards

The prototype boat, B-500, which had in-line seating and a small roll bar, was trialled at several stations, including Hartlepool, Mudeford and Appledore, and the first Atlantic 21 went into service at Hartlepool. In 1980 B-500 went on display at Bristol, later going to Chatham (pictured).

B class Atlantic 21 inshore lifeboats

22'9" x 7'6" Atlantic 21 • Halmatic/RNLI Inshore Lifeboat Centre, Cowes
Numbered B-500 to B-595 • First built 1970 • Last built 1993

The Atlantic 21 rigid-inflatable was developed by the RNLI in the 1970s and evolved into a highly effective rescue craft. While the early boats were built of plywood and subdivided into watertight compartments, when full-scale production began they were moulded from glass reinforced plastic (GRP).

B class Atlantic 21 inshore lifeboats

22'9" x 7'6" Atlantic 21 • Halmatic/RNLI Inshore Lifeboat Centre, Cowes
Numbered B-500 to B-595 • First built 1970 • Last built 1993

The Atlantic 21 varied in its layout as the build programme continued and experience was gained with using high-speed inshore lifeboats. More powerful engines were used, more equipment was added, and on some boats, such as B-585 Peter and Grace Ewing, a small windscreen was added.

B class Atlantic 75 inshore lifeboats

7.38m x 2.64m Atlantic 75 • Souter/RNLI Inshore Lifeboat Centre, Cowes
Numbered B-700 to B-796 • First built 1993 • Last built 2003

The Atlantic 75 was a development of the 21 and was designed at the RNLI's Inshore Lifeboat Centre (ILC) at Cowes. The 75 was 38cm longer and 20cm broader than the 21, and was powered by twin 70hp outboards giving a top speed of thirty-two knots, while the seating and roll bar remained the same.

B class Atlantic 85 inshore lifeboats

8.3m x 2.8m Atlantic 85 • RNLI Inshore Lifeboat Centre, Cowes
Numbered from B-801 • First built 2004 • In build 2012

The Atlantic 85 was a development of and replacement for the Atlantic 75 but was faster and more powerful, with twin 115hp outboards. Seats for four crew were provided, and radar and VHF DF was fitted. The craft can be operated in daylight in force six to seven and at night in force five to six.

Twin-engined inflatable inshore lifeboats

19' twin-engined inflatable • Various builders
Numbered from C-500 to C-504 • First built 1972 • Last built 1973

In the 1970s the RNLI developed more capable inflatable ILBs. Five boats, all based on the 19ft Zodiac Mk.V except one supplied by RFD, were acquired and tested. Although the C class were capable craft, the larger Atlantic 21 proved to be more suitable and no more boats of this type were built.

Zodiac C class inflatable inshore lifeboats

17'6" x 7'1" C class inflatable • Various builders
Numbered from C-505 to C-523 • First built 1978 • Last built 1990

The Zodiac Mk.IV twin-engined inflatable was developed during the late 1970s, and was essentially a larger and more powerful D class ILB. They gave good service at a number of stations, including Cardigan (pictured), but in the 1990s were phased out and replaced by Atlantic rigid-inflatables.

D class inflatable inshore lifeboats

Fully inflatable, single-engined • Various builders since 1963
Numbered from D-1 • First built 1963, over 700 built since

The inflatable inshore lifeboat was developed during the early 1960s to meet changing demands made on lifeboats. The 16ft inflatables, made from tough nylon coated with neoprene/hypalon, were crewed by two, powered by a 40hp outboard engine, and could be launched quickly and easily.

RFD PB16 D class inflatable inshore lifeboats

15'6" x 6'3" inflatable • R. F. D. Company Ltd, Godalming, Surrey
Numbered from D-1 to D-310 • First built 1963

The first inshore lifeboats were manufactured by the RFD Company and their inflatable RFD PB16 Z-Boat design was used during the 1960s and 1970s, and into the 1980s. Various other designs, notably the Zodiac Mk.II, were also used at this time, but the RFD PB16 was the most widespread.

Avon D class inflatable inshore lifeboats

16'3" x 6'7" inflatable ILB • RNLI Inshore Lifeboat Centre, Cowes
Built 1983-2002 • Numbered D-311, D-315 to D-339, D-343 to D-575

The Avon EA16 type inshore lifeboat was developed and built by the RNLI during the early 1980s. At 16ft 3in in length, it was larger than the RFD PB16 type, and weighed 745lbs. The boats were powered by a single 40hp marinised outboard, and had a top speed of about 20 knots.

IB1 D class inflatable inshore lifeboats

16'3" x 6'7" inflatable ILB • RNLI Inshore Lifeboat Centre, Cowes
Built 2002 on • Numbered D-600 on (D-750 was completed in 2011)

The Inshore Boat 1 (IB1) was developed by the RNLI between 2000 and 2003. The new design was faster, incorporated the latest advances in material and equipment technology, and was more consistent in its performance. The 50hp outboard engine gave it a top speed of 25 knots.

Y class inflatable

11'6" x 5'4" Inflatable • RNLI ILB Centre • Up to Y-245 (2012)
Used on 17m Severn and 16m Tamar lifeboats • Over 240 built

The first Y class inflatables were built in 1971 for use on the 54ft and 52ft Aruns, and the original Y boats were Zodiac Mk.1 types. They were later used on Severns and Tamars, being launched over the stern of the Arun on rails, via a davit from the Severn, and from a ramp at the stern of the Tamar.

X class inflatable boat

9'2" (2.79m) x 4'4" (1.32m) inflatable • weight 40lbs (18kg)
Avons Redcrest • 1982 to tie in with 47ft Tyne build • Up to X-197 (2012)

The small X boats are used on board 47ft Tyne and 12m Mersey lifeboats, although they are not carried all the time by these lifeboats. The boat, which is manually inflated by the crew, is used to reach casualties inshore and is manually propelled and usually operated by two crew.

XP inflatable boat

2.84m x 1.59m Inflatable • RNLI Inshore Lifeboat Centre
Kept on board 14m Trent • First built 2001 • Up to XP-51 (2012)

The small XP boat, a powered X boat, is used as an inflatable daughter boat aboard 14m Trent all-weather lifeboats. It has to be inflated before use, and is powered by a 5hp outboard engine which gives it a speed of six knots. This small craft is used to access areas where the lifeboat cannot reach.

Rescue Water Craft (RWC)

3.22m x 1.17m Yamaha VX700 Waverunners • Yamaha
Seven XL700 and 49 VX700 in service (2012) • Lifeguard beaches

The RNLI have been using Rescue Water Craft (RWC) since 2002 at beaches where Lifeguards operate. Yamaha models have been used, modified with a rescue sled to take up to four people. The single petrol engine of 80hp gives good acceleration and speed, and RWC can operate in very shallow waters.

A class Arancia beach rescue boats

3.88m x 1.73m Arancia • 6 built at ILC (A-64 to A-69) • 66 built by Arancia, New Zealand • 77 built • Numbered A-01 to A-77

The Arancia inshore rescue boat (IRB) was developed for surf lifesaving in New Zealand in the 1970s. Brought into the RNLI in 2001, the IRBs are sturdy enough for heavy surf, light enough for two people to launch, and became a common sight at with the RNLI Beach Lifeguard service.

A class Arancia inshore rescue boats

3.88m x 1.73m Arancia • Built by Arancia, modified by RNLI at ILC
Numbered A-76 (Criccieth), A-77 (Gorleston), A-78 (Aberystwyth)

After proving its worth on the beaches with the RNLI's Lifeguards, the Arancia IRB was deemed suitable to be co-located with ILBs at a number of lifeboat stations, such as at Criccieth (pictured), to be used in shallow water and estuaries. It was modified with the addition of more equipment.

The E class lifeboats

The E class lifeboats were introduced in January 2002 for service at three new stations on the river Thames (pictured). Six boats were built, powered by waterjets to give a speed of 40 knots, and modified by the RNLI in 2003 and 2004. An E class Mk.II was introduced in 2011, of which three were built.

E-001 Public Servant (Civil Service No.44)

9m x 2.8m Tiger Marine • FBM Babcock Naval Shipyard, Rosyth
Built 2001 • Gravesend/Chiswick/Tower 2002-12

E-001 was provided by the CISPOTEL Lifeboat Fund and was named on 11 June 2002 at St Katharine Docks, London, by Lady Tebbit, wife of Sir Kevin Tebbit. She served until June 2012, and was then scrapped.

E-002 Olive Laura Deare

9m x 2.8m Tiger Marine • FBM Babcock Naval Shipyard, Rosyth
Built 2001 • Gravesend/Chiswick/Tower 2002-12

E-002 was provided by the bequest of Mrs Olive Laura Deare, Gravesend, and was initially based at Gravesend. She was named on 26 April 2003 at Fort Gardens, Milton Place, Gravesend by Mrs Mary Straight.

E-003 Chelsea Pensioner

9m x 2.8m Tiger Marine • FBM Babcock Naval Shipyard, Rosyth
Built 2001 • Gravesend/Chiswick/Tower 2002-12

E-003 was funded from the bequest of Dr Patricia Mary Martyn Baguley of Cockermouth, and named on 19 July 2002 at the Royal Hospital, Chelsea, by Bert Spurdin in recognition of the support given by the Chelsea Pensioners.

E-004 Ray and Audrey Lusty

9m x 2.8m Tiger Marine • FBM Babcock Naval Shipyard, Rosyth
Built 2001 • Gravesend/Chiswick/Tower 2002-12

E-004 was funded from the legacy of Raymond and Audrey Lusty, Farnham, and was named in 2004 during a ceremony at Lensbury, Broom Road, Teddington. She was taken out of service in October 2012.

E-005 Legacy

9m x 2.8m Tiger Marine • FBM Babcock Naval Shipyard, Rosyth
Built 2001 • Gravesend/Chiswick/Tower 2002-

E-005 was funded from the bequest of Lieutenant Philip Francis Spencer King and named during a ceremony on 27 May 2004 at Southwark Cathedral by England rugby captain, Lawrence Dallaglio.

E-006 Joan and Kenneth Bellamy

9m x 2.8m Tiger Marine • FBM Babcock Naval Shipyard, Rosyth
Built 2001 • Gravesend/Chiswick/Tower 2002-

E-006 was provided from the bequest of Ken and Joan Bellamy, of
Kidderminster, and named on 29 June 2005 at The Boathouse, Putney,
by Mr John Young, Chairman of Young's Brewery.

E-07 Hurley Burly

10.5m x 3.5m (with collars) E class Mk.II • MST, Liverpool
Built 2011 • Chiswick/Tower 2011-

The first of the new E class Mk.II fast response boats, E-07, was provided
from the gift of Mrs Kay Hurley MBE, and was named on 31 October 2011
at Tower lifeboat station, Lifeboat Pier, on the Thames by the donor.

E-08 Dougie and Donna B

10.5m x 3.5m (with collars) E class Mk.II • MST, Liverpool
Built 2012 • Chiswick/Tower 2012-

E-08 was funded by the generous bequest of Mrs Rosemary Battams and
was named on 28 September 2012 at Chiswick lifeboat station (pictured) by
Olympic medal-winning rower Greg Searle.

E-09 Brawn Challenge

10.5m x 3.5m (with collars) E class Mk.II • MST, Liverpool
Built 2012 • Chiswick/Tower/Relief 2012-

E-09 was funded by an RNLI fundraising drive entitled 'The Brawn Lifeboat
Challenge' and was named on 27 September 2012 at Chiswick lifeboat
station (pictured) by motor sport engineer Ross Brawn.

Inshore Rescue Hovercraft

Hovercraft

The inshore rescue hovercraft was introduced in 2002 to meet the
demand for a rescue craft capable of crossing terrain such as tidal
marshes and mudflats that can be inaccessible by boat. Six hovercraft
were built between 2002 and 2005, with a seventh added in 2009 for
service in the Relief Fleet and freeing up one for training. The Griffon
470TD hovercraft built by Griffon Hovercraft of Southampton was the
most suitable craft. The 470TD has two propeller-fans driven by twin
85hp Volkswagen intercooled and turbo-charged diesel engines.

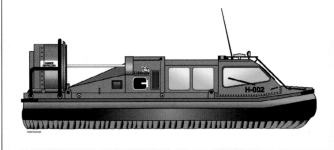

H-001 Molly Rayner

7.6m x 2.55m Griffon 450TD • Griffon Hoverwork Ltd
Built 2002 • Trials 2001-02, Relief 12.2003-

H-001 was funded by Mr Donald Rayner, Buckinghamshire, in memory of
his wife and named on 11 July 2003 at RNLI Depot, Poole by Mr Rayner.

H-002 The Hurley Flyer

7.6m x 2.55m Griffon 470TD • Griffon Hoverwork Ltd
Built 2002 • Morecambe 12.2002-

H-002 was funded from the gift of Mrs Kay Hurley MBE, Oxfordshire, and formally named at Central Promenade, Morecambe on 31 May 2005 by the donor. She is transported by and launched from lorry HT03 Crew Cab.

H-003 Hunstanton Flyer (Civil Service No.45)

7.6m x 2.55m Griffon 470TD • Griffon Hoverwork Ltd
Built 2003 • Hunstanton 7.2003-

H-003 was funded by The Lifeboat Fund (staff and pensioners of the Civil Service, Royal Mail and BT), and named on 21 May 2005 at the lifeboat station at Old Hunstaonton by David Rowlands.

H-004 Vera Ravine

7.6m x 2.55m Griffon 470TD • Griffon Hoverwork Ltd
Built 2004 • Southend-on-Sea 7.2004-

H-004 was funded from the bequest of Vera Ravine, Grays, London and named on 11 June 2005 at the Lifeboat Station, Southend-on-Sea by Mrs M. Orchard. She is launched from a house on the shore adjacent to the pier.

H-005 Hurley Spirit

7.6m x 2.55m Griffon 470TD • Griffon Hoverwork Ltd
Built 2004 • New Brighton 10.2004-

H-005 was provided from the gift of Mrs Kay Hurley, MBE, of Oxfordshire and named by the donor on 25 June 2005 at West Cheshire Sailing Club, Harrison Drive, New Brighton. She is transported by a lorry.

H-006 John Russell

7.6m x 2.55m Griffon 470TD • Griffon Hoverwork Ltd
Built 2005 • Relief 2005-

H-006 was funded from a bequest of the late John Russell and was named on 20 October 2006 at the RNLI Depot, Poole, by Mrs Diane Edginton. She is used as a relief hovercraft operating around the country.

H-007 Samburgh

7.6m x 2.55m Griffon 470TD • Griffon Hoverwork Ltd
Built 2009 • Relief 1.2009-

H-007 was funded from the legacy of Lille Florence Samborough, of London, in memory of her late father-in-law, and named on 29 January 2009 at the RNLI Depot, Poole (pictured), by Carl Tansill.

William Myatt

Completed in 1931, the 25' x 8' wooden boarding boat William Myatt was built for service at Dover, she was used for rescue work at Walton during the war, and was also stationed at Padstow (pictured) from 1955 to 1965; she was sold in 1965 and became a fishing boat.

BB-31 City of Leicester

Built in 1932, City of Leicester measured 25' by 8'3" and served at Walton and Frinton until 1985. She was funded by the Leicester Mercury Fund. After her long career at Walton, she was placed on display outside the town's old lifeboat house (pictured).

BB-188

A wooden boarding boat, BB-188 measured 25' x 8'3" and was another boat to serve at Walton and Frinton (pictured), where the lifeboat was kept moored off the pier. BB-188 was fitted with a motor in 1992 and served the station until 2005.

BB-901

The fibreglass boarding boat used at a number of stations, notably Howth, Ballycotton and Portrush (pictured), is generally employed where lifeboats are moored in a sheltered harbour. They are powered by a single 15hp Mariner longshaft outboard engine.

BB-185

The wooden boarding boat BB-185 was built in 1981 for St Mary's, where she was kept in the boathouse (pictured). She was approximately 20ft overall, of clinker construction and was the RNLI's only slipway-launched boarding boat. She was sold by the RNLI in 2011.

BB-234

The wooden boarding boat BB-243 was built at International Boatbuilding College at Lowestoft in 2000 for St Mary's (Isles of Scilly) and is kept in the boathouse to be launched down the slipway. The station also has an old D class inflatable for use as a boarding boat.

BB-195 Punt

The lifeboat at Islay is moored just far enough from the boarding platform to warrant the use of a small punt (pictured). This unusual and unique craft is hauled between boat and platform by ropes. The station also has an old D class inflatable for when other moorings are used.

BB-575 D class inflatable

Since 2000 the RNLI has used old D class inflatables, which have been replaced in service, as boarding boats, redesignating them using a BB-prefix, so BB-575 (pictured) was in operational service as D-575 (named Hounslow), being used as a boarding boat at Porthdinllaen.

Single-engined inflatable boarding boat

Wooden boarding boats were replaced by a variety of inflatable boarding boats, with the single-engined ones being very similar to the D class ILB for stations where the moorings were relatively sheltered. They are also used on an everyday basis by full-time mechanics.

Sillinger twin-engined inflatable

Twin-engined Sillinger inflatables have been used as boarding boats for stations where moorings are relatively exposed, such as Aran Islands (pictured) and Arranmore, and where extra power is needed, particularly in bad weather.

BB-240

BB-240 (pictured) and BB-239 were wooden-hulled boarding boats purpose-built at Lowestoft for the Humber station at Spurn Point, where they were used until 2012. They were based on the 18ft McLaughlin design and were powered by twin 50hp Mariner outboards.

BB-243

The foam-filled fibreglass boarding boat BB-243 was built in 2012 by Boston Whaler and is based on a 2010 Model 21ft Justice boat specifically for use at the Humber station at Spurn Point. The hull is self-bailing with scuppers and was adapted for the conditions at Spurn.

Appendices

Lifeboats abroad, on display, builders, launching, stations

The core of this book covers the RNLI's lifeboats and where they are now, or where they were last reported. The appendices group together lifeboats which have been sold abroad to foreign lifeboat services for continued use as rescue boats, as well as listing lifeboats which are on display. Many lifeboats, particularly in the last 20 years, have been sold abroad and some countries, notably Iceland and China, have rescue services which predominantly operate former RNLI lifeboats.

As well as old lifeboats being sold abroad, an increasing number are now restored and on display at a variety of museums and heritage centres. The largest collection of former RNLI lifeboats is the RNLI Historic Lifeboat Collection at

the Historic Dockyard in Chatham, Kent. These boats represent well over 100 years of lifeboat design and are maintained by a team of dedicated volunteers.

Details of lifeboat builders and launch methods have also been included to provide an idea of where lifeboats have been built and how they put to sea. A wide variety of boatbuilders have been used to construct lifeboats, with boatyards in London used in the 19th century. Cowes on the Isle of Wight was the main centre of construction for the RNLI during much of the 20th century, along with various yards on the south coast. Since fibre glass and composite materials have been used for hulls, lifeboats have usually been constructed at one yard while fitted out at another.

In 2009 the RNLI purchased Green Marine, a Lymington boatbuilder and the only manufacturer in the UK able to produce, to the RNLI's exacting standards, the technologically advanced composite hulls required for the 21st century lifeboat fleet. The yard was put up for sale and as its closure would have had serious consequences for future lifeboat construction, the RNLI acquired the facility and renamed it SAR Composites.

The final appendix lists lifeboat stations operated by the RNLI, with the dates they were established and when motor and inshore lifeboats were first placed on station. Another list provides information about independent and private lifeboat stations, which have proliferated during the second half of the 20th century.

The 52ft Arun Duke of Atholl (ON-1160), named Gunnar Friðriksson at Ísafjörður, is one of many former RNLI lifeboats sold for service in Iceland. (Nicholas Leach)

Lifeboats sold abroad

ON	Sold	Country	Current location
704	1957	Uruguay	Retired in Colonia, Montevideo
705	1956	Chile	Display on quay at Valparaiso
734	1959	Guatemala	Location unknown
747	1951	Liberia	Location unknown
779	1959	Netherlands	Pleasure boat at Aalsmeer
780	1959	Netherlands	Location unknown
794	1963	Valparaiso	Wrecked after service
799	1958	Guatemala	Location unknown
850	1973	Portugal	Fishing boat at Sesimbra
860	1980	Chile	Pleasure boat at Torpoint, Plymouth
914	1969	New Zealand	Trip boat at New Plymouth
934	1985	Uruguay	Display at Colonia, Montevideo
988	1989	Iceland	Pleasure boat at Largs Yacht Haven
998	1993	Estonia	Pleasure boat at Dirhami
999	1992	New Zealand	Pleasure boat at Glenbrook
1002	1999	Australia	Serving at Botany Bay
1003	1999	Australia	Work boat at Fremantle
1005	1999	Australia	Work boat at Fremantle
1006	1999	Australia	Spare lifeboat at Mosman, Sydney
1009	1994	Estonia	Display at Lennusadam Museum
1011	1993	Australia	For sale at Sandy Bay, Hobart
1012	1995	Uruguay	Serving at Puerto de Colonia
1019	1994	Uruguay	Serving at Punta Del Este
1021	1992	Tenerife	Pleasure boat at Portishead
1026	1999	Namibia	Serving at Luderitz
1028	1999	New Zealand	Serving at Taranaki
1029	1999	Australia	Work boat at Melbourne
1032	1998	New Zealand	Serving at Lyttelton
1033	1999	Canada	Pleasure boat at Ladner, BC
1035	1999	Australia	Work boat at Mornington, Victoria
1043	1997	New Zealand	Work boat at Lyttleton
1044	1997	Uruguay	Serving at Puerto del Bueco
1045	1999	New Zealand	Pleasure boat at Auckland
1048	1995	New Zealand	Pleasure boat at Lyttelton
1049	1999	Finland	Serving at Porkkala
1050	1998	Iceland	Serving at Sandgerði
1051	1998	Chile	Serving at Valparaiso
1053	2002	Iceland	Serving at Rif
1056	1999	Australia	Serving at Port Stephens
1057	2002	Iceland	Serving at Reykjavík
1058	2002	Australia	Serving at Ulladulla
1059	2001	Finland	Serving at Hanko
1060	1999	New Zealand	Work boat at Freemantle
1061	2002	Iceland	Relief lifeboat at Njarðvik
1065	1995	New Zealand	Charter boat at Auckland
1067	2003	Madeira	Stored at Canical, to become lifeboat

ON	Sold	Country	Current location
1068	1994	Uruguay	Work boat at Montevideo
1073	2003	New Zealand	Tutukaka Marina
1074	2007	China	Serving at Waigaoqiao
1075	2007	China	Serving at Ningbo
1076	2002	Finland	Serving at Kaskinen
1077	2003	Madeira	Serving at Santa Cruz
1078	2003	Iceland	Serving at Hafnarfjörður
1079	1999	New Zealand	Cruiser at Picton
1081	2005	China	Serving at Fuzhou
1082	2005	China	Serving at Donghai, Shanghai
1086	2003	Finland	Serving at Kemi
1087	1990	South Africa	Serving at Mossel Bay
1088	1994	South Africa	Serving at Hermanus
1089	2002	South Africa	Serving at Hout Bay
1090	2002	South Africa	Serving at Simon's Town
1093	2005	China	Serving at Beihai
1094	2007	China	Serving at Rongcheng
1095	2007	China	Serving at Tianjin
1096	2007	China	Serving at Rongcheng
1097	2008	China	Serving at Shenzhen
1098	2005	China	Serving at Zhangjiang
1099	2002	Finland	Serving at Uusikaupunki
1100	2007	Iceland	Serving at Grindavík
1101	2007	South Africa	Serving at Port Elizabeth
1102	2007	South Africa	Destroyed by fire in December 2010
1103	2005	Faroe Islands	Serving at Klaksvik, Faroe Islands
1104	2002	South Africa	Serving at Durban
1105	1993	New Zealand	Serving at Port Nelson
1106	2006	China	Serving at Qinhuangdao
1107	2005	China	Serving at Dalian
1108	2004	Iceland	Serving at Höfn
1109	2010	Uruguay	Serving at Colonia
1110	2008	China	Serving at Guangzhou
1111	2008	China	Serving at Haikou
1113	2004	Iceland	Serving at Neskaupstaður
1114	2011	Uruguay	To be allocated, Uruguay
1118	2004	Iceland	Serving at Raufarhöfn
1123	2005	China	Serving at Wenzhou, Zhejiang
1134	2005	Iceland	Serving at Vopnafjörður
1135	2006	Iceland	Serving at Patreksfjörður
1136	2004	Iceland	Serving at Skagaströnd
1143	2005	China	Serving at Shantou
1144	2005	Iceland	Serving at Siglufjörður
1150	2007	China	Serving at Waigaoqiao
1159	2007	China	Serving at Xiamen (Amoy)
1160	2007	Iceland	Serving at Ísafjörður

ON-1003 in Australia.

ON-1144 in Iceland.

ON-432 at Walton.

ON-856 at Chatham.

ON	Ex Lifeboat Name	Type	Sold	Location
112	Queen Victoria	SR	1902	Arreton Barns, Isle of Wight
353	Alfred Corry	NS	1919	Old boathouse, Southwold
397	Edward Birkbeck	NS	1925	Returned to Winterton for restoration
406	St Paul	NS	1931	Chatham Historic Dockyard
432	James Stevens No.14	NSM	1928	Titchmarch Marina, Walton-on-the-Naze
461	Chapman	LP	1939	Hoylake Maritime Museum
489	Ryder	SR	1930	Afloat at Polperro (summer), Polruan (Winter)
521	James and Mary Walker	W	1933	Under restoration at Wester Kellie for Anstruther display
536	J. C .Madge	L	1936	The Mo, Sheringham
551	Selina	WB	1923	Stored for possible display at Newport, IOW
563	Charterhouse	SRM	1932	Under restoration at Lower Fishguard for display
578	William Cantrell Ashley	L	1949	Stored for display at Cardiff Maritime Museum
583	Charles Henry Ashley	W	1932	Restored as training/display boat at Cemaes, Anglesey
594	William Riley of Birmingham and Leamington	SRR	1931	Afloat, or kept out of water at Cross Butts Farm, Whitby
597	Lizzie Porter	SR	1936	Chatham Historic Dockyard
607	James Leith	NS	1936	Chatham Historic Dockyard
623	Louisa II	SRR	1939	Power of Water Exhibition, Glen Lyn Gorge, Lynmouth
636	James and John Young	L	1939	EISCA collection, Eyemouth Maritime Centre, Eyemouth
669	Robert and Ellen Robson	SRR	1957	Old lifeboat house, Whitby
670	John & Mary Meiklam of Gladswood	NSM	1950	Old lifeboat house, Gorleston
676	Langham	SRM	1952	Under restoration at Arreton Barns, Isle of Wight
687	B. A .S .P.	WM	1955	Chatham Historic Dockyard
705	Capitan Christiansen	R	1955	Lifeboat in Valparaiso, Chile, on display out of water
722	J. and W.	WS	1957	Under restoration at SWP Engineering, Berwick
759	Thomas McCunn	W	1972	Old lifeboat house, Longhope
777	H. F. Bailey	W	1973	Cromer Lifeboat Museum
786	Foresters Centenary	LS	1961	The Mo, Sheringham
797	Howard D.	LS	1964	St Helier Marina, Jersey
809	Helen Blake	HS	1959	Chatham Historic Dockyard
811	Thomas Kirk Wright	Surf	1963	Old lifeboat house, Poole
819	Julia Park Barry of Glasgow	WM	1979	To go on display at Peterhead after restoration
822	Jesse Lumb	WM	1981	Imperial War Mus, Duxford

ON	Ex Lifeboat Name	Type	Sold	Location
828	Princess Royal	WM	1976	Hartlepool Marina
849	William Gammon	WM	1983	Stored at Landore for display at Swansea Maritime Museum
856	Susan Ashley	WM	1981	Chatham Historic Dockyard
862	Thomas Corbett	LM	1982	Under restoration at Hoylake Maritime Museum
870	William and Laura	LM	1980	Ulster Folk and Transport Museum, Cultra, Co Down
873	George Elmy	LM	1972	Display at Seaham Harbour
884	St Cybi (C. S. No.9)	B	1986	Chatham Historic Dockyard
885	Sir Samuel Kelly	WM	1976	Car park, Donaghadee
888	North Foreland	WM	1982	Chatham Historic Dockyard
900	Herbert Leigh	WM	1988	New Dock Museum, Barrow
906	Shirley Jean Adye	LM	1968	Old Caister lifeboat house
915	Friendly Forester	LM	1983	Blackgang Chine Adventure Park, Isle of Wight
922	Watkin Williams	WM	1983	Stored at Cardiff Maritime Museum, for display
927	Grace Darling	LM	1985	Chatham Historic Dockyard
938	Rowland Watts	B	1985	Stored at Murphy Marine, Valentia, for display
942	J. G. Graves of Sheffield	Oak	1994	Chatham Historic Dockyard
960	Manchester Unity of Oddfellows	Oak	1991	The Mo, Sheringham
962	T. G. B.	WM	1986	Scottish Maritime Museum, Irvine from 7.1986
972	Will and Fanny Kirby	Oak	1994	Chatham Historic Dockyard
975	Sir James Knott	Oak	1990	Kirkleatham Old Hall Museum, Redcar
979	Amelia	Oak	1992	Shipwreck and Heritage Museum, Charlestown
984	Mary Joicey	Oak	1989	Newbiggin Maritime Centre
985	Valentine Wyndham-Quin	Oak	1988	Old lifeboat house, The Green, Harwich
989	James and Catherine Macfarlane	Oak	1988	Lands End
990	Ruby and Arthur Reed	Oak	1989	Hythe Marina, Southampton Water
996	Birds Eye	Oak	1991	Sea Watch Centre, Moelfre
1037	Edward Bridges (Civil Service & P.O. No.37)	Ar	1994	Chatham Historic Dockyard
1247	Katie Hannan	SE	2008	Stored at Babcock, Plymouth for possible future display
–	Bedford	NC	1939	EISCA collection, Eyemouth Maritime Centre, Eyemouth
–	Tyne	NC	1887	Between South and North Marine Parks, South Shields
–	Zetland	NC	1880	Zetland Museum, Redcar
–	44-001	WA	1996	Chatham Historic Dockyard

Launch methods

Getting a lifeboat to sea is obviously crucial to undertaking a rescue. Numerous methods have been employed to get lifeboats afloat, all of which are determined by local conditions and the station's location. In the early days boats were kept on land wherever practical and the launch method was determined by the type of beach, the presence of a harbour or in some cases local preference. The following launch methods have been employed around the country:

Carriage The lifeboat is mounted on a carriage, which would almost always be kept in a boathouse. The carriage was pulled to the water by manpower, horses or, since the 1920s, motorised tractors. Once the carriage was far enough in the water so the lifeboat could float, the boat would be released and launched by a rope and pulley system.

Skids A series of skids would be placed at intervals up the beach so that the lifeboat could be hauled out of the water. It would then be hauled up onto the carriage which would be tipped to form a temporary slipway. At some stations the lifeboat was kept on the beach and launched over skids, which were laid down to the sea, usually by hand, a method which required a large number of shorehelpers.

Cradle At a few locations the boat would be kept on the beach in a cradle which would be tipped to form a launch way from which the boat was hauled across the beach to the surf using skids.

Trolley A trolley on rails down a slipway was used for all-weather lifeboats at some stations; today trolleys are used to launch ILBs.

Slipway The lifeboat is kept in a boathouse at the head of a slipway, which runs down to the sea. Most slipways have rollers in a central channel, on which the keel of the lifeboat rests as it is launched. Other parts of the slipway support the lifeboat's bilge keels ensuring the boat remains upright during launching.

Hoist At two stations, Buckie and Sunderland, a platform or cradle inside a boathouse supported the lifeboat. In order to launch the lifeboat, the platform would be lowered by hoists so that the boat was in a position to either float or slip into the water, depending on the state of the tide. The building took up less room than a conventional boathouse and slipway.

Davit Many inshore lifeboats are on a trolley which is wheeled out of a boathouse across a quayside to a davit. The crew sit in the boat as it is lowered into the water.

Crane At one station, Workington, the all-weather lifeboat is held on a cradle, which is on rails so that the boat can be moved out of the boathouse; it is then lifted by a large crane, or davit, and lowered over the dock wall. As with some ILBs, the crew board the boat before it is floated out of the lifting strops.

Moored Mooring a lifeboat afloat is the easiest and fastest method of launching, but only with the advent of reliable anti-fouling paints has it become widespread. Lifeboats were moored out and a boarding boat used to reach the boat. The majority of lifeboats kept afloat are now moored alongside a quay or pontoon so the crew can access the boat more quickly and safely.

Pen Where a pier or jetty is available, a pen is used so that the lifeboat can be moored safely. The crew can board the boat via a walkway and the lifeboat is also sheltered.

Floating boathouse The ILB is kept inside the boathouse on a cradle, which is raised to keep the boat clear of the water. Walkways down each side provide access to the boat.

Hydrohoist/air berth In a few locations the ILB is driven onto a floating platform, which then keeps the boat clear of the water. The ILB is given a degree of protection by being sheeted over.

Lifeboat house and slipway

The lifeboat house and slipway was developed during the second half of the 19th century as a method of getting a larger lifeboat to sea. Since the 1990s the RNLI has been rebuilding slipway stations to accommodate 16m Tamar lifeboats, such as at Barrow (pictured).

Cradle on beach

Keeping lifeboats on cradles at the head of a beach was quite common along the east coast, at stations such as Aldeburgh (pictured), Dungeness and Walmer, where shingle beaches precluded the use of carriages until more powerful launching tractors had been developed.

Floating boathouses

Floating boathouses are relatively recent developments, and have been used at Poole, Burnham-on-Crouch (where two are used, as pictured), Brighton and Fenit for accommodating inshore lifeboats. The buildings are mostly berthed in marinas and reached from an adjacent pontoon.

D class inflatable and trolley

Launching D class inflatable inshore lifeboats from a trolley, using a tractor (such as at Port Talbot, pictured), Land Rover or other launch vehicle, is one of the fastest methods of launching and enables the ILB, the RNLI's most numerous lifeboat type, to quickly get to a rescue.

Lifeboat construction background

Commercial boatbuilding firms have been widely employed by the RNLI to build lifeboats sine the 19th century. In many cases both choice of builder and design were influenced by local preference, such as in East Anglia where Norfolk & Suffolk type lifeboats were predominantly built by local builders. Once the RNLI had completed a review of lifeboat standards in the late 19th century, one firm, Thames Iron Works, became the predominant builder and between 1896 and 1912 built 260 lifeboats.

After TIW got into financial difficulties in 1912 and of ten boats in build one had to be completed by the RNLI and the other nine by S. E. Saunders, the RNLI had to look elsewhere for lifeboat construction. A number of builders based on the Isle of Wight were then employed, with Saunders (later Saunders-Roe) dominating lifeboat construction until the 1930s. Two other Cowes-based firms, which became synonymous with lifeboat building, then took on the work, Groves & Guttridge and J. S. White. Although they were the favoured builders, a number of lifeboats were built by other firms. Another well-known lifeboat builder, William Osborne of Littlehampton, built lifeboats for 48 years until 1999.

In the late 1970s the RNLI looked at using other materials with which to build lifeboat hulls. Glass reinforced plastic (GRP) was deemed suitable and as a result Halmatic of Havant 'moulded' the GRP hulls for Arun lifeboats, with other firms completing the boats' fit-out. The steel-hulled Waveneys and Tynes were usually completed by a single builder, such as Brooke Marine, Berthon and Fairey Allday Marine, although ten Tyne hulls were manufactured by a steel fabricator as distinct from a boat builder.

The start of the Mersey programme saw two further innovations by the RNLI. The first ten were built with aluminium hulls and the remaining hulls of fibre reinforced composite (FRC), initially built by FBM and then by FRC specialist Green Marine, who have moulded all subsequent lifeboat hulls from Severns to Shannons. The fitting out work was undertaken by FBM, Souter Shipyard and William Osborne.

The Severn and Trent class boats, as well as the later Aruns, were all built this way using a variety of builders. The Tamar class lifeboats were all fitted out by DML in Plymouth. The Shannon class lifeboats will be built by Berthon Boat Company at Lymington, who also fitted out the first production boat.

In 2011 the RNLI acquired the firm of Green Marine, the major supplier of FRC moulded hulls, and, under the name SAR Composites, used the company's workforce to produce lifeboat hulls. A further change came in 2012 when the RNLI announced that its Poole site will be rebuilt in 2013-14 to create a state-of-the-art lifeboat construction facility where all future lifeboat building will be undertaken.

ON-1220 self-righting trial, Souter, Cowes, 30.10.1997.

ON-1298 self-righting trial, Plymouth, 15.6.2010.

Building yards and their locations

Directory	Builder	Location
Alexander Robertson	Alexander Robertson and Sons	Sandbanks, Argyll
Aluminium Shipbuilders	Aluminium Shipbuilders	Porchester
Arancia	Arancia Industries Ltd	Auckland, New Zealand
Babcock	Babcock Marine	Plymouth
Berthon	Berthon Boat Co.	Lymington
Bideford Shipyard	Bideford Shipyard	Bideford
Brooke Marine	Brooke Marine	Lowestoft
Camper and Nicholson	Camper and Nicholson	Gosport
Chantiers Augustin Normand	Chantiers Augustin Normand	Le Havre, France
DML	Devonport Marine Limited	Plymouth
Dell Quay	Dell Quay Marine	Chichester
Edward Oliver	Edward Oliver	South Shields
Fairey Allday Marine	Fairey Allday Marine	West Cowes
Fairey Marine	Fairey Marine	West Cowes
FBM	Fairey Brooke Marine	West Cowes
Forrestt	Forrestt and Son	Limehouse, London
Green Marine	Green Marine	Lymington
Griffon Hoverwork Ltd	Griffon Hoverwork Ltd	Woolston, Southampton
Groves & Guttridge	Groves and Guttridge	East Cowes
Habbeké Shipyard	Habbeké Shipyard	Volendam
Halmatic	Halmatic Ltd	Havant
Hardy Marine	Hardy Marine Ltd	North Walsham, Norfolk
Harrison	Harrison	Amble
Henri Oltmanns Bootwerft	Henri Oltmanns Bootwerft	Bremerhaven
Henry Greathead	Henry Greathead	South Shields
Herd & Mackenzie	Herd and Mackenzie Ltd	Buckie
ILC	RNLI Inshore Lifeboat Centre	East Cowes
J. I. Thornycroft	John I. Thornycroft & Company Ltd	Woolston, Southampton
J. S. White	J. S. White	Cowes
James and Caddy	James and Caddy	Weymouth
James Beeching	James Beeching Brothers	Great Yarmouth
Keith Nelson	Keith Nelson	Bembridge
Lambert	Lambert	South Shields
Lochin	Lochin Marine Ltd	Newhaven
M. S. T.	Marine Specialised Technology Ltd	Liverpool
Marshall	Marshall Branson Marine Ltd	Amble
Morgan Giles	Morgan Giles	Teignmouth
Morris & Lorimer	Morris and Lorimer	Sandbanks, Argyll
R. and H. Green	R. and H. Green	Blackwall, London
RFD	R. F. D. Company Ltd	Godalming, Surrey
Ramage and Ferguson	Ramage and Ferguson and Co Ltd	Leith
Robson	Robsons	South Shields
Rowhedge Iron Works	Rowhedge Iron Works	Rowhedge
Rutherford	A. Rutherford and Co	Birkenhead
SAR Composites	SAR Composites	Lymington
Saunders	S. E. Saunders	East Cowes
Saunders-Roe	Saunders-Roe Ltd	East Cowes
Souter	W. A. Souter and Son	West Cowes
Souter Marine	Souter Marine Ltd	West Cowes
Souter Shipyard	Souter Shipyard Ltd	West Cowes
Summers and Payne	Summers and Payne	Southampton
Sussex Yacht Co	Sussex Yacht Company	Shoreham
Thames Iron Works	Thames Iron Works	Blackwall, London
Tiger Marine	Tiger Marine	Anglesey
Vosper Thornycroft	Vosper Thornycroft	Woolston, Southampton
William Osborne	William Osborne Ltd	Littlehampton
Wm Ellis	William Ellis	Lowestoft
Woolfe	Woolfe	Shadwell, London
Wright	Wright Steel Fabricators	Derby
Yarrow	Yarrow and Co	Scotstoun, Glasgow

12m Mersey class lifeboats 1171 to 1175 under construction at FBM Ltd boatyard, Cowes, 15 January 1991.

ENGLAND

Berwick-upon-Tweed	Op (at Spittal) RNIPLS 1835, Cl 1852; Reop RNLI 1855, moved (to town) 1901, moved (to Spittal) 1927, M 1930, Temp Cl 1939-40, Cl 1976; Reop RNLI M 1993 (named Berwick-on-Tweed to 1956); Op RNLI ILB 1976-93 and 1995
Holy Island	Op Crewe Trust 1802, Cl 1827; Reop 1829, Cl 1852; Reop RNLI 1865, M 1925, Cl 1968; No.2 Op Newcastle Trinity House Op 1827, Cl 1838; Reop RNLI 1868, Cl 1934
Bamburgh	Op Crewe Trust (at Bamburgh Castle) 1786, Cl p.1824; Reop RNLI 1882, Cl 1897
Seahouses	Op Crewe Trust 1827, To RNLI 1859, M 1936, ILB 1964 (named North Sunderland until 1999)
Craster	Op RNLI 1969-
Boulmer	Op RNIPLS 1825, To RNLI 1853, M 1931, Cl 1968; Op RNLI ILB 1968, Cl 1968
Alnmouth	Op Duke of Northumberland 1852, To RNLI 1854, Cl 1935
Amble	Op RNIPLS 1842, Cl 1856; Reop RNLI M 1939, ILB 1966
Hauxley	Op Duke of Northumberland 1852, To RNLI 1853, Cl 1939
Cresswell	Op RNLI 1875, Cl 1944
Newbiggin	Op Duke of Northumberland 1852; To RNLI 1853, M 1938-81, RNLI ILB 1981
Blyth	Op Ridley Estate Trust 1808, Cl 1810; Reop RNIPLS 1826, Cl 1841, Reop Blyth LBA 1845, To RNLI 1866, M 1921-2004, ILB 1965, No.2 Op (Cambois) Blyth LBA 1854, To RNLI 1866, Cl 1927
Cullercoats	Op Duke of Northumberland 1852, To RNLI 1853, M 1937-69, Temp Cl 1939-40, RNLI ILB 1965
Tynemouth	Op RNIPLS 1832, Cl 1842; Reop (Priors Haven) RNLI 1862, moved (to North Shields) M 1905, ILB 1965; No.2 (Black Middens) Op RNLI 1865, Cl 1905
North Shields	Op Tyne Lifeboat Inst 1798, Cl 1941
South Shields	Op Tyne Lifeboat Inst (Coble Landing) 1790, Temp Cl 1830-33; Cl 1937; 2nd boat Op c 1845, Cl 1937; Op (at South Beach) c.1862, M c.1930, Cl 1947; Op (Heard Groyne) 1937, Cl 1939
Whitburn	Op Sunderland Comm 1818, To Local Comm 1830, To RNLI 1854, Cl 1918
Sunderland (Roker)	Op Sunderland Hum Soc 1800, Cl 1818, Reop 1831, Cl 1851; Reop 1859, To RNLI 1871, moved (North Dock) 1900, Cl 1916 (named No.1 until 1889)
Sunderland (No.2)	Op (North Side) Sunderland Hum Soc 1866, To RNLI 1871, Cl 1887
Sunderland (South Pier)	Op Sunderland Hum Soc 1858, To RNLI 1871, Cl 1900 (named No.3 until 1887, No.2 until 1889)
Sunderland (South Outlet)	Op (South Outlet) 1872, Cl 1912 (named No.3 until 1887, No.2 until 1899)
Sunderland (South Side)	Op Shipowners ass. No.1 1808, Cl 1843; Op 1819,Cl >1851 (named No.2 until 1850); No.2 Op 1850, Cl 1864
Sunderland	Op Fishermens' Lifeboat 1845, Cl 1850; Op Seamens' Ass. 1856, Cl 1864; No.2 Op 1850, Cl 1871; Reop RNLI 1911, Cl 1914; Reop M 1916-2004, ILB 1966, 2nd ILB 2004
Hendon Beach	(Manned from South Outlet) Op RNLI 1902, Cl 1912
Seaham Harbour	Op Marquis of Londonderry 1855, Cl p.1870;2nd boat Seamens' Friendly Ass. Op 1856, Cl p.1870; Reop RNLI 1870, Cl 1911; No.2 Op RNLI M 1909, Cl 1979 (named No.1 from 1911)
Crimdon Dene	Op RNLI ILB 1966, Cl 1993
Hartlepool No.1	Op (at North Shore) Tees Bay LBS 1841, To Hartlepool LB Ass. 1847, To RNLI 1875, Cl 1915
Hartlepool No.2	Op (Watergate) Local Comm 1803, To (Old Pier) Tees Bay LBS 1836, To Hartlepool LB Ass 1847, To RNLI 1875, Cl 1923
Hartlepool	Op (Harbour) Hartlepool LB Ass 1858, To RNLI 1875, M 1923, Cl 1968; Reop RNLI 1977- (named Hartlepool No.3 until 1923) (operated frm Middleton 1903-1968 and 2000); RNLI ILB 1968
Hartlepool	Op (at Old Harbour) Seamens' LBS 1854, Cl 1875
West Hartlepool No.1	Op (South Beach) West Hartlepool Harbour and Dock Co 1847, To RNLI 1869, Cl 1903 (No.2 until 1874)
West Hartlepool No.2	Op (Dock) West Hartlepool Harbour and Dock Co 1854, To RNLI 1869, Cl 1894 (No.1 until 1874)
Seaton Carew	Op Local Comm 1804, To Tees Bay LBS 1823, To RNLI 1857, Cl 1922
Seaton Snook	Op RNLI M 1907, Cl 1909
Middlesbrough	Op Tees Bay LBS 1854, To RNLI 1858, Cl 1895
Teesmouth	Op RNILPS 1829, Cl c.1842, Reop Tees Bay LBS 1843, Cl c.1854; Reop RNLI M 1911, Cl 2006
Redcar	Op Local Comm 1802, To Tees Bay LBS 1825, To RNLI 1858, M 1931-86; ILB 1963, 2nd ILB 1986; Op Fishermen's Comm 1864, Cl 1884; Op Free Gardeners 1877, Cl 1898
Saltburn	(Manned from Redcar) Op Tees Bay LBS 1849, To RNLI 1858, Temp Cl 1916-1917 Cl 1922
Staithes	Op RNLI 1875, Cl 1922; Reop RNLI 1928, Cl 1938; Reop RNLI ILB 1978 (named Staithes and Runswick)
Runswick	Op RNLI 1866, M 1933, Cl 1978
Upgang	(Manned from Whitby) Op RNLI 1865, Cl 1919
Whitby No.1	Op (West Side) Whitby LBA 1802, Cl 1817; Reop 1822, To RNLI 1861, Cl 1934
Whitby No.2	Op (East Side) Whitby LBA 1822, To RNLI 1861, Cl 1957
Whitby	Op Fishermens' Lifeboat 1861, Cl 1872
Whitby	Op (at Fish Pier, East Side) RNLI M 1919, ILB 1966
Robin Hood's Bay	Op CG 1830, Cl 1843; Op Local Comm 1839, Cl c.1855; Reop RNLI 1881, Cl 1931
Scarborough	Op Local Comm 1801, To RNLI 1861, M 1923, ILB 1965
Filey	Op Local Comm 1804, To RNLI 1852, M 1940, ILB 1966
Flamborough No.1	Op (North Landing) RNLI 1871, M 1934, Cl 1993
Flamborough No.2	Op (South Landing) RNLI 1871, Cl 1938; Reop RNLI 1993
Bridlington	Op Local Comm 1805, To RNLI 1853, M 1931 ILB 1966; Op Fishermens' Lifeboat 1866, Cl 1886; Op Sailors and Working Mens' Lifeboat 1871, Cl 1898
Barmston	(Manned from Bridlington) Op RNLI 1884, Cl 1898
Hornsea	(Manned from Bridlington) Op Local Comm 1851, To SFMRBS 1852, To RNLI 1854, Cl 1924
Withernsea	Op RNLI 1862, Cl 1913; Reop RNLI ILB 1974
Easington	Op RNLI 1913, Cl 1933
Humber	Op Trinity House of Hull 1810, To Humber Cons Board 1908, To RNLI 1911, Temp Cl 1917-1918, M 1919; No.2 Op 1930-32 and 1968-69 (named Spurn to 1924), ILB 1964-64
Grimsby	Op RNLI 1882, Temp Cl 1901-03; Cl 1927, No.2 Steam LB Op 1898, Cl 1903
Cleethorpes	Op RNLI 1868, Cl 1882, Reop RNLI ILB 1987
Humber Mouth	Op RNLI ILB (at Humberston) 1965, Cl 1980
Donna Nook	Op Lincs Coast Shipwreck Ass 1829, To RNLI 1864, Cl 1931; 2nd boat op Lincs Coast SW Ass 1851, Cl 1864
Saltfleet	Op Lincs Coast Shipwreck Ass 1827, Cl 1829
Theddlethorpe	Op Lincs Coast Shipwreck Ass 1828, Cl 1831; Reop Lincs Coast Shipwreck Ass 1832, To RNLI 1864, Cl 1882
Mablethorpe	Op RNLI 1883, Temp Cl 1917, Cl 1920; Reop RNLI ILB (on Promenade) 1965, 2nd ILB 2001
Sutton	Op Lincs Coast Shipwreck Ass 1843, To RNLI 1864, Cl 1913
Huttoft	Op Lincs Coast Shipwreck Ass 1835, Cl 1843
Chapel	Op RNLI 1870, Cl 1898
Skegness	Op Lincs Coast Shipwreck Ass 1830, To RNLI 1864, M 1932, ILB 1964
Gibralter Point	Op RNIPLS 1825, To Lincs Coast Shipwreck Ass 1827, Cl 1830
Hunstanton	Op Norfolk Shipwreck Ass 1824, Cl 1843; Reop RNLI 1867, Cl 1931; Reop RNLI ILB 1979, Hovercraft 2003
Brancaster	Op Norfolk Shipwreck Ass 1823, Cl 1843; Reop RNLI 1874, Cl 1935
Wells	Op Norfolk Shipwreck Ass 1830, Cl 1851; Reop RNLI 1869, M 1936, ILB 1963
Blakeney	Op Norfolk Shipwreck Ass 1824, Cl 1843; Reop RNLI 1862, Cl 1935
Sheringham	Op Upcher Family 1838, Cl 1935; Op RNLI 1867, moved (to Old Hythe) 1902-36, M 1936-92; ILB 1986-86 and 1992
Cromer	Op Local Comm 1805, To Norfolk Shipwreck Ass. 1823, To RNLI 1857, M 1923, ILB (on East Beach) 1967; No.2 (on East Beach) Op RNLI 1923, M 1934, Cl 1967
Mundesley	Op Cromer Comm 1811, To RNLI 1857, Cl 1895
Bacton	Op Local Comm 1822; To Norfolk Shipwreck Ass.1823, To RNLI 1857, Cl 1882
Happisburgh	Op RNLI 1866, Cl 1926; Reop RNLI ILB 1965, 2nd ILB 2009
Palling	Op Norfolk Shipwreck Ass 1852, To RNLI 1857, Cl 1930; No.2 Op RNLI 1870 Cl 1929
Winterton	Op Norfolk Shipwreck Ass 1823, To RNLI 1857, Cl 1925; Op B Hume for Beachmen 1868, Cl 1878: No.2 Op RNLI 1879, Cl 1925
Scratby	Op (California) Beachmen 1854, Cl c.1875
Caister	Op Norfolk Shipwreck Ass 1845, To RNLI 1857, Cl 1929; No.2 Op RNLI 1867, M 1941, Cl 1969
Great Yarmouth	Op Norfolk Shipwreck Ass 1825, To RNLI 1857 Cl 1883; No.2 Op Norfolk Shipwreck Ass. 1833, To RNLI (No.2) 1857, Cl 1919
Great Yarmouth and Gorleston	Op Local Comm 1802, Cl 1807; Op Ranger Co.1855, Cl 1867; Op Storm Co 1863, To Gorleston VLBA 1881, Cl 1939; Op RNLI 1866, M 1924 (named Gorleston until 1926), ILB 1963, 2nd ILB 1974-77; Op No.2 RNLI 1883, Cl 1924; Op No.3 RNLI 1892, Cl 1904; Op No.4 RNLI Steam 1897-98 and 1903-08
Corton	Op RNLI 1869, Cl 1879
Lowestoft	Op Lowestoft LBS 1801, Cl 1802; Reop Suffolk Hum Soc 1807, To RNLI 1855, M 1921; Op No.2 RNLI 1870, Cl 1912; Op Lowestoft Vol LBS 1883, Cl 1893

Pakefield	Op Suffolk Hum Soc 1840, To RNLI 1855, Cl 1886, Reop 1890, Cl 1922; No.2 Op RNLI 1871, Cl 1895; Op Beachmen 1861, Cl 1870
Kessingland	Op Beachmen 1855, Cl 1869; Op RNLI 1867, Cl 1936; No.2 (Benacre) Op RNLI 1870, Cl 1918; No.3 Op 1884, Cl 1896
Southwold	Op Southwold LBS 1841, To RNLI 1854, M 1925, Cl 1940; No.2 Op RNLI 1866, Cl 1920; Reop RNLI ILB 1963
Dunwich	Op RNLI 1873, Cl 1903
Sizewell	Op Suffolk Hum Soc 1826, Cl 1851
Thorpeness	Op Suffolk Hum Soc 1853, To RNLI 1855, Cl 1900; No.2 Op RNLI 1860, Cl 1863
Aldeburgh	Op Suffolk Hum Soc 1851, To RNLI 1855, Temp Cl 1928-29, M 1930, ILB 1977; No.2 Op RNLI 1905, Temp Cl 1929-30, M 1940, Cl 1959
Orford	Op RNIPLS 1826, Cl 1835
Hollesley Bay/ Bawdsey	Op Local Comm 1801, To Suffolk Hum. Soc. 1805, Cl 1825
Woodbridge Haven	Op RNIPLS 1825, Cl 1853
Landguard Fort	Op Ipswich LB Ass 1821, Cl 1826; Reop Admiralty 1845, Cl c.1864
Harwich	Op Essex LB Ass.1821, Cl p.1843; Reop RNLI 1876, Temp Cl 1902-1904, Cl 1912; Op RNLI Steam 1890, Temp Cl 1892-1894 & 1897-98, Cl 1917; Reop RNLI ILB 1965, M 1967
Walton and Frinton	Op RNLI 1884, M 1906- (named Walton-on-the-Naze until 1931); Op Beachmen 1894, Cl c.1911
Frinton-on-Sea	Op Cook & Co. 1901, To Frinton Vol LB Soc 1904, Cl 1917
Clacton-on-Sea	Op RNLI 1878, M 1912, Cl 1984, ILB 1966, 2nd ILB 1984
West Mersea	Op RNLI ILB 1963
Burnham-on-Crouch	Op RNLI ILB 1966, 2nd ILB 1996
Southend-on Sea	Op RNLI 1879, Cl 1891; 2nd boat Op 1885, M 1928-76; ILB (land) 1965, 2nd ILB (Pier) 1969, 3rd ILB (Pier) 1987, Hovercraft 2004
Gravesend	Op RNLI ILB (2 boats) 2002-09, (1 boat) 2009
Tower	Op RNLI ILB (up to 3 boats) 2002
Chiswick	Op RNLI ILB (2 boats) 2002
Teddington	Op RNLI ILB 2002, 2nd ILB 2002
Sheerness	Op RNLI M 1969, ILB 1972
Whitstable	Op RNLI ILB 1963
Margate	Op Town Council 1857, To RNLI 1860, M 1925, ILB 1966; No.2 Op RNLI 1898, Cl 1927; Boatmens' LB Op 1857, Cl 1928, Reop 1939-40 as Emergency LB
Kingsgate	Op RNLI 1862, Cl 1897
Broadstairs	Op Boatmen 1850, Cl 1868; 2nd boat Op Boatmen 1853, Cl 1868; To RNLI 1868, Cl 1912
Ramsgate	Op Ramsgate Harbour Trust 1802; Cl 1824; Reop 1851, To RNLI/Board of Trade 1863, To RNLI 1922, M 1925, ILB 1969
North Deal	Op RNLI 1865, Cl 1932; 2nd boat War Emergency Op 1915, Cl 1921
Walmer	Op RNLI 1856, Cl 1912; Reop RNLI 1927, M 1933-90, ILB 1964, 2nd ILB 1990
Kingsdowne	Op RNLI 1866, Cl 1927
Dover	Op (at Townsend) Dover Hum Soc 1837, To RNLI 1855, Moved (to Clock tower) 1865, Cl 1914; Reop RNLI Steam (at Camber) 1919, Cl 1922; Reop RNLI M (at Camber) 1930, Cl 1941; Reop RNLI M (at Eastern Docks) 1947, moved (to Western Docks) 1984
Channel Lightvessel No.6	Op RNLI 1971, Cl 1972 (manned by full-time Trinity House crew)
Folkestone	Op RNLI 1893, Cl 1930
Hythe	Op (at Sandgate) RNLI 1876 (named Hythe, Sandgate & Folkestone to 1894), moved (to Hythe) 1893 (named Hythe), M 1929, Cl 1940
Dymchurch	Op RNIPLS 1826, Cl 1838 (named Dungeness No.27 Tower until 1836)
New Romney	Op RNLI 1871, Cl 1928 (named Dungeness until 1874)
Littlestone-on-Sea	Op RNLI ILB 1966
Dungeness	Op (No.1 Battery) RNLI 1854, Cl 1871; Op (Lydd) RNLI 1874, M 1933; No.2 Op RNLI 1892, Cl 1939; (named Lydd, Dungeness 1874-1892)
Rye	Op (at No.31 Tower) Local Comm 1803, Cl c.1825: Reop RNIPLS 1832, moved (to Rye Camber) 1856, Cl 1901
Rye Harbour	Op RNLI 1856, Cl 1928 (named Winchelsea until 1910); Reop RNLI ILB 1966
Hastings	Op Local Subs 1835, Cl 1851; Reop RNLI 1858, M 1931, ILB 1964
Eastbourne	Op John Fuller 1822, To Local Comm 1833,To RNLI 1853, M 1921, moved (to Sovereign Marina 1993), No.2 Op 1903 Cl 1924, Reop 1929, Cl 1930; ILB 1964
Newhaven	Op Local Comm 1803, Cl 1809, No.2 Op Local Comm 1807, CL c.1831; Op RNIPLS 1824, Cl 1829; Reop SFMRBS 1852, To RNLI 1854, M 1907

Brighton	Op (West Pier) Local Comm 1809, Cl p.1816; Reop RNLI 1825, Cl 1837;Reop RNLI 1858, Cl 1931; Op Brighton Hum Soc 1837, Cl p.1854; Op John Wright 1854, Cl p.1854; Op Town Lifeboat 1840, Cl 1932, Reop RNLI (on Promenade) ILB 1965, moved (to Brighton Marina) 1978
Shoreham Harbour	Op Harbour Comm 1845, To RNLI 1865, Cl 1924; Reop RNLI M 1929, ILB 1967 (named Shoreham until 1924)
Worthing	Op Local Comm 1852, To RNLI 1865, Cl 1930; Reop RNLI ILB 1964, Cl 1967
Littlehampton	Op Pier Commissioners 1859-?; Reop RNLI 1884, Cl 1921; Reop RNLI ILB 1967, 2nd ILB 2002
Selsey	Op RNLI 1861, M 1922, ILB 1968; No.2 Op 1894-96
Chichester Harbour	Op (West Wittering) RNLI 1867, Cl 1884
Hayling Island	Op RNLI 1865, Temp Cl 1917-19, Cl 1924; Reop Hayling Island Rescue ILB 1973, joint with RNLI 1975, To RNLI 1978, 2nd ILB 1995
Portsmouth	Op RNLI ILB 1965, 2nd ILB 1967, 3rd ILB 1968-69 (named Eastney to 1978, Portsmouth (Langstone Harbour) to 1995)
Southsea	Op RNLI 1886, Cl 1918
Ryde	Op Local Comm 1869, To RNLI 1894, Cl 1923
Bembridge	Op RNLI 1867, M 1922, ILB 1964
Shanklin	Op Local Comm 1884, Cl 1916
Atherfield	Op Coastguard 1843, Cl ?; Reop RNLI 1890, Cl 1915
Brightstone Grange	Op RNLI 1860, Cl 1915
Brooke	Op Coastguard c.1843, Cl ?; Reop RNLI 1860, Cl 1937
Totland Bay	Op Local Comm 1870, Cl 1884; Reop RNLI 1885, Steam 1915-19, Cl 1924
Yarmouth	Op Local Comm 1868, Cl 1870; Reop RNLI M 1924, ILB 1964-78
Cowes	Op RNLI ILB 2008
Calshot	Op RNLI M 1970-2012, ILB 2001, 2nd ILB 2012
Lymington	Op RNLI ILB 1965
Hurst Castle	Op Coastguard 1824, Cl 1825
Christchurch	Op Local Comm 1804, Cl?
Mudeford	Op RNLI ILB 1963
Bournemouth	Op RNLI ILB 1965, Cl 1972
Poole	Op (at Sandbanks) RNLI 1865, moved (to Quay) 1882, M 1939, moved (to Lilliput Marina) 1974, moved (to Poole Bridge) 1988 (named Poole and Bournemouth 1917-53), ILB 1964, 2nd ILB 1969-70, 1977- & 1994-95
Studland	Op RNIPLS 1826, Cl 1848
Swanage	Op RNLI 1875, M 1928, ILB 1993
Chapman's Pool	Op RNLI 1866, Cl 1880
Kimmeridge	Op RNLI 1868, Cl 1896
Weymouth	Op RNLI 1869, M 1924, ILB 1995
Portland	Op RNIPLS 1826, Cl 1851
Lyme Regis	Op RNIPLS 1825, Cl p.1827; Reop RNLI 1853, Cl 1932; Reop RNLI ILB 1967

CHANNEL ISLANDS

Alderney	Op (St Anne) RNLI 1869, Cl 1884; Reop (at Braye Harbour) RNLI M 1984, ILB 1997-2009
St Helier	Op States 1830, Cl p.1880; Reop RNLI 1884, M 1937, ILB 2005
St Catherine	Op RNLI ILB 1969
St Peter Port	Op States 1802, Cl 1857; Reop RNLI 1881, M 1929
St Sampson	Op Carrington and Peek 1857, To RNLI 1861, Cl 1878
La Lande	Op RNLI 1878, Cl 1881

ENGLAND

Sidmouth	Op RNLI 1869, Cl 1912
Exmouth	Op L Com 1803, Cl 1815; Reop RNLI 1858, M 1933, moved (to harbour) 1960, ILB 1966, moved (to Maer Rocks) 2009
Teignmouth	Op SFMRBS 1851, To RNLI 1854, Cl 1940, Reop ILB 1990
Torquay	Op RNLI 1876, Cl 1923; Op (Torquay Harb) RNLI 1917, Cl 1928
Torbay	Op RNLI 1866, M 1922 (named Brixham to 1917, Brixham and Paignton to 1924), ILB 1964
Dartmouth	Op RNLI 1878, Cl 1896; Reop RNLI ILB 2007 (named Dart)
Salcombe	Op (South Beach) RNLI 1869, Temp Cl 1916-17, Cl 1925; Reop RNLI M 1931, ILB 2003
Hope Cove	Op RNLI 1878, Cl 1930
Yealm River	Op (Newton Ferrers) 1878, Cl 1927
Plymouth	Op Local Comm 1803, Cl c.1820; Op (at Cawsand) RNIPLS 1825, Cl 1840; Reop (at Millbay) RNLI 1862, M 1926, ILB 1967-83 and 2004
Looe	Op RNLI 1866, Cl 1930, Reop RNLI ILB 1992, 2nd ILB 2003
Fowey	Op RNLI 1922, M 1928, ILB 1996
Polkerris	Op RNLI 1859, Cl 1922 (named Fowey 1859-93, Polkerris & Fowey 1896-1905)
Mevagissey	Op (at Porth Mellon) RNLI 1869, moved (to Mevagissey Harbour) 1888, Cl 1930
Portloe	Op RNLI 1870, Cl 1887

Falmouth	Op RNLI 1867, M 1931, ILB 1967-67 and 1980-
Porthoustock	Op RNLI 1869, Cl 1942
Coverack	Op RNLI 1901, M 1934-72, ILB 1972, Cl 1978
Cadgwith	Op RNLI 1867, M 1941, Cl 1963
The Lizard	Op (at Polpeor) RNLI 1859, M 1918, moved (to Kilcobben Cove) 1961; No.2 (at Church Cove) Op 1885, Cl 1899 (named Lizard-Cadgwith 1963-1987)
Mullion	Op RNLI 1867, Cl 1908
Porthleven	Op RNLI 1863, Cl 1929
Marazion	Op RNLI (at St Michael's Mount) ILB 1990, Cl 2001
Penzance	Op Local Comm 1803, Cl 1812; Reop RNIPLS 1826, Cl p.1851; Reop RNLI 1853, Cl 1917
Newlyn	Op RNLI 1908, Cl 1913
Penlee	Op (at Penlee Point) 1913, M 1922, moved (to Newlyn) 1983, ILB 2001
St Agnes	Op RNLI 1890, Cl 1920
St Mary's	Op RNIPLS 1837, Cl 1839 and 1840, Cl 1855; Reop RNLI (at Porth Cressa) 1874, M 1919, Moved (to Carn Thomas) 1919
Sennen Cove	Op RNLI 1853, M 1922, ILB 1994
St Ives	Op Local Comm 1840, Cl 1860; Reop RNLI 1861, M 1933, ILB 1964
Hayle	Op RNLI 1866, Cl 1920
St Agnes	Op (at Trevaunance Cove) RNLI ILB 1968
Newquay	Op RNLI 1860, Cl 1934, Reop RNLI M 1940, Cl 1945, Reop RNLI ILB 1965, 2nd ILB Op 1995
Padstow	Op (at Hawker's Cove) Local Comm 1827, To RNLI 1856, M 1931-62; No.2 Op (at harbour) 1899, steam LB 1899-1900, Steam Tug & LB 1901-29, M 1929, moved (to Trevose Head) 1967
Rock	Op RNLI ILB 1994
Port Isaac	Op RNLI 1869, Temp Cl 1917-19, Cl 1933; Reop ILB 1967
Bude	Op Local Comm 1837, Cl c.1852; Reop RNLI 1853, Cl 1923; Reop RNLI ILB 1966
Clovelly	Op RNLI 1870, M 1936, Cl 1988; Reop RNLI ILB 1998
Appledore (Northam Burrows)	Op (Northam Burrows) RNIPLS 1852, To RNLI 1855. Cl 1897; 2nd boat RNLI 1856, Cl 1862, Reop RNLI 1870, Cl 1889
Appledore (Braunton Burrows)	Op (at Braunton Burrows) RNIPLS 1848, To RNLI 1855, Temp Cl 1917, Cl 1919
Appledore	Op (Appledore) RNIPLS 1825, To RNLI 1855, Cl 1856; 2nd boat RNIPLS 1831, Cl 1852; Reop (at Badsteps) RNLI 1889, M 1922, ILB 1973
Morte Bay	(Manned from Ilfracombe) Op (at Woollacombe) RNLI 1871, Cl 1900
Ilfracombe	Op Experimental LB 1828, Cl 1843; Reop Local Comm 1850, Cl 1860; Reop RNLI 1866, M 1936, ILB 1991
Lynmouth	Op RNLI 1869, Cl 1944
Minehead	Op RNLI 1901, M 1939-73; ILB 1970, 2nd ILB 1974
Watchet	Op RNLI 1875, Cl 1944
Burnham-on-Sea	Op Bridgwater Harb. Trust 1836, Cl 1857; Reop RNLI 1866, Cl 1930; Reop RNLI ILB 2003, 2nd ILB 2003
Weston-super-Mare	Op RNLI 1882, M 1933-69, ILB 1966, 2nd ILB 1969
Pill	Op RNLI ILB 1971, Cl 1974
Portishead	Op RNLI ILB (due to open 2013 or 2014)

WALES

Penarth	Op RNLI 1861, Cl 1905, Reop RNLI ILB 1980, 2nd ILB 1996
Barry Dock	Op RNLI 1901, M 1922, No.2 M 1973-79
Atlantic College	Op (at St Donat's Castle) College/RNLI ILB 1963, To RNLI 1973

Porthcawl	Op RNLI 1860, Cl 1902, Reop RNLI ILB 1965, 2nd ILB 2012
Port Talbot	Op RNLI ILB (at Aberavon Beach) 1966
The Mumbles	Op (at Mumbles) Swansea Harbour Trust 1835, moved (to Swansea) 1841, To RNLI 1863, moved (to Mumbles) 1866, M 1924 (named Swansea until 1904), ILB 1965
Horton & Port Eynon	Op (at Horton) RNLI ILB 1968
Port Eynon	Op RNLI 1888, Temp Cl 1916, Cl 1919
Llanelli	Op SFMRBS 1852, To RNLI 1854, Cl 1863; Reop 1869, Cl 1871
Burry Port	Op RNLI 1887, Cl 1914; Reop RNLI ILB 1973, 2nd ILB 2010
Pembrey	Op RNLI 1863, Cl 1887
Ferryside	Op RNLI 1860, M 1941, Cl 1960
Carmarthen Bay	Op (Laugharne) RNIPLS 1835, Cl 1843
Tenby	Op SFMRBS 1852, To RNLI 1854, M 1923- ILB 1972-
Angle	Op RNLI 1868, Cl 1910; Reop 1915, Temp Cl 1918-19, M 1929, ILB 1994; No.2 Op Steam 1908, Cl 1915
Little Haven	Op RNLI 1882, Cl 1921; Reop RNLI ILB 1967 (named Little and Broad Haven)
Solva	Op RNLI 1869, Cl 1887
St Davids	Op RNLI (at Porthstinian) 1869, M 1912, ILB 1997
Fishguard	Op Privately 1822, Cl 1846; Reop RNLI 1855, Cl 1907; No.2 Op (at Pen Cw) 1869, M 1908, ILB 1995
Newport	Op (Cwmdewi) RNLI 1884, Cl 1894
Cardigan	Op (Penryn Castle) Local Comm 1849, To RNLI 1851, Cl 1932, Reop (at Poppit Sands) RNLI ILB 1971, 2nd ILB 1998
New Quay	Op RNLI 1864, M 1948, ILB 1967
Aberystwyth	Op Harbour Trust 1843, Cl c.1861; Reop RNLI 1862, M 1932-64; ILB 1963, 2nd ILB 2011
Borth	Op Private c.1830, Cl 1850; Op RNLI ILB 1966
Aberdovey	Op Harbour Auth 1837, To RNLI 1853, Cl 1931; Reop RNLI ILB 1963
Barmouth	Op Harbour Trust 1828, Cl 1851; Reop RNLI 1853, M 1939, ILB 1967
Criccieth	Op SFMRBS 1853, To RNLI 1854, Cl 1931; Reop RNLI 1953, M 1953-68 (named Portmadoc until 1892), Op ILB 1967, 2nd ILB 2009
Pwllheli	Op RNLI 1891, M 1931, ILB 1964
Abersoch	Op (at Penrhyndu) RNIPLS 1844, Cl 1853; Reop (at Abersoch) RNLI 1869, moved (to Penrhyndu) 1894, Cl 1931, Reop RNLI ILB 1965
Porthdinllaen	Op RNLI 1864, M 1926
Llanaelhaiarn	Op (Gwydir) RNLI 1883, Cl 1901
Clynnog	Op Caernarfon Harb Trust 1847, Cl 1853
Caernarfon	Op Caernarfon Harb Trust 1835, Cl c.1891; No.2 1844-p.52
Llanddwyn	Op Caernarfon Harb Trust 1826, Cl 1835; Reop Anglesey Ass. 1840, To RNLI 1855, Cl 1907
Rhosneigr	Op RNLI 1872, Cl 1924
Rhoscolyn	Op Anglesey Ass 1830, To RNLI 1855, Cl 1929
Trearddur Bay	Op RNLI ILB 1967, 2nd ILB 2001
Porth Rhuffydd	(Manned from Holyhead) Op RNLI 1891, Cl 1904
Holyhead	Op Anglesey Ass 1829, To RNLI 1855, M 1928, ILB 1967; No.2 Op RNLI 1890, Cl 1930; No.3 Op RNLI Steam 1892-93 and 1897-98
Cemlyn	Op Anglesey Ass 1828, To RNLI 1855, Cl 1872; Reop RNLI 1877, Cl 1919
Cemaes	Op (Porth Wylfa) RNLI 1872, Cl 1932
Bull Bay	Op RNLI 1868, Cl 1926
Moelfre	Op Anglesey Ass 1848, To RNLI 1855, M 1930, ILB 1965
Penmon	Op (Trwyndu) Anglesey Ass 1831, To RNLI 1855, Cl 1915

Tenby lifeboat station in South Wales; the lifeboat house and slipway were built in 2004-05 for 16m Tamar lifeboat.

Lytham St Annes lifeboat station in Lancashire; the lifeboat house was built in 2002-03 for a 12m Mersey lifeboat.

Beaumaris	Op RNLI 1891, Cl 1896; Reop RNLI M 1914-91, ILB 1967
Conwy	Op RNLI ILB 1966
Llandudno	Op RNLI 1861, M 1933, ILB 1965
Llanddulas	Op RNLI 1869, Cl 1932
Abergele	Proposed 1867 but boat sent to Rhyl temporarily and in 1869 sent to Llanddulas
Rhyl	Op SFMRBS 1852, To RNLI 1854, M 1939; No.2 Op RNLI 1878, Cl 1899; ILB 1967, 2nd ILB 1986-86
Point of Air	Op (Gronant) Liverpool Dock Trust (later Mersey Docks and Harbour Board) 1826, To RNLI 1894, Cl 1894; No.2 Op 1839, Cl 1891, Reop 1893, To RNLI 1894, Cl 1894
Point of Ayr	Op (Talacre) 1894, Cl 1923; No.2 Op (Cross Gully) 1896, Cl 1898
Mostyn	Op RNIPLS 1835, Cl 1850
Flint	Op RNLI ILB 1966

ISLE OF MAN

Ramsey	Op RNIPLS 1829, Cl c.1842; Reop RNLI 1868, M 1931
Douglas	Op Local Comm 1802, Cl 1814; Reop 1824, To RNIPLS 1826, Cl p.1851; No.2 Op & Cl 1825; Reop RNLI 1868, M 1924; No.2 Op 1874-95
Castletown	Op RNIPLS 1826, Cl 1842; Reop RNLI 1856, Cl 1922
Port St Mary	Op RNLI 1896, M 1936, ILB 1966
Port Erin	Op RNLI 1883, M 1925-92, ILB 1992
Peel	Op RNIPLS 1828, Cl 1843; Reop RNLI 1885, M 1937-72 and 1992, ILB 1972-92

ENGLAND

West Kirby	Op RNLI ILB 1966
Hilbre Island	(Manned from Hoylake) Op Liverpool Dock Trust (later Mersey Docks and Harbour Bd) 1848, To RNLI 1894, Cl 1939
Hoylake	Op Liverpool Dock Trust (later Mersey Docks and Harbour Board) 1803, To RNLI 1894, M 1931; No.2 Op 1839-48
New Brighton	Op RNLI 1863, Cl 1890; Reop (steam) 1893, M 1923-73; No.2 Op RNLI 1864, M 1938-50; No.3 Op RNLI 1884-87; RNLI ILB 1973, Hovercraft 2004
Magazines	Op (at Wallasey) Liverpool Dock Trust (later Mersey Docks and Harbour Board) 1827, Cl 1863; No.2 Op 1839, Cl 1863
Liverpool	Experimental LB 1802; Op Liverpool Dock Trust 1839, Cl 1894; No.2 Op 1840, Cl 1894
Formby	Op Liverpool Corp 1776, Cl 1889; Reop Mersey Docks and Harbour Board 1892, To RNLI 1894, Temp Cl 1917, Cl 1919; Private boat Op 1815, Cl 1825
Southport	Op Southport Lifeboat Soc p.1812, Cl 1817; Reop Liverpool Dock Trust (later Mersey Docks and Harbour Board) 1840, To RNLI 1860, Cl 1902; No.2 Op RNLI 1888, Cl 1925
Lytham St Annes	Op SFMRBS 1851, To RNLI 1854, M 1931 (moved to St Annes 1999), ILB 1967 (named Lytham until 1931)
St Annes	Op RNLI 1881, Cl 1925; No.2 Op RNLI 1888, Cl 1910
Blackpool	Op RNLI 1864, M 1937-75, Op ILB 1965, 2nd ILB 1975, 3rd ILB 1996
Fleetwood	Op RNLI 1859, Cl 1930, Reop RNLI M 1933, ILB 1966; No.2 Op 1887-94
Morecambe	Op Morecambe and Heysham Lifebat Ass 1894, M 1934, Cl ? Reop RNLI ILB 1966, Hovercraft 2002
Barrow	Op (at Roa Island) RNLI 1864, moved (to Barrow) 1889, moved (to Roa Island) 1898, M 1927, ILB 1964 (named Piel until 1889, Barrow until 1898, Piel (Barrow) until 1935)
Seascale	Op RNLI 1875, Cl 1895
St Bees	Op RNLI ILB 1970
Whitehaven	Op Whitehaven Harbour Trust 1803, To RNLI 1865, Cl 1924
Workington	Op RNLI 1886, Cl 1905; Reop RNLI M 1948, ILB 2004
Maryport	Op RNLI 1865, M 1931, Cl 1949
Silloth	Op RNLI 1860, Cl 1896, Reop RNLI ILB 1967

SCOTLAND

Kippford	Op RNLI ILB 1966
Balcary	Op RNLI 1884, Cl 1931
Kirkcudbright	Op (in town) RNLI 1862, moved (to Cutler's Pool) 1892, M 1928-89, ILB 1988
Whithorn	Op RNLI 1869, Temp Cl 1917, Cl 1919
Port Logan	Op RNLI 1866, Cl 1932
Portpatrick	Op RNLI 1877, M 1922, No.2 Op RNLI 1922-24
Stranraer	Op (at Agnew Park) RNLI ILB 1974
Ballantrae	Op RNLI 1871, Temp Cl 1917, Cl 1919
Girvan	Op RNLI 1865, M 1931
Ayr	Op Harb Trust 1803, Cl p.1840; Reop RNLI 1859, Cl 1932
Troon	Op RNLI 1871, M 1929, ILB 2004
Irvine	Op Harbour Trust 1834, To RNLI 1860, Cl 1914
Ardrossan	Op Local Comm 1807, To RNLI 1869, Cl 1930
Largs	Op RNLI ILB 1964
Helensburgh	Op (at Rhu Marina) RNLI ILB 1965

Tighnabruaich	Op RNLI ILB 1967
Campbeltown	Op RNLI 1861, M 1912, ILB 1993; No.2 Op RNLI 1910-31
Southend	Op (at Dunaverty Bay) 1869, Cl 1930
Macrihanish	Op RNLI 1912, Cl 1930
Arran (Lamlash)	Op RNLI ILB 1970
Kildonan (Arran)	Op RNLI 1870, Cl 1901
Oban	Op RNLI 1972-80, M 1978
Tobermory	Op RNLI M 1938, Cl 1947; Reop RNLI M 1990
Islay	Op (at Port Askaig) RNLI M 1934 (named Port Askaig to 1948)
Mallaig	Op RNLI M 1948
Barra Island	Op (at Castlebay) RNLI M 1931
Kyle of Lochalsh	Op RNLI ILB 1995
Portree	Op RNLI M 1991
Ullapool	Op (cruising lifeboat) RNLI 1966, Cl 1967
Lochinver	Op RNLI M 1967
Leverburgh	Op RNLI M 2012
Stornoway	Op RNLI 1887, M 1929
Thurso	Op (at Scrabster) RNLI 1860, M 1929
Longhope	Op RNLI 1874, M 1926
Kirkwall	Op RNLI M 1969; RNLI M 1972
Stromness	Op RNLI 1867, M 1909
Stronsay	Op RNLI M 1909, Temp Cl 1915, Cl 1920; Reop RNLI 1952, Cl 1972
Lerwick	Op RNLI M 1930
Aith	Op RNLI M 1933
Huna	Op RNLI 1877, Cl 1930
Ackergill	Op RNLI 1878, Cl 1932
Wick	Op British Fishery Society 1848, To RNLI 1895, Cl 1913; Reop RNLI M (at Salmon Rock) 1921
Helmsdale	Op Local Comm 1909, Cl 1939
Dornoch Firth & Embo	Op (at Embo) RNLI 1886, Cl 1904
Invergordon	Op RNLI M 1974, ILB 1976-79
Cromarty	Op RNLI 1911, M 1928, Cl 1968
Kessock	Op RNLI ILB 1993 (named North Kessock until 2001)
Nairn	Op RNLI 1878, Cl 1911
Lossiemouth	Op RNLI 1859, Cl 1923
Buckie	Op RNLI 1860, M 1922-
Whitehills	Op RNLI 1924, M 1932, Cl 1969
Banff and Macduff	Op (Banff) 1860, moved (to Palmers Cove) 1867, Temp Cl 1917-21, Cl 1924 (named Banff until 1902)
Macduff	Op RNLI M 1974, Cl 1984; Reop RNLI ILB 1986
Fraserburgh	Op Harbour Comm 1806, Cl 1851; Reop RNLI 1858, M 1915, Cl 1970, Reop RNLI M 1979
Whitelink Bay	Op RNLI 1878, Cl 1905
Peterhead	Op RNLI 1865, M 1928; No.2 Op RNLI M 1912
Port Errol	Op (Cruden Bay) RNLI 1877, Temp Cl 1914-15, Cl 1921
Newburgh	Op RNIPLS 1828, Cl 1841; Reop RNLI 1877, M 1941, Cl 1965
Aberdeen	Op (Beach) Harb Comm 1803, Cl 1820; Reop 1841, To RNLI (No.2) 1925, M 1939-43 & 1947-62; Op (Harbour) Harb Comm 1875, To RNLI (No.1) 1925, M 1926, ILB 1968
Stonehaven	Op Kincardineshire LB Ass 1854, Cl p.1866; Reop RNLI 1868, Cl 1934; Reop RNLI ILB 1967, Cl 1984
Gourdon	Op RNLI 1878, M 1936, Cl 1969; Fishermen's Surf LB Op 1890, last used 1938
Johnshaven	Op RNLI 1891, Cl 1928
Montrose No.3	Op (at Kirkside) RNLI No.3 1885, Cl 1892
Montrose	Op Local Comm 1800, To Town Council 1818, To Harb Trust 1838, To RNLI 1869, M 1926, ILB 1994, No.2 Op RNLI 1869, M 1940, Cl 1950
Arbroath	Op Local Comm 1803, To RNLI 1865, M 1932, ILB 1968
Westhaven	Private LB mentioned 1851
Budden Ness	Op River Tay LBS 1830, To RNLI 1861, Temp Cl 1863-67, Cl 1894
Broughty Ferry	Op River Tay LBS 1859, To RNLI 1861, M 1910, ILB 1964
Ferryport-on-Craig	Op Dundee Humane Society 1833, Cl 1860
St Andrews	Op Local Comm 1802, To RNLI 1860, Cl 1938
Boarhills	Op Private LB 1860, Cl 1891
Crail	Op RNLI 1884, Cl 1923
Anstruther	Op RNLI 1865, Temp Cl 1917-19, M 1933, ILB 2003
Buckhaven	Op RNLI 1900, Cl 1932
Kinghorn	Op RNLI ILB 1965
Queensferry	Op (at South Queensferry) RNLI ILB 1967
Leith	Op Local Comm 1805, Cl 1825
North Berwick	Op RNLI 1860, Cl 1925, Reop RNLI ILB 1967
Dunbar	Op Local Comm 1808, Cl 1821, Reop RNLI 1864, M 1931 (moved to Torness 1995), ILB 1968
Skateraw	Op RNLI 1907, Cl 1943
St Abbs	Op RNLI 1911, M 1911-74, ILB 1974
Eyemouth	Op RNLI 1876, M 1937, Temp Cl 1963-64

IRELAND

Portrush	Op RNLI 1860, moved (to Lansdowne) 1901, M 1924, moved (to harbour) 1928, ILB 1993
Red Bay	Op (at Cushendall) RNLI ILB 1972
Larne	Op RNLI ILB 1994, M 1996
Carrickfergus	Op RNLI 1896, Cl 1913
Bangor	Op RNLI ILB 1965
Groomsport	Op RNLI 1858, Temp Cl 1919, Cl 1920
Donaghadee	Op RNLI M 1910
Ballywalter	Op RNLI 1866, Cl 1906
Cloughey/ Portavogie	(Manned fron Cloughey) Op RNLI M 1965, Temp Cl 1978, Cl 1981
Cloughey	Op RNLI 1888, M 1931, Cl 1965
Portaferry	Op RNLI 1980
Killough	Op (at Rossglass) RNLI 1901, Cl 1914
St John's Point	Op RNIPLS 1835, Cl 1843
Rossglass	Op RNIPLS 1825, Cl 1835; Private LB Cl c.1854
Tyrella	Op RNIPLS 1838, Cl 1851; Reop RNLI 1860, Cl 1899
Newcastle	Op RNIPLS 1830, Cl 1833; Reop RNLI 1854, M 1937, ILB 1994
Kilkeel	Op RNLI 1986
Greenore	Op RNLI 1894, Temp Cl 1917, Cl 1920
Clogher Head	Op RNLI 1899, M 1931
Giles Quay	Op (Dundalk, North Side) RNLI 1879, Cl 1912
Black Rock	Op (Dundalk, South Side) RNLI 1859, Temp Cl 1879-80, Cl 1935
Drogheda No.1	Op (North Side at Baltray) RNLI 1856, Cl1899
Drogheda No.2	Op (South Side at Mornington) RNLI 1872, Cl 1926
Balbriggan	Op RNLI 1875, Cl 1898
Skerries	Op RNIPLS 1833, Cl 1838; Reop RNLI 1854, Cl 1930, Reop RNLI ILB 1981
Rogerstown	Op RNLI 1874, Cl 1882
Howth	Op Dublin Ballast Board 1817, To RNLI 1862, M 1930, ILB 1967
Sutton	Op Dublin Ballast Board 1805, Cl 1834
Clontarf	Op Dublin Ballast Board 1801, Cl 1825
Pigeon Dock	Op Dublin Ballast Board 1804, Cl 1825
Pigeon House	Op Dublin Ballast Board 1816, Cl 1820; Reop Dublin Ballast Board 1825, Cl 1831
Poolbeg	Op Dublin Ballast Board 1820, To RNLI 1862, M 1938, Cl 1959
Dun Laoghaire	Op Dublin Ballast Board 1817, To RNLI 1862, Cl 1911; No.2 Op RNLI 1890, Cl 1895; Reop RNLI 1898, M 1919 (named Kingstown until 1922), ILB 1986
Sandy Cove	Op Dublin Ballast Board 1803, Cl 1861
Bullock	Op Dublin Ballast Board p,1808, Cl c.1834
Greystones	Op RNLI 1872, Cl 1895
Wicklow	Op RNLI 1857, M 1911, ILB 1995
Arklow	Op RNIPLS 1826, Cl 1830; Reop RNLI 1857, M 1915
Courtown	Op RNLI 1865, Cl 1925, Reop RNLI ILB 1990
Cahore	Op RNLI 1857, Cl 1916
Wexford	Op RNLI (No.1) (at Rosslare Spit) 1859, M 1921, Cl 1927 (at Wexford Quay 1925-27); No.2 Op (at Rosslare Spit) RNLI 1858, Cl 1897; Reop RNLI ILB (at harbour) 2002

Rosslare Fort	Op (at Rosslare Spit) RNIPLS 1838, Cl 1855
Rosslare Harbour	Op RNLI 1896, Cl 1921; Reop RNLI M 1927
Carnsore	Op RNLI 1859, Cl 1897
Kilmore Quay	Op RNLI 1847, Cl 1857; Reop RNLI 1884, M 1937 (named Kilmore until 1986), moved (to marina) 2003
Fethard	Op RNLI 1886, Cl 1914, Reop RNLI ILB 1996
Duncannon	Op RNLI 1869, Cl 1886
Dunmore East	Op RNLI 1884, M 1914-19, Temp Cl 1919-25, M 1925
Tramore	Op RNLI 1858, Cl 1923; Reop RNLI (at Elizabeth Cove) ILB 1964
Dungarvan	Op RNLI (at Ballincourty) 1859, Cl 1900
Helvick Head	Op RNLI (at Crowe Point) 1900, M 1930, Cl 1969 (named Dungarven Bay (Helvick Head) to 1930); Reop RNLI ILB 1997
Ardmore	Op RNLI 1858, Cl 1895
Youghal	Op Harbour Trust 1839, To RNLI 1857, M 1931-84, ILB 1984
Ballycotton	Op RNLI 1858, M 1930
Queenstown	Op RNLI 1866, Cl 1899; No.2 Op 1890, Cl 1920
Crosshaven	Op RNLI ILB 2000
Kinsale	Op 1818, Cl 1824, Reop RNLI ILB 2003
Courtmacsherry Harbour	Op RNIPLS 1825, Cl c.1829; Reop RNLI 1867, moved (to Barry's Point) 1901, Temp Cl 1924-25, Cl 1928; Reop RNLI M (in harbour) 1929 (named Courtmacsherry until 1928)
Baltimore	Op RNLI M 1919, ILB 2008
Castletownbere	Op RNLI M 1998
Derrynane	Op RNIPLS 1844, Cl 1855
Valentia	Op RNLI (at Reenard Point) 1864, moved (to Knight's Town) 1869, Cl 1896; Reop RNLI M 1946
Fenit	Op RNLI 1879, M 1928, Cl 1969 (named Fenit (Tralee Bay) to 1969), Reop RNLI M 1994, ILB 1999
Kilrush	Op RNLI ILB 1996
Galway	Op RNLI ILB 1996
Aran Islands	Op RNLI M (at Kilronan) 1927 (named Galway Bay to 1995)
Clifden	Op RNLI ILB 1988, 2nd ILB (at Beach) 1997
Westport	Op RNLI (at Inishlyre) 1857, Cl 1862
Achill Island	Op RNLI M (at Kildavnet) 1996
Ballyglass	Op RNLI M 1989, ILB (at Belmullet) 2002
Sligo Bay	Op RNLI ILB (at Rosses Point) 1998
Bundoran	Op RNLI ILB 1994
Killybegs	Op RNLI M 1941, Cl 1945
Aranmore	Op 1883, M 1929
Lough Swilly	Op (at Ned's Fort) RNLI ILB 1988, 2nd ILB 1995-2005, M (at Buncrana) 2000
Culdaff	Op RNLI 1892, Cl 1913
Greencastle	Op RNLI 1864, Cl 1928

INLAND WATERWAYS

South Broads	Op (at Oulton Broad) RNLI ILB 2001, 2nd ILB 2002-04, Cl 2011
Loch Ness	Op RNLI (at Drumnadrochit) ILB 2008
Enniskillen	Op (Lower Lough at Kiladeas) RNLI ILB 2001, 2nd ILB (Upper Lough at Carry Bridge) 2002
Lough Derg	Op RNLI ILB (at Dromineer) ILB 2004
Lough Ree	Op RNLI ILB (at Coosan Point) ILB 2012

Invergordon lifeboat station in the Scottish Highland, with 14m Trent Douglas Aikman Smith (ON-1206) moored at the pontoon.

Kinsale lifeboat station in southern Ireland; the lifeboat house was built in 2008-09 for Atlantic 75 ILB, which is davit launched.

Independent Lifeboat Stations in geographic order

In addition to the stations operated and funded by the RNLI, more than 40 independent organisations fund, build and operate lifeboats around the coasts of the UK and Ireland. The number such of independent rescue organisations has steadily grown since the 1960s with local people putting in much time, effort and money to buy and operate their own rescue boats. Most of the stations use small, fast rigid-inflatable boats, with two stations, Caister and Blyth, operate larger offshore lifeboats. Because no umbrella organisation exists to manage or co-ordinate the independent lifeboats, information about them and their activities is difficult to obtain, and this list may not be comprehensive.

ENGLAND

Boulmer	1969	Boulmer Volunteer Rescue Service
Blyth	2006	Blyth All Weather Lifeboat
Runswick	1978	Runswick Bay Rescue Boat
Hornsea	1993	Hornsea Inshore Rescue
Humber	1990	Humber Rescue
Cleethorpes	1969	Cleethorpes Rescue
Mundesley	1972	Mundesley Volunteer Lifeboat
Hemsby	1977	Hemsby Volunteer Inshore Rescue Club
Palling	1974	Palling Volunteer Rescue Service
Caister	1969	Caister Volunteer Rescue Service
Norwich	2001	Norwich Riverside Lifeboat
Felixstowe	1997	Felixstowe Volunteer Coast Patrol Rescue Service
Folkestone	?	Folkestone Inshore Rescue
Pett Level	1970	Pett Level Rescue Boat Association
Birling Gap Safety Boat	1983	Birling Gap Safety Boat Association
Portsea	1933	Portsmouth & Southsea Voluntary Lifeguards
Gosport & Fareham	1969	Gosport & Fareham Inshore Rescue Service
Hamble	1968	Southampton Water Inshore Rescue Service (Hamble Rescue)
Cowes	1989	Cowes Inshore Lifeboat (taken over by RNLI 2008)
Ryde	1956	Ryde Inshore Rescue
Sandown & Shanklin	1972	Sandown & Shanklin Independent Lifeboat (based at Sandown)
Freshwater	1975	Freshwater Independent Lifeboat
Stanswood	?	Stanswood Beach Rescue
Solent (at Lepe)	1971	Solent Rescue (based at Lepe Country Park)
Venturers	1961	Venturers Search and Rescue
Sidmouth	1968	Sidmouth Lifeboat
Hope Cove	2010	Hope Cove Life Boat (HCLB)
Jersey (Channel Is)	?	Jersey Fire and Rescue Service
Guernsey (Channel Is)	?	St John Ambulance and Rescue Service
Clovelly	1988	Clovelly Estate, taken over by RNLI 1997
Burnham-on-Sea	1994	Burnham Area Rescue Boat (BARB)
Portishead	1995	Portishead and Bristol Lifeboat (due to be taken over by RNLI 2013 or 2014)
Severn Area	1986	Severn Area Rescue Association (SARA) (operates lifeboats at Sharpness and Beachley)
Upton upon Severn	2005	Mercia Inshore Rescue

WALES

Cardiff and Vale	1998	Cardiff and Vale Rescue Association (CAVRA)
Loughor	1969	Loughor Rescue Service
Ferryside	1966	Ferryside Inshore Rescue (affiliated with St John's Ambulance, Wales)

ENGLAND

Liverpool	1984	Merseyside Fire & Rescue Service Marine Rescue Unit
Southport	1988	Southport Offshore Rescue Trust
Flookburgh/Bay	2001	Bay Search & Rescue
Ulverston	2004	Ulverston Inshore Rescue
Duddon	1969	Duddon Inshore Rescue
Haverigg	1973	Haverigg Inshore Rescue Team
Maryport	1978	Maryport Inshore Rescue

SCOTLAND

Nith	1981	Nith Inshore Rescue (based in Glencapel)
Loch Lomond	1977	Loch Lomond Rescue Boat
Mossgate (Fleet Bay)	?	Fleet Bay Inshore Rescue (Mossyard)
Port William (Luce Bay)	1982	
Dornoch	1969	East Sutherland Rescue Association
Moray Firth	2005	Moray Inshore Rescue Organisation (based at Findhorn Boatyard and Marina)
Stonehaven		Marine Rescue International (closed 2013)

IRELAND

Lough Neagh	1989	Lough Neagh Rescue (operates lifeboats at Ardboe and Kinnego)
Cahore	1994	Cahore Inshore Rescue Service
Waterford	?	Waterford City River Rescue
Tramore	?	Tramore Sea Rescue Association
Bonmahon	1986	Bonmahon Inshore Rescue Service
Schull	2005	Schull Community Inshore Rescue Service
Bantry	1987	Bantry Inshore Rescue Association
Derrynane	1995	Derrynane Inshore Rescue
Banna	1982	Banna Community Sea Rescue
Ballybunion	1986	Ballybunion Sea & Cliff Rescue
Limerick City (Shannon)	?	
Kilkee	1981	Kilkee Inshore Rescue Service
Lahinch		Lahinch Rescue CIRS
Carna	?	
Corrib/Mask Lakes	?	
Ballinskelligs	2006	Ballinskelligs Inshore Rescue Ltd

SARA 2 Dave Moore is one of several inshore lifeboats, of varying sizes, operated by the Severn Area Rescue Association (SARA).

Preparing Maryport lifeboat EON Spirit of Maryport for service; Maryport Inshore Rescue service was founded in 1978.

The future of lifeboat building

RNLI to build lifeboats from 2014

In 2013 the build programme for the 16m Tamar class lifeboats came to an end, with the final two boats, operational numbers 16-26 and 16-27, being completed. By then, the RNLI was already planning the future production of all-weather lifeboats, with the future building programme focussing on the new 13m Shannon class, which made its debut in autumn 2012, with the boats costing £1.5 million each.

In December 2012 a radical step was taken when the RNLI announced plans to bring future production and maintenance of all-weather lifeboats to its headquarters in Poole, Dorset. The new facility will be built on RNLI land next to Holes Bay and will create 90 jobs. The initial outlay will be £11.2 million in set-up costs, but the RNLI believes that bringing the work in-house will save £3.7 million a year. Work on the project is scheduled to be undertaken in 2013-14 and the site will be operational from 2014.

Up to now the RNLI has contracted out lifeboat building to commercial boatbuilders, but undertaking the construction work in-house will mean contractors' profits are removed along with other overheads, making economic as well as practical sense. Refit and overhaul work will also be carried out at the new site, starting in spring 2014. Hull and deck moulding, which was done at the boatyard owned by the RNLI, SAR Composites at Lymington, will move over by 2019.

As the technology used in constructing all-weather lifeboats has advanced, the pool of suppliers who fulfil the work has reduced. Bringing building work in-house means the RNLI can control costs and minimise any risks to the supply chain. The RNLI has a 20-year strategy that requires the building of six all-weather lifeboats every year, as well as maintaining the existing fleet, and so the new facility will safeguard the future of all-weather lifeboat construction. It will revolutionise lifeboat construction and maintenance, bringing every stage of the production process under one roof, and ensuring that the RNLI is fully equipped to build the next generation of lifeboats – the Shannon class – and continue saving lives at sea for years to come.

13m Shannon lifeboat build programme (2013 on)

ON	Op No	Name	Allocated
1308	13-01	Sir Jock and Lady Slater	Relief
1309	13-02	The Morrell	Dungeness
1310	13-03	R. & J. Welburn	Exmouth
1311	13-04	Storm Rider	Relief
1312	13-05	Patsy Knight	Lowestoft
1313	13-06		Hoylake
1314	13-07	Frederick William Plaxton	Scarborough
1315	13-08		Selsey
1316	13-09		St Ives
1317	13-10		Ilfracombe

Future allocations beyond the above: Lough Swilly, Montrose (named Ian Grant Smith), Relief, Llandudno, Swanage and Skegness

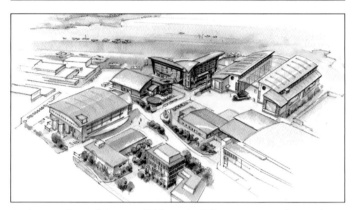

An impression of the new lifeboat building centre co-located with the RNLI's other buildings at Poole, Dorset.

Capsize trials of Shannon lifeboat ON-1308 (13-01) at Lymington on 30 January 2012 as part of her trials programme. (Peter Edey)

The second production Shannon class lifeboat, ON.1309, in build at Berthon Boat Company, Lymington. (By courtesy of RNLI)

Photo credits

The index covers lifeboat names used when boats were in service; numbers after lifeboat names are their Official Numbers; where a lifeboat has no ON or where further mentions of it appear, the reference is a page number; where 'The' was used at the start of a name, this has not been indexed.